AIR P GLOSSARY & REFERENCE GUIDE

Compiled by
DAVID BRUFORD

Editing and Technical Assistance
Brian Marindin
Ex-Cathay Pacific Airways Senior Check & Training Captain
Chief Instructor, Airways Flight Training, Exeter, Devon

Additional Assistance
The IR & CPL Instructors and staff at
Airways Flight Training (Exeter) Ltd

Airlife
England

Visual Flight Rules Chart reproduced with the assistance of the CAA Aeronautical
Information Services, Heathrow.

British Library Cataloguing in Publication Data
A catalogue record for this book
is available from the British Library

ISBN 1 85310 483 3

Printed in England by Livesey Ltd., Shrewsbury.

Airlife Publishing Ltd.

101 Longden Road, Shrewsbury SY3 9EB, England

Contents

THE AIR PILOT'S GLOSSARY AND REFERENCE GUIDE

Introduction

The Air Pilot's Glossary and Reference Guide provides quick and easy access to abbreviations, codes and terms used by pilots, air traffic control, aeronautical publications and reports.

A few tips may save you some time in finding the right subject. The book is in two sections. The glossary contains an alphabetical list of abbreviations and subjects. Where required the abbreviations will refer to an explanation of their meaning elsewhere in the glossary. If a more detailed explanation is available this will refer you to the reference section. The reference section contains very detailed explanations of most aeronautical subjects. Finally the quick reference section contains a list of conversion tables and emergency procedures which hopefully you will never need.

If, for instance, you want to know about ILS, look it up in the glossary. This will tell you that it means Instrument Landing System. Look up Instrument Landing System again in the Glossary and it will give you a brief description of what the system does. If further information is available (as there is in this example) look up the subject in the reference section under the heading indicated. Where the glossary reference is a term and not an abbreviation, the explanation will refer you to further text in the reference section if more is available.

This reference guide has been produced to be useful. We have tried to include everything that a student pilot, a qualified PPL or a career pilot training towards a CPL or IR will need. We have precised all the text as far as possible and have had to leave out some advanced subjects. If you feel that something essential to a comprehensive guide has been left out please write and let us know. We will make sure it is included in the next edition.

David Bruford

THE AIR PILOT'S GLOSSARY

A

a   Used at advanced levels of meteorology to express the Equatorial Radius of the Earth.

a   Speed of sound at sea level & standard temperature. The standard temperature is based on the criteria set out under the international standard atmosphere. See text in the reference section under International Standard Atmosphere.

A   Amber. The colour of a light. Usually shown on airfield approach charts or in relation to aerodrome lighting.

A   Approach lighting, usually shown on airfield approach charts.

A   A suffix indicating local time. Relating to the operating hours of an airfield or flight related facilities.

A   Meteorological, indicating that a QNH is given in inches and hundredths.

A1A/A2A   Terms used to describe types of non-directional beacon transmitters used in radio navigation. A1A = unmodulated carrier wave interrupted with Morse groups. A2A = amplitude modulated carrier wave overlaid with Morse. Refer to text in the reference section under Marker Beacons.

A/A   Air to Air. See Glossary text under that heading.

AA   Minimum altitude. (NOTAM decode 2nd & 3rd letters). See Glossary text under Minimum Safe Altitude.

AAA   Airfield Avoidance Area. Shown on the appropriate charts.

AAC   Aviation Administration Communications.

AACA   Aviation Airworthiness Certification Authority.

AACC   Airports Associations Co-ordinating Council.

AAD   Assigned Altitude Deviation.

AAF   Anti-Icing Fluid. See Glossary text under that heading.

AAF   Army Air Field.

AAG   Aeronautical information service Automation Group.

AAI   Angle of Approach Indicator. See Glossary text under that heading.

AAIB   Air Accidents Investigation Branch.

AAL   Above Aerodrome Level. See Glossary text under that heading.

AAM   Airline Administrative Messages.

AARA   Air to Air Refuelling Area. See Glossary text under that heading.

AAS   Airport Advisory Service.

AASC   Airworthiness Authorities Steering Committee.

AB   Air Base (Military).

AB   Automatic weather Broadcast. See Glossary text under Automatic Terminal Information Service and Very High Frequency Meteorological Report.

ABAC	Association of British Aviation Consultants.
Abbreviated Precision Approach Path Indicators	A light system mounted near a runway threshold which by a changing colour will indicate if an aircraft's approach glideslope is correct (usually at 3°). See further text in the reference section under Precision Approach Path indicators.
ABC	Advance Booking Charter.
A-BCAS	Active Beacon Collision Avoidance System.
ABE	Aerodrome Beacon. See Glossary text under that heading.
Abeam	A position given as 90° to an aircraft's track. See further text in the reference section.
ABI	Aerodrome Boundary Information.
ABM	Abeam. See Glossary text under that heading.
ABN	Aerodrome Beacon. See Glossary text under that heading.
ABNML	Abnormal. See Glossary text under that heading.
Abnormal	Usually relating to turbulence on an approach when wind is from particular direction although in NOTAMS it may refer to other situations.
Abort	The cancellation of a take-off after the aircraft has started rolling.
Above Aerodrome Level	Also AFL (above field level) and AGL (above ground level). The altimeter setting to obtain this height is QFE. See text in the reference section under Above Ground Level
Above Ground Level	Height above the Earth's surface. See further text in the reference section.
Above Mean Sea Level	The heights shown for fixed objects and terrain on aeronautical charts are shown AMSL. The altimeter sub-scale setting to show AMSL is QNH.
Absolute Altitude	An aircraft's height above ground level. See text in the reference section under Above Ground Level.
Absolute Instability	Atmospheric state which exists when the environmental lapse rate is greater than the dry and saturated adiabatic lapse rates. See text in the reference section under Adiabatic Lapse Rates.
Absolute Stability	Atmospheric state which exists when the environmental lapse rate is less than the dry and saturated adiabatic lapse rates. See text in the reference section under Adiabatic Lapse Rates.
Absolute Temperature	See text in the reference section under Temperature.
ABT	About.
ABV	Above.
ac	Aircraft.
a.c.	Alternating Current. See Glossary text under that heading.
Ac	Altocumulus cloud. See Glossary text under that heading.

A/C	Aircraft.
A/C	Approach Control.
AC	Advisory Circular.
AC	Air Carrier.
AC	Air Conditioning.
AC	Control zone. (NOTAM decode 2nd & 3rd letters).
AC	Withdrawn for maintenance. (NOTAM decode 4th & 5th letters).
ACAS	Airborne Collision Avoidance System.
ACC	Area Control Centre.
Accelerate Stop Distance	The distance required to for a multi-engined aircraft to stop following an engine failure. see the full definition in the reference section. For other distances and areas see text in the reference section under Aerodrome – Surface Definitions.
ACCID	Notification of an aircraft Accident.
ACC-R	Area Control Radar.
ACE	Altimeter Control Equipment.
ACFT	Aircraft.
ACL	Altimeter Check Location. See Glossary text under that heading.
Aclinal Line	A line joining points that exhibit forces of equal magnetic dip. See further text in the reference section.
ACN	Aircraft Classification Number.
ACPT	Accept or Accepted.
ACR	Aerodrome Control Radar.
ACR	Area Control Radar.
ACSL	Altocumulus Standing Lenticular. Clouds which form on the leeward side of mountains or large hills.
ACT	Active or activated.
Actual	Meteorological aerodrome report. See Glossary text under that heading.
ACTV	Active.
ACYC	Anticyclone or high pressure weather system. See Glossary text under High Pressure Area.
AD or A/D	Aerodrome.
AD	Air defence identification zone. (NOTAM decode 2nd & 3rd letters).
AD	Airworthiness Directive.
AD	Available for daylight operations. (NOTAM decode 4th & 5th letters).
ADA	Advisory Airspace.

ADA	Advisory Area.
ADC	Aerodrome Control(ler).
ADCUS	Advise Customs.
ADDN	Additional.
ADELT	Automatically Deployed Emergency Locator Transmitter. See Glossary text under Emergency Locator Transmitter.
ADF	Automatic Direction Finding (equipment). See Glossary text under that heading.
ADI	Attitude Director Indicator.
Adiabatic	A thermodynamic process in which heat is absorbed or released within a contained system. See further text in the reference section under Adiabatic Lapse Rates.
Adiabatic Cooling	A drop in atmospheric temperature caused solely by a reduction in pressure. See further text in the reference section under Adiabatic Lapse Rates.
Adiabatic Heating	A rise in atmospheric temperature caused solely by an increase in pressure. See further text in the reference section under Adiabatic Lapse Rates.
Adiabatic Lapse Rates	The rate of change of temperature with height. See further text in the reference section.
ADIZ	Air Defence Identification Zone.
ADJ	Adjacent.
ADNL	Additional.
ADR	Advisory Route. See Glossary text under that heading.
ADR	Advisory Rule.
ADREP	Accident/incident Data Reporting system.
ADSEL	Address Selective secondary surveillance radar.
ADTS	Approved Departure Times.
ADV	Advise.
ADV	Advisory Area.
Advection Fog (Land)	Formed when warm air moves over a colder surface causing a drop in temperature and the relative humidity to increase to its dewpoint. Formation requires a light wind of 3 – 10 knots. See further text in the reference section.
Advection Fog (Sea)	Formed when warm moist air flows over a comparatively cold sea and is cooled to its dewpoint. See further text in the reference section.
Advisory Route	Not an airway but with similar dimensions and terrain clearances. See further text in the reference section.
Advisory Service Area	A designated area where an air traffic advisory service is available. See further text in the reference section under Advisory Route.
ADVN	Advance.

ADVY	Advisory.
ADZ	Advise.
ADZY	Advisory.
Ae	Meteorological Aerodrome report. See Glossary text under that heading.
AE	Control area. (NOTAM decode 2nd & 3rd letters).
AEF	Air Experience Flight.
AER	Approach End Runway.
AERADIO	Air Radio.
Aerad Navigational Charts	Radio navigation charts published and updated by British Airways. Jepperson publish similar charts.
Aerodrome Beacon	White flashing strobe light provided as a homing beacon. See text in the reference section under Aerodrome Identification Beacon.
Aerodrome Circuit	The circuit is organized to promote an orderly and safe traffic flow. Refer to the Glossary text on its constituent legs, Crosswind, Downwind, Base and Final leg or the reference section for the purposes and radio calls to be made on each leg under Aerodrome Circuit.
Aerodrome Closure	Licenced aerodromes may only be closed at times specified by NOTAM or in the Air Pilot, when the landing area is unfit or essential runway facilities are unserviceable.
Aerodrome Elevation	The highest point on the landing area and aerodrome QFE datum. The elevation is shown in the Air Pilot.
Aerodrome Flight Information Service	Provided where no aerodrome control service exists and a licenced AFISCO is available. Most facilities are provided with the exception of traffic separation. See further text in the reference section.
Aerodrome Identification Beacon	Light beacon flashing a two letter Morse identification group every 12 seconds at 7 words per minute. Coloured red at military aerodromes, green at civil. See further text in the reference section.
Aerodrome Meteoriological Report	Abbreviated to METAR, it is a report of the actual observed weather at an aerodrome at the time given in the report. Sometimes abbreviated to Ae. See further text in the reference section under Meteorological Aerodrome Report.
Aerodrome Operating Minimas	A published list showing aerodrome operating minimas for individual aerodromes that show the minimum cloud bases and visual ranges below which an approach to land may not be made.

Aerodrome Radio Contact	A call should not be made later than the greater of 15nm or 15 minutes flight time from the air traffic zone boundary. To avoid interference with other aerodromes calls should not be made before 25nm and 10,000 feet for approach and 25nm and 4,000 feet for tower frequencies. For details of the call content and aerodrome information available refer to the reference section.
Aerodrome Signals	A signals square is provided at many aerodromes to convey circuit direction, type of aircraft activity and taxying instructions. Refer to the reference section for a full listing of signals and markings.
Aerodrome Surfaces	See text in the reference section for a full list and definitions.
Aerodrome Traffic Zone	See text in the reference section for full definitions.
Aerofoil	A structure shaped to generate lift when propelled through the air such as a propeller, helicopter rotor blade, tailplane or wing. See further text in the reference section.
Aerological Diagram	A graph used to plot the pressure, temperature and humidity of an air mass.
Aeronautical Information Circulars	Published every 28 days and colour coded as: Green – maps and charts, pink – safety, mauve – airspace amendments, white – administrative matters and yellow – operational matters. They lapse 5 years from the issue date. See further text in the reference section.
AES	Aerodrome Emergency Service.
AEW	Airborne Early Warning.
AF	Audio Frequency.
AF	Flight checked and found reliable. (NOTAM decode 4th & 5th letters).
AF	Flight information region. (NOTAM decode 2nd & 3rd letters). See Glossary text under that heading.
AFB	Air Force Base.
AFC	Area Forecast Centre.
AFC	Automatic Frequency Control.
AFCT	Affect.
AFI	Assistant Flying Instructor.
AFIL	Flight Plan filed In the Air.
AFIS(O)	Aerodrome Flight Information Service (Officer).
AFIS	Automatic Flight Inspection.
AFISCO	Aerodrome Flight Information Service Control Officer.
AFL	Above Field Level, also AAL (above aerodrome level) and AGL (above ground level). The altimeter setting to obtain this height is the QFE.

AFM	Yes, affirm, affirmative, correct.
AFN	Aeronautical Fixed Telecommunications.
AFO	Airport Fire Officer.
AFS	Aerodrome Fire Service.
AFS	Aeronautical Fixed Service.
AFS	Air Force Station.
AFT	After ... (time or place).
Aftercast	A meteorological report of observed weather conditions prepared to determine if weather was a contributory factor in an aircraft accident.
AFTN	Aeronautical Fixed Telecommunications Network.
AFTN	Afternoon.
A/G	Air/Ground communication station.
AG	Arrester Gear, fitted at some military airfields near the runway threshold and used for stopping equipped aircraft.
AG	Operating but ground checked only, awaiting flight check. (NOTAM decode 4th & 5th letters).
AGA	Aerodromes, air routes and Ground Aids, a sub-section of the Air Pilot.
AGCS	Air Ground Communications System.
Ageostrophic Wind	The vector difference between the geostrophic wind and an actual wind.
AGL	Above Ground Level, also AFL (above field level), and AAL (above aerodrome level). The altimeter setting to obtain this height is the QFE.
AGN	Again.
AGNIS	Azimuth Guidance Nose-in Stand. A system for very large aircraft to line up with a parking and passenger stand.
Agonic Line	A line joining points of zero magnetic deviation.
AH	Artificial Horizon. See Glossary text under that heading.
AH	Hours of service are now ..... (NOTAM decode 4th & 5th letters).
AH	Upper control area. (NOTAM decode 2nd & 3rd letters).
AHD	Ahead.
AHRS	Attitude and Heading Reference System.
AI	Attitude Indicator. See Glossary text under Artificial Horizon.
AIAA	Area of Intense Aerial Activity. See Glossary text under that heading.
AIC	Aeronautical Information Circular. See Glossary text under that heading.
AIDS	Aircraft Integrated Data System.
AIF	Attitude Instrument Flying.

Ailerons	Pivoted part of the wing surface used to provide lateral control in the roll of an aircraft. See text in the reference section for details of aileron types.
AILS	Automatic Instrument Landing System.
AIP	Aeronautical Information Publication. See text in the reference section under Air Pilot.
AIR	Airworthiness of Aircraft.
Airbrake	A hinged section of a wing which when raised or lowered into the airstream increases drag.
Aircraft Categories (Performance)	Aircraft with a weight not exceeding 5,700kg. C = aircraft for which a forced landing should not be required in the event of one engine failing. D = no specific performance after an engine failure. E = not exceeding 2,370KG and limited performance scheduling. See further text in the reference section.
Aircraft Categories (Pilot Licencing)	Group A = single engine aircraft not exceeding 5,700Kg. Group B = certain multi-engined aircraft not exceeding 5,700Kg. Group C = aircraft exceeding 5,700Kg or of a complex nature. See further text in the reference section.
Aircraft Categories (Nominal Threshold)	Aircraft classification is based on nominal threshold speeds in knots. A = 0 – 90. B = 91 – 120. C = 121 – 140. D = 141 E = 166 – 210. See further text in the reference section.
Aircraft Categories (Weight)	Microlight – not exceeding 390Kg, wing loading not exceeding 25Kg per sq metre, fuel capacity not exceeding 50 litres, not designed to carry more than 2 persons. Wake turbulence UK separation classification: Light aircraft = 17,000 Kg or less. Small aircraft = 40,000 Kg or less and more than 17,000 Kg. Medium aircraft = less than 136,000 Kg and more than 40,000 Kg. Heavy aircraft = 136,000 Kg or greater.
Aircraft Categories (Weight) Aerodrome Operating Minima	Aeroplanes Not Exceeding 5,700 Kg MTWA. A = piston engine or turboprop aeroplanes. B = turbo jet aeroplanes. Aeroplanes exceeding 5,700 Kg MTWA. A = exceeding 5,700 Kg MTWA and less than 25,000 Kg MLWA. B = 25,000 Kg MLWA and up to 68,000 Kg MLWA*. C = over 160,000 Kg MLWA. * AERAD Group B1, AERAD group B2 is more than 68,000 Kg MLWA and up to 160,000 Kg MLWA.
Aircraft Documents	Documents required to enable legal flight in the UK. See text in the reference section for a full listing.
Aircraft Surface Movement Indicator	Primary radar system used to display all objects, fixed or moving within an aerodrome movement area. See text in the reference section under Radar – Primary.
Aircraft Weight Schedule	A schedule required under the Air Navigation Order for a pilot to calculate a weight and balance criteria. See further text in the reference section.
Airfield Elevation	The height of an airfield above mean sea level. See further text in the reference section.

Air Masses	A large area of air, several hundred miles in size and diameter, with a constant temperature and humidity which may be modified by movement over sea or land. For more information and classifications see text in the reference section.
Air Mass Thunderstorm	Very active cumulonimbus clouds that occur when insolation is at its peak, especially during a weak depression. See further text in the reference section.
AIRMET	A premium rate oral telephone recording forecast system. See further text in the reference section.
Airmiss	A situation where a pilot considers his aircraft was in definite risk of collision with another aircraft. See further text in the reference section.
Air Pilot	Synonym for the UK Aerodrome Information Publication. Information is in eight sections. AGA – aerodrome classification and limitations. COM – radio communication and navigation frequencies. FAL – arrival, departure and transit procedures. GEN – general. MAP – maps and charts. MET – meteorological information. RAC – rules & procedures. SAR – search and rescue procedures. See further text in the reference section.
Airport Elevation	The highest point on the landing area given as height in feet above mean sea level. The QFE datum. See text in the reference section under Airfield Elevation.
AIRAC	Aeronautical Information Regulation and Control. See text in the reference section under NOTAM.
AIREP	Air Report, reporting position and meteorological conditions in flight.
Airspeed Definitions	See text in the reference section for a full listing and definitions.
Airspeed Indicator	Device used to indicate airspeed by feeding combined static and dynamic pressure via a pitot tube to a capsule which expands rotating a indicator needle on a numbered dial. See further text in the reference section.
Air to Air	Relating to radio transmissions between aircraft. Under normal circumstances messages to other aircraft should be passed through the ATC unit both aircraft are using.
Air to Air Refuelling Area	Normally only shown on radio navigation charts. It is not restricted airspace but pilots are warned that the military aircraft using the airspace may not be complying with quadrantal flight rules.
Air Traffic Advisory Service	A flight information service provided on advisory routes giving separation from known traffic. The service is not based on accurate information and relies on information from other participating aircraft.
Air Traffic Zone	A PPR entry zone. Ground level to 2,000 feet AGL with a radius of 2nm if the longest runway is 1,850m or less or 2.5nm if the longest runway is more than 1,850m.

Airways	Class A airspace of various lengths, 10nm wide. The minimum altitudes (airway base) provides adequate terrain clearance. Each segment is delineated by a radio navigation aid. They are reference by a letter and number. For example, A25, Alpha 25. See further text in the reference section.
Airways Reporting Points	Points are shown on airways charts and identified by a five letter code. Points are either compulsory or when advised by air traffic control. See text in the reference section under Marker Beacons and Airways.
AIS	Aeronautical Information Services.
AK	Resumed normal operation. (NOTAM decode 4th & 5th letters).
AL	Instrument Approach and Landing charts.
AL	Minimum usable flight level. (NOTAM decode 2nd & 3rd letters). See Glossary text under Transition Level.
AL	Operative (or re-operative) subject to previously published limitations/conditions. (NOTAM decode 4th & 5th letters).
ALA	Alighting Area.
Alarm Flag	A flag provided on ILS and VOR display to advise the pilot that any displayed information should be ignored.
Albedo	Dissimilar substances absorb heat at different rates. The ratio of the amount of electromagnetic radiation reflected by a body, to the amount incident upon it, is known as albedo. The amount of albedo is expressed by percentage. See further text in the reference section under Insolation.
ALERFA	Alert phase of a mayday call. See Glossary text under that heading.
Alert Phase	A period where apprehension exists as to the safety of an aircraft and its occupants. See further text in the reference section.
ALF	Aloft.
ALF	Auxiliary Landing Field.
ALFENS	Automated Low Flying Enquiry and Notification System.
ALG	Along.
Alpha Time	British summer time, Greenwich mean time + 1 hour.
ALQDS	All Quadrants.
ALR	Alerting Message.
ALS	Approach Light System.
ALS	Automatic Landing System.
ALSF-1	Approach Light system with Sequenced Flashing lights in instrument landing system category 1.
ALSF-2	Approach Light system with red barrettes and Sequenced Flashing lights in instrument landing system category 2.

ALSTG	Altimeter Setting.
ALT	Altitude. See Glossary text under that heading.
Alternate Aerodrome	An aerodrome selected prior to departure to which a flight may proceed when a landing at the original destination is not possible. See further text in the reference section.
Alternating Current	A current flow which is reversed in polarity at regular intervals. See further text in the reference section.
Altimeter	An aneroid barometer linked to a needle or needle and dial display to indicate a height above the datum set on an adjustable subscale. The display shows an increase in height in direct proportion to a reduction in static pressure. See further text in the reference section.
Altimeter Check Location	A position provided at some airfields where, with a specific sub-scale setting being set, the accuracy of an altimeter may be checked.
Altimeter Setting	Various subscale settings used dependent on the flight circumstances. See further text in the reference section.
Altimeter Setting Region	The UK is divided into 15 regions, each with its own QNH setting based on the lowest estimated pressure level forecast for the next hour.
Altitude	Height above sea level. The height shown on an altimeter when a QNH is set on the sub-scale.
ALTN	Alternate aerodrome. See Glossary text under that heading.
ALTN	Alternating. A light alternating in colour.
Altocumulus	Medium level, base 7,000 – 20,000 feet, cumulus cloud.
Altocumulus Flocus	Medium level, base 7,000 – 20,000 feet, active cumulus cloud with various upper levels
Altocumulus Lenticularis	Almond shaped medium level, base 7,000 – 20,000 feet, cumulus clouds.
Altocumulus Standing Lenticular	Clouds which form in the leeward side of mountains or large hills.
Altocumulus Stratiformes	Medium level, base 7,000 – 20,000 feet, layered formations of cumulus clouds.
Altostratus Cloud	Medium level, base 7,000 – 20,000 feet, layer cloud.
ALTRV	Altitude Reservation.
Am	Amber.
AM	Amplitude Modulation. See Glossary text under that heading.
AM	Military operations only. (NOTAM decode 4th & 5th letters).
AMA	Area Minimum Altitude.
AMC	Acceptable Means of Compliance.
AMD	Amend or Amended.
AME	Authorized Medical Examiner.

Amplitude Modulation	A method by which a frequency is combined with a carrier wave. The carrier is added at transmission and removed by the receiver to leave an audible signal. See further text in the reference section under Radio Waves.
AMR	Airport Movement Radar.
AMS	Aeronautical Mobile Service.
AMS	Air Mass. See Glossary text under Air Masses.
AMSL	Above Mean Sea Level. See Glossary text under that heading.
AMST	Advanced Medium Short Takeoff and landing transport.
AMT	Amount.
AN	Area Navigation route. (NOTAM decode 2nd & 3rd letters).
AN	Available for night operation. (NOTAM decode 4th & 5th letters).
Anabatic Wind	A wind caused by solar radiation warming the air nearest the surface. The resultant rising air blows up the side of a range of mountains or hills. See further text in the reference section.
Anafront	The condition where a warm front rises over the cold air ahead of its path.
ANC	Air Navigation Commission.
Anemograph	An instrument used to record wind speed or wind speed and direction.
Anemometer	An instrument used for measuring and displaying wind speed.
Angle of Approach Indicator	A visual aid using lights to indicate to a pilot that his aircraft is on the correct approach slope (usually 3°) to land.
Angle of Attack	The angle between the chord line and the relative airflow of a aerofoil section.
Angle of Incidence	The angle at which the wing is fixed to the airframe relative to the longitudinal axis.
ANGR	Air Navigation (General) Regulations.
ANM	Aeronautical Notification Message.
ANO	Air Navigation Order.
Anoxia	Total lack of oxygen. See Glossary text under Hypoxia.
ANP	Air Navigation Plan.
Anticyclone	An area of high pressure. Also known as a high. See text in the reference section under Anticyclone.
Anti-Icing Fluid	A fluid, usually alcohol based, that will not freeze and if sprayed over an icy aircraft will cause the ice to melt. Some types will prevent light icing from forming.
Anvil Cloud	An anvil shape formed at the top of a large cumulonimbus cloud projecting in the direction of the prevailing wind at that altitude.
AO	Aircraft Operator.
AO	Oceanic control area. (NOTAM decode 2nd & 3rd letters).

AO	Operational. (NOTAM decode 4th & 5th letters).
AOA	Aerodrome Operation Area.
AOA	At Or Above.
AOB	Angle Of Bank of an aircraft in relation to its lateral axis.
AOB	At Or Below.
AOC	Aerodrome Obstruction (or Obstacle) Chart.
AOE	Airport Of Entry (from abroad).
AOG	Aircraft On Ground.
AOM	Aerodrome Operating Minimas. See Glossary text under that heading.
AOP	Aerodrome Operations.
AOPA	Aircraft Owners & Pilots Association.
Ap	Approach Lights. Lights which lead to the runway along the approach path.
A/P	Airport.
AP	Airport.
AP	Available, prior permission required. (NOTAM decode 4th & 5th letters).
AP	Autopilot. See Glossary text under that heading.
AP	Reporting point. (NOTAM decode 2nd & 3rd letters).
APAPI	Abbreviated Precision Approach Path Indicator. See Glossary text under that heading.
APC	Approach Control(ler).
APC	Approach Positive Control.
APCH	Approach.
AP/DF	Approach & Direction Finding facility approach. A system using UHF/VHF radio with which ATC can guide an aircraft towards an airfield.
APHAZ	Aircraft Proximity Hazard
APP	Approach.
APP	Approach control.
Apparent Drift	An inherent directional gyro indicator error. It is counteracted by use of a latitude nut set to the appropriate latitude at which the aircraft normally operates. See further text in the reference section under Directional Indicator and Gyroscopes.
Apparent Wander	An error affecting a directional gyro's accuracy caused by the rotation of the Earth inducing the DI to over read in the northern hemisphere and under read in the southern hemisphere. See further text in the reference section under Directional Indicator and Gyroscopes.
APPL	Approach Precision Position Location equipment.

Appleton Layers	The layer of atmosphere surrounding the stratosphere is known as the ionosphere. It starts at around 50km and extends to as high as 500km. It is made up of several layers, the F1 and F2 layers are known as the Appleton Layers. See further text in the reference section under Ionosphere.
APP-R	Approach control Radar.
Approach Lights	Lights which lead to the runway along the approach path.
Apron	The part of an aerodrome reserved for loading, unloading, embarking & disembarking of passengers or cargo and aircraft parking for maintenance or refuelling.
APRX	Approximate or Approximately.
APS	Aircraft Prepared for Service (less passengers & fuel).
APSG	After Passing.
APT	Airport.
APT	Automatic Picture Transmission. See Glossary text under that heading.
AP/TR	Approach and Tower facility.
APV	Approve, Approved, Approval.
APWI	Airborne Proximity Warning Indicator.
AQZ	Area QNH Zone.
A/R	Altitude Reporting.
AR	Air traffic services Route. (NOTAM decode 2nd & 3rd letters).
AR	Available on Request. (NOTAM decode 4th & 5th letters).
ARB	Airworthiness Requirements Board.
ARCC	Airworthiness Requirements Co-ordinating Committee.
ARCS	Airline Request Communication System.
Arctic Maritime Air	At source, stable, very cold, humid air. On reaching the UK very cold, unstable & moist bringing heavy showers or snow which die out to leave cold weather with good visibility. For more information and classifications See text in the reference section under Air Masses.
Arctic Sea Smoke	Fog formation resulting from a very cold air mass moving away from a below 0°C land area over a comparatively warm sea. Synonyms are evaporation fog, frost smoke and steam fog.
Area Navigation System	A computer linked ILS, VOR, VORTAC & DME receiver coupled to a course deviation indicator. The system is able to determine a waypoint or phantom station position and display bearing, track and distance to that point. See further text in the reference section.
Area of Intense Aerial Activity	Areas used for military aircraft to manoeuvre and practice. Training aircraft are referred to as being *in the box* by the military. It is not restricted airspace.
ARFF	Airport Rescue / Fire Fighting.

ARFOR	Area Forecast.
ARMET	Area forecast, upper winds and temperatures at specific points.
ARND	Around.
ARNG	Arrange.
ARO	Air traffic services Reporting Office.
ARP	Airport Reference Point.
ARPT	Airport.
arr	Arrangement.
ARR	Arrive, Arrival.
Arrester Gear	Fitted at some military airfields near the runway threshold and used for stopping equipped aircraft.
ARSR	Air Route Surveillance Radar.
ARTCC	Air Route Traffic Control Centre.
Artificial Horizon	Primary aircraft instrument which displays an aircraft's bank angle and climb or descent attitude against a simulated horizon by means of a miniature aircraft linked to an Earth tied gyro. See further text in the reference section.
ARTS	Automated Radar Terminal System.
As	Altostratus Cloud. See Glossary text under that heading.
ASA	Advisory Service Area. See Glossary text under that heading.
ASA	Air Services Agreements.
ASA	Aviation Safety Authorities.
ASA	Radar Advisory Service Area. See Glossary text under Radar Advisory Service.
ASDA	Accelerate Stop Distance Available. See Glossary text under that heading.
ASDE	Airport Surface Detection Equipment.
ASE	Altimetry System Error.
ASI	Air Speed Indicator. See Glossary text under that heading.
ASL	Above Sea Level. See Glossary text under the more commonly used Above Mean Sea Level.
ASM	Airspace Management.
ASMI	Aircraft Surface Movement Indicator. See Glossary text under that heading.
ASP	Aircraft Servicing Platform.
ASPH	Asphalt.
Aspre	Warm breeze in southern France.
ASR	Airport Surveillance Radar.
ASR	Altimeter Setting Region. See Glossary text under that heading.

Associated Equipment	Radio navigation equipment co-located or are situated so close that no difference is apparent when used for navigational purposes. See further text in the reference section under Co-Located Navigation or Approach Equipment.
ASSR	Airport Surface Surveillance Radar.
ASSW	Associated with, meteorological.
Astro-Navigation	Traditional navigation using the positions of the sun and stars.
ASTVOL	Advanced Short Takeoff and Vertical Landing aircraft.
Asymmetric Flight	A flight made in a multi-engined aircraft where one or more engines are shut down causing an imbalance of forward thrust.
AT	At, meteorological.
AT	Terminal control area. (NOTAM decode 2nd & 3rd letters).
ATA	Actual Time of Arrival.
ATC	Air Traffic Control.
ATCC	Air Traffic Control Centre.
ATCI	Air Traffic Control Investigations.
ATCO	Air Traffic Control Officer.
ATCRBS	Air Traffic Control Radar Beacon System.
ATCRU	Air Traffic Control Radar Units.
ATCT	Air Traffic Control Tower.
ATCU	Air Traffic Control Unit.
ATD	Actual Time of Departure.
ATD	Automatic Threat Detection system.
ATE	Air Traffic Engineer.
ATE	Automatic Test Equipment.
ATFM(U)	Air Traffic Flow Management (Unit).
ATIS	Air Traffic Information Service.
ATIS	Automatic Terminal Information Service. See Glossary text under that heading.
ATLB	Air Transport Licencing Board.
ATM(C)	Airspace and Traffic Management (Centre).
ATM(G)	Airspace and Traffic Management (Group).
ATN	Aeronautical Telecommunications Network.
ATP	At ... (time or place).
ATPL	Airline Transport Pilot's Licence.
ATS	Air Traffic Services.
ATSA	Air Traffic Service Assistant.
ATSORA	Air Traffic Services Outside Regulated Airspace.
ATSPM	Air Traffic Services Planning Manual.
ATSU	Air Traffic Services Unit.

ATTITB	Air Transport and Travel Industry Training Board.
Attitude Indicator	Synonym for artificial horizon. See text in the reference section under Artificial Horizon.
ATTN	Attention.
AT-VASI	Abbreviated T Visual Approach Slope Indicator. A smaller version of a T shaped light based glide slope indicator. See text in the reference section under Visual Approach Slope Indicators.
ATZ	Aerodrome Traffic Zone. See Glossary text under that heading.
AU	Not available. (NOTAM decode 4th & 5th letters).
AU	Upper flight information region. (NOTAM decode 2nd & 3rd letters).
AUS	Airspace Utilisation Section.
AUTH	Authorised or Authorisation.
Automatically-Deployed Emergency Locator Transmitter	See Glossary text under Emergency Locator Transmitter.
Automatic Direction Finding	The receiving (fitted in the aircraft) end of a non-directional beacon. The direction to, or from, the beacon is shown by an indicator pointer on a compass face. The needle always points directly at the beacon. See further text in the reference section.
Automatic Picture Transmission	Term used to describe the transmission of normal and infra-red satellite cloud pictures. Usually obtainable by METFAX.
Automatic Terminal Information Service	A VHF recorded audio message providing aerodrome arrival, departure or combined information service issuing weather and runway information. See further text in the reference section.
Autopilot	A gyroscopically controlled electronic aid which may control one or all aspects of an aircraft's heading, height and yaw.
AUW	All Up Weight.
AV	Abbreviated Visual approach slope indicator system. A smaller version of a larger light based glideslope indicator. See Glossary text under Visual Approach Slope Indicator.
AV	Upper advisory area. (NOTAM decode 2nd & 3rd letters). See Glossary text under Upper Airspace and Advisory Service Area.
AVAD	Automatic Voice Alerting Device.
AVASIS	Abbreviated Visual Approach Slope Indicator System. See text in the reference section under Visual Approach Slope Indicators.
AVG	Average.
AVGAS	Aviation Gasoline. See text in the reference section under Avgas

AVTUR	Aviation Turbine Fuel. See text in the reference section under JET A-1.
A/W	Airway. See Glossary text under Airways.
AW	Aerodrome Warning.
AW	Airworthiness.
AW	Completely Withdrawn. (NOTAM decode 4th & 5th letters).
AWAC	Airborne Warning and Control.
AWO	All Weather Operations.
Awy	Airway. See Glossary text under Airways.
AX	Intersection. (NOTAM decode 2nd & 3rd letters).
AX	Previously promulgated shutdown has been cancelled. (NOTAM decode 4th & 5th letters).
AZ	Aerodrome traffic Zone. (NOTAM decode 2nd & 3rd letters). See Glossary text under Air Traffic Zone.
AZ	Azimuth.
Azimuth Guidance Nose-in Stand	A system for very large aircraft to line up with an airport parking and passenger stand.
AZM	Azimuth.

B

(b)	Bi directional.
B	Aerodrome or identification beacon. See Glossary text under Aerodrome Beacon.
B	Bar.
B	Blue. The colour of a light. Usually shown on airfield approach charts or in relation to aerodrome lighting.
BA	Braking Action.
Back Beam	The beam put out by an instrument landing system which is at 180° to the approved approach beam. Although indications will be received approaches based on them are not approved in the UK.
Backing Wind	An expression used to describe a wind direction moving anti-clockwise when observed from a fixed point.
BACS	Beacon Collision Avoidance System.
Balance Tabs	Fixed or pivoted. The fixed balance tab is a small metal tab easily bent by hand but retains its rigidity in flight. It is used to correct a trim fault and is fitted to the appropriate control surface. See further text in the reference section.
Banner Cloud	Clouds formed where air goes around a peak rather than over the top. Some of the air is lifted upwards in back eddies and forms 'windsock' like clouds dispersing downwind. Also referred to a cloud banners.
Barometer	An instrument used to measure and display atmospheric pressure.
Barometric Pressure	Atmospheric pressure displayed by a barometer.
Barometric Tendency	A change of barometric pressure observed during a specified period and noted in meteorological reports.
BASE	Cloud Base. Always given as height above ground level.
Base Leg	The aerodrome circuit leg between the downwind and final legs and at 90° to them. See the reference section for the purposes and radio calls to be made on each circuit leg under Aerodrome Circuit.
Basic Decision Height	A height at which, if no visual reference may be made, a descent must be discontinued and a climb initiated.
Basic Minimum Descent Height	A height at which, if no visual reference may be made, a further descent must not be initiated.
BB	Back Beam. See Glossary text under that heading.
BC	Back Course. See Glossary text under Back Beam.
BC	Patches, meteorological, relating to fog or mist.
BCARs	British Civil Airworthiness Requirements.
bcd	Binary coded decimal.

BCFG	Fog patches.
BCH	Basic decision Height. See Glossary text under that heading.
BCKG	Backing. See Glossary text under Backing Wind.
BCM	Back Course Marker. See Glossary text under Back Beam.
BCN	Beacon (aeronautical ground light). See Glossary text under Aerodrome Identification Beacon and Aerodrome Beacon.
BCOP	Broken Clouds or better. An expression used to describe 5 - 7 Oktas (or eighths) of cloud cover, or better.
BCP	Breakcloud Procedure. See Glossary text under that heading.
BCST	Broadcast.
BDH	Basic Decision Height. See Glossary text under that heading.
BDRY	Boundary.
Bearing	An expression used to relate the position of an aircraft to another aircraft or fixed ground position. Expressed either as degrees or by a clock face. See also Glossary text under True Bearing and Relative Bearing.
Beat Frequency Oscillator	A device used in aircraft based automatic direction finding (ADF) equipment. See further text in the reference section under Automatic Direction Finding.
Beaufort Wind Scale	A scale devised to categorize wind speeds. See full text and specifications in the reference section.
BECMG	Becoming, meteorological. See text in the reference section under TREND.
Bergernon Process	An ice particle theory which dictates that before precipitation can commence there must be ice particles present in the upper part of the cloud. See further text in the reference section.
Bernoulli's Principle	At any point in a tube through which a fluid (or air) is flowing, static and dynamic pressure equal a constant. See further text in the reference section.
BFDK	Before Dark.
BFO	Beat Frequency Oscillator. See Glossary text under that heading.
BFR	Before.
BGA	British Gliding Association.
BGN	Begin, Began.
BHAB	British Helicopter Advisory Board.
BHGA	British Hang Gliding Association.
BHND	Behind.
BHP	Brake Horsepower.
Billow Clouds	Roll cloud, resembling closely spaced lenticular clouds, generated by an area of vertical wind shear.
BINOVC	Breaks In Overcast.

Bird Sanctuaries	Classed as a prohibited or restricted area and marked on navigational maps with a reference to the upper height limits and the months of activity. See further text in the reference section.
Bird Strikes	All bird strikes require a mandatory report to the CAA whether or not structural damage occurs. Form CA 1282 is used. See further text in the reference section.
Bise	Cold and dry north easterly wind which accompanies heavy cloud and low pressure in the Languedoc region of France.
BKN	Broken Cloud. An expression used to describe 5 – 7 Oktas (eighths) of cloud cover.
Bl	Blue. The colour of a light. Usually shown on airfield approach charts or in relation to aerodrome lighting.
BINA ERS	British Isles/N. America En Route Supplement.
BL	Between Layers. Clear air between layers of stratus cloud.
BL	Blowing, meteorological, used to describe the action of wind on snow.
Blaast	Scottish term for a cold squall.
Black Blizzard	See Glossary text under Dust Devils.
BLDG	Building, meteorological, used to describe the increasing pressure of an air mass.
Bleed Air	High pressure air bled from an engine for cabin pressurization.
BLN	Balloon.
BLO	Below clouds.
Blocking	Term used to describe the effect of an anticyclone halting the progress of a depression and associated fronts. See Glossary text under Quasi-Stationary Front.
Block to Block Time	The period between an aircraft first moving under its own power to the time it stops after flight.
Blowing Snow	Ice crystals blown into the air (hydrometeor) reducing visibility to less than 1,000 metres. See further text in the reference section under Visibility.
BLSN	Blowing Snow. See Glossary text under that heading.
BLW	Below ...
BLZD	Blizzard.
BM	Back Marker. See Glossary text under Marker Beacons.
BMAA	British Microlight Aircraft Association.
BMDH	Basic Minimum Descent Height. A height at which, if no visual reference may be made, a descent must be discontinued.
BNDRY	Boundary.
BNTH	Beneath.
BO	Boundary lights.

BOH	Break Off Height. A height at which, if no visual reference may be made, a descent must be discontinued.
Bomb/Bombing	American expressions describing a rapidly deepening depression where the central pressure falls by 12 millibars or more in a 12 hour period.
Booking In **Booking Out**	Where an aerodrome control service exists all flights must be logged in and out.
Boom Carpet	An area of ground upon which the sonic boom from a supersonic aircraft can be heard.
Boundary Layer	Synonym for friction layer. See text in the reference section under surface winds.
BOVC	Base of Overcast. The estimated or measured cloud base above ground level.
BPA	British Parachuting Association.
BR	Mist, derived from the French word *brouillard.*
BRAF **BRAG** **BRAN** **BRAP**	Braking Action Fair ⎫ Grades of report passed to Braking Action Good ⎪ approaching aircraft referring Braking Action Nil ⎬ to the braking action a pilot Braking Action Poor ⎭ may expect upon landing.
Breakcloud **Procedure**	Breakcloud or cloudbreak procedures are those which assist pilots in descending to a pre-determined height at which, if they are unable to make a visual ground reference, a climb must be initiated and an approach made elsewhere.
Breeze	See Glossary text on Light Breeze and Gentle Breeze.
BRG	Bearing. See Glossary text under that heading.
BRKG	Braking. Relating to runway braking action.
Brocken Spectre	A coloured ring of light surrounding the shadow of an aircraft projected onto the surface of a cloud.
Broken Cloud	An expression used to describe 5 – 7 Oktas (or eighths) of cloud cover.
BS	Commercial Broadcasting Station. See Glossary text under that heading.
BTL	Between Layers. A flight carried out between layers of stratus cloud.
BTN	Between.
Buys Ballot's Law	If an observer in the northern hemisphere stands with his back to the wind then the area of low pressure will be to his left. The opposite applies in the southern hemisphere. See further text in the reference section.

C

c	Compass
c	Coulomb. See Glossary text under that heading.
C	Centre. The suffix used for runway identification in the case where an airfield has three runways, each with the same magnetic direction.
°C	Degrees Celsius (centigrade). See Glossary text under Celsius.
C	Civil.
C	Tower/Control/operations. A black 'C' on a yellow background denotes the office at an airfield where landing fees may be paid.
C/A	Clear/Acquisition code. A term used in a satellite navigation or global positioning system. See further text in the reference section under Global Positioning System.
CA	Activated. (NOTAM decode 4th & 5th letters).
CA	Air/ground radio facility. (NOTAM decode 2nd & 3rd letters).
CA 48	Flight Plan form also referred to as RAF F2919.
CA 1094	Airmiss report form.
CA 1282	Bird strike report form.
CAA	Civil Aviation Authority.
CACC	Civil Aviation Communications Centre.
CAF	Cleared As Filed, referring to a submitted flight plan.
CAIP	Civil Aircraft Inspection Procedures.
Calibrated Airspeed	An expression used in the United States to describe the UK's equivalent of rectified airspeed (RAS). It is the indicated airspeed corrected for pressure error (due to inherent instrument and position errors).
CALF	Chart Amendments – Low Flying.
Calm	Wind speed not registering on measuring equipment. Force 0.
Camber	The distance between the mean camber line and the chord line.
Canard	An aircraft design which has the main wing at the rear and a stabilator at the front.
Candella	An expression used to describe the measurable brilliance of a light bulb. Originally based on candle power.
CANP	Low level Civil Aircraft Notification Procedure. See Glossary text under that heading.
Cantilever Wing	A wing supported only at its join to the fuselage and having no support strut or wires.
CAP	Civil Aviation Publication.
CAP	Contact Approach.
Cap Cloud	An apparently stationary cloud forming over the summit of a mountain taking the shape of a giant cap. See further text in the reference section.

Carburettor Heat	Used as a precaution against the formation, or for the dissipation of carburettor ice. A heat exchange unit provides a temperature rise of up to 50° C to an alternate air feed which is directed to the carburettor intake. See further text in the reference section under Icing – Carburettor.
Carburettor Icing	A reduction in pressure at the carburettor venturi can result in moisture in the induction air forming ice by adiabatic cooling. The ice attaches to the venturi walls causing a restriction and progressive reduction in power. See further text in the reference section under Icing – Carburettor.
Carrier Wave	A wave that is transmitted at a constant frequency and amplitude. It is designated as a NON emission. See further text in the reference section under Radio Waves.
CAS	Calibrated Air Speed. See Glossary text under that heading.
CAS	Close Air Support.
CAS	Collision Avoidance System.
CAS	Controlled Airspace.
CAST	High turretted castellanus clouds.
Castellanus	High Turretted cumulonimbus clouds with great vertical extent.
CAT	Category.
CAT	Clear Air Turbulence. See Glossary text under that heading.
CAT	Commercial Air Transport.
CATO	Civil Air Traffic Operations.
CAVOK	Ceiling and Visibility OK. See further text and a full specification in the reference section under C.A.V.O.K.
CB	Cumulonimbus Cloud. See Glossary text under that heading.
CBR	Cloud Base Recorder.
CC	Completed. (NOTAM decode 4th & 5th letters).
CC	Counter Clockwise.
CC	Cirrocumulus Cloud. See Glossary text under that heading.
CCA/B/C	Correction. Used in relation to weather reports.
CCF	Central Control Function. See Glossary text under that heading.
CCF	Combined Control Function.
CCT	Centre of Control for Traffic.
CCW	Counter Clockwise.
Cd	Candella. See Glossary text under that heading.
CD	Coded.
CD	De-activated. (NOTAM decode 4th & 5th letters).
C_D	Drag Coefficient.
CD5B...	Calvert coded approach light system with 5 bars suffixed for ILS Category... A system used to visually indicate if an aircraft is on the correct approach glideslope.

C_{DI}	Coefficient of Induced Drag.
CDI	Course Deviation Indicator. See further text in the reference section under Omni-Bearing Indicator.
C_{DP}	Coefficient of Profile Drag.
CE	En-route surveillance radar. (NOTAM decode 2nd & 3rd letters). See Glossary text under Secondary Surveillance Radar.
CE	Erected. (NOTAM decode 4th & 5th letters).
Ceiling	Used to denote the maximum height of an aircraft or upper level of cloud.
Ceilometer	Device used to measure a cloudbase. There are two types, nodding beam or lazer.
Cell	Term used to describe the circulation of an active cumulus cloud.
Celsius	Temperature scale with the freezing point of water at 0°C and boiling point at 100°C. See text in the reference section under Temperature.
Centimetric	Frequencies in the super high frequency or microwave range, 3,000 – 30,000Mhz.
Central Control Function	An integral part of the UK air traffic control system responsible for the control of aircraft at FL155 and below within the London TMA and including Heathrow and Gatwick.
Centreline Thrust Aircraft	A twin engine aircraft where the engines are fitted fore and aft of the fuselage on the lateral axis. See further text in the reference section.
Centre of Gravity	The point at which the total weight of an aircraft is considered to act.
Centrifugal Force	Meteorologically, a cyclostrophic force acting away from the centre of a high pressure system in the northern hemisphere, with the opposite effect in the southern hemisphere. See text in the reference section under Cyclostrophic Force.
Centripetal Force	Meteorologically, a cyclostrophic force acting towards the centre of a high pressure system in the northern hemisphere,with the opposite effect in the southern hemisphere. See text in the reference section under Cyclostrophic Force.
Certificate of Airworthiness	A requirement for legal flight on all aircraft except those operated under a permit to fly. It is issued by a CAA licenced maintenance organisation and is valid for 3 years. See further text in the reference section.
Certificate of Experience	A certification that a pilot has achieved the required of number of hours to enable him/her to continue to use the privileges conferred under the original licence or rating.
Certificate of Maintenance Review	A requirement for legal flight on all aircraft engaged in public transport or aerial work. See further text in the reference section.

Certificate of Registration	A requirement for legal flight. Any alterations of ownership must be advised to the CAA within 28 days of the change. See further text in the reference section.
Certificate of Release to Service	A document applying either to an aircraft or to a part fitted to an aircraft confirming that it has been manufactured and/or examined to be within a specific standard or performance requirement.
CETD	Calculated Estimated Time of Departure.
CETO	Calculated Estimated Time of Overflight of a fixed ground object.
CF	Change Frequency to.
CF	Operating frequency(s) changed to ..... (NOTAM decode 4th & 5th letters).
CFI	Chief Flying Instructor.
CFMU	Central Flow Management Unit.
CFN	Confirm.
CG	Centre of Gravity. See Glossary text under that heading.
CG	Downgraded to ..... (NOTAM decode 4th & 5th letters).
CG	Ground controlled approach system. (NOTAM decode 2nd & 3rd letters).
CGL	Circling Guidance Lights.
CH	Changed. (NOTAM decode 4th & 5th letters).
CH	Channel, a specified radio frequency.
CH	Critical Height. See Glossary text under Minimum Descent Height.
Chaff	A method of alerting radar controllers to an emergency and radio failure situation by dropping packets containing strips of aluminium foil into the slipstream of the aircraft in distress. They paint a distinct following trail from an aircraft on the radar screen.
Charlie Bangers	Slang term used to describe thunderstorms, derived from the meteorological abbreviation CB, cumulonimbus.
Chart Types	See Glossary text under Equivalence Charts, Lambert Projection Charts, Mercator Projection Charts and Orthomorphic Charts.
Chart Scales	See text in the reference section.
Check Out	A flight in which a pilot's competence is checked by a supervisory or examining pilot.
CHG	Change.
Chord	The length of a chord line. See Glossary text under Chord Line.
Chord Line	A straight line joining the ends of the curved camber line.
CHT	Cylinder Head Temperature gauge. See Glossary text under that heading.
CI	Cirrus cloud. See Glossary text under that heading.

CI	Identification or radio call sign changed to ..... (NOTAM decode 4th & 5th letters).
CIG	Ceiling. See Glossary text under that heading.
Circling Area	A designated area having a published safe circling altitude where aircraft may hold awaiting an approach to land.
Circuit	See Glossary text under Aerodrome Circuit.
Circuit Breaker	A restorable electrical fuse. See further text in the reference section.
CIRNAV	Circumnavigate.
Cirrocumulus Cloud	Regular cloud patterns of ice crystals formed on the leading edge of a warm front.
Cirrostratus Cloud	High level, thinly overcast cloud, base 20,000 feet or more, composed of ice crystals.
Cirrostratus Nebulosus	Very high level cirrus cloud composed of ice crystals that appear to form a halo around the sun.
Cirrus Castellanus	High turretted cirrus clouds.
Cirrus Cloud	High level, base 20,000 feet or more, cloud formed in the upper levels of the troposphere consisting of snow flakes and ice crystals which form long, thin, streaky clouds. See further text in the reference section.
Cirrus Uncinus	Cirrus cloud formations which link together.
CIT	Near or over large towns.
CIV	Civil.
CK	Check.
CL	Centre line. Relating to a runway.
CL	Centre line Lights. Relating to a runway.
CL	Realigned. (NOTAM decode 4th & 5th letters).
CL	Selective calling system. (NOTAM decode 2nd & 3rd letters). See Glossary text under that heading.
CL..m	Centreline with figures indicating light spacings.
C/L	Centre Lights. Relating to a runway.
C/L	Centre Line. Relating to a runway.
C$_L$	Lift Coefficient.
CLA	Clear Ice. See Glossary text under that heading.
Clag/Claggy	Slang expression used to describe overcast low cloud.
CLBR	Calibration.
CLCD	Colour Coded centreline, white, alternate white/red, red.
CLD	Cloud.
Clean	Used to describe the condition of an aircraft with landing gear and flaps retracted.

Clear Air Turbulence	Turbulence encountered near or within a jet stream with no meteorological phenomenon to indicate its presence. See further text in the reference section.
Clear Ice	Also known as glaze ice. Formed on aircraft flying through sub-zero temperatures in rain. See text in the reference section under Icing—Airframe – In Flight
Clearway	A rectangular area, commencing at the end of the take off run selected and prepared as a suitable area over which an aircraft may make a portion of its initial climb to a specified height. For other areas see text in the reference section under Aerodrome – Surface Definitions.
CLL	Centre Line Lighting will be provided.
C$_{Lmax}$	Maximum Lift Coefficient.
CLNC	Clearance.
Cloud	A mass of air in which condensation has occurred. See further text in the reference section.
Cloud Banners	See Glossary text under Banner Cloud.
Cloudbreak Procedures	See Glossary text under Breakcloud Procedure.
Cloud Heights	Classified by base heights: Low = below 7,000 feet. Medium, alto, 7,000 to 20,000 feet. High, cirro, above 20,000 feet.
Cloudy Ice	Formed by an aircraft flying through a cloud containing large super-cooled water droplets. On impact part of each droplet instantly freezes into rime crystals, the temperature of the remainder is raised by the latent heat release and runs back in the airflow to freeze more slowly as clear ice. Also known as rime ice. See further text in the reference section under Icing.
CLR	Clear(s), Cleared to ..., Clearance.
CLRS	Clear & Smooth.
C$_{LS}$	Lift Coefficient at which stall commences.
CLSD	Closed.
cm	Centimetre.
CM	Surface movement radar. (NOTAM decode 2nd & 3rd letters).
CM	Displaced. (NOTAM decode 4th & 5th letters). See Glossary text under Displaced Threshold.
CMATZ	Combined Military Air Traffic Zones.
CMB	Climb.
CMPL	Complete, Completion, Completed.
CN	Cancelled. (NOTAM decode 4th & 5th letters).
CNL	Cancellation (of a flight plan).
CNS	Continuous. Used in respect of rain or snow.
CNTR	Centre.

CNTRL	Central.
CO	Operating. (NOTAM decode 4th & 5th letters).
Coalescence Theory	Theorises that precipitation occurs by water droplets colliding and merging until they are too big to be supported by updrafts. See further text in the reference section.
Coarse Deviation Needle	An indicator used in a VOR and ILS localiser display to show the distance off track. See further text in the reference section under Omni-Bearing Indicator.
Coastal Refraction	An error affecting non directional beacon transmissions. Radio waves travel faster over water than land and where a signal is received at any other angle than 90° it will be progressively refracted. See text in the reference section under Non Directional Beacon.
C of A	Certificate of Airworthiness. See Glossary text under that heading.
C of E	Certificate of Experience. See Glossary text under that heading.
Col	An area surrounded by two diagonally opposed depressions and two diagonally opposed anticyclones.
Cold Front	A front of cold air which moves in a predictable line replacing the warm air ahead of it. See text in the reference section under Fronts.
Cold Front Wave	An ruffling effect in a long cold front marking the formation of a secondary depression. See Glossary text under Secondary Depression.
Co-Located Equipment	See text in the reference section under Co-Located Navigation or Approach Equipment.
COM	Communications.
Commercial Broadcasting Station	Transmitters often used by pilots via their ADF equipment for bearing and homing information. Their use is not approved by the CAA and they should not be used in IMC.
COM/NAV	Communication & Navigation Aids.
COMO	Compass Locator.
Compass Deviation	See Glossary text under Deviation.
Compass (Magnetic)	A standby or E2B compass, used to calibrate the directional gyro indicator or as the prime direction indicator in the event of a DGI failure. See further text in the reference section.
Compass Swing	A check and calibration procedure where a magnetic compass may be adjusted for accuracy. It is a mandatory operation following a lightning strike.
CON	Consol beacon.
CONC	Concrete.
COND	Condition.
Condensation	The process where water vapour changes to liquid, normally by cooling. See Glossary text under Latent Heat of Condensation and the reference section under Condensation.

Condensation Nuclei	Minute particles of salt, ash and unsaturated hydrocarbons suspended in the atmosphere which cause water vapour to concentrate into mist or cloud water droplets when sufficient humidity exists.
Condensation Level	The height above which the water vapour in rising air will condense to form cloud. See Glossary text under Saturation.
Condensation Trail	An initially thin track of water vapour or ice crystals created from the water vapour from a high flying jet engine. If the air is sufficiently humid the increase in temperature along this track can modify the air causing it to reach its saturation point and grow into a trailing cloud formation.
Conditional Stability	Atmospheric state which exists when the environmental lapse rate is between the dry and saturated adiabatic lapse rates. See text in the reference section under Adiabatic Lapse Rates.
Conduction	The movement of heat from one place to another by molecular agitation and without motion of the medium.
Cone of Confusion	A blind area when a VOR signal cannot be received. See further text in the reference section under Omni-Bearing Indicator.
Confluence	Meteorologically used to describe converging streamlines. See Glossary text under Streamline.
CONST	Construction.
Constant Speed Propeller	See Glossary text under Constant Speed Unit.
Constant Speed Unit	Used in engines fitted with a variable pitch propeller. The unit allows the engine revolutions to remain constant and the thrust changed by altering the propeller's angle of attack. See further text in the reference section under Propeller.
cont	Continuous.
CONT	Continue.
Contour Charts	Charts plotting upper winds by pressure contours. Charts available are 700, 500, 200, 100 millibars representing 10,000, 18,000, 30,000 and 53,000 feet respectively.
Contour Gradient	The difference in height over the horizontal spacing between two contour lines.
Contrail	Abbreviation for condensation trail. See Glossary text under that heading.
Convection	The movement of heat by physical motion of a heated medium from one place to another.
Convection Heating	Meteorologically, the effect of the sun warming the Earth's surface causing the air above it to rise and become less dense. See further text in the reference section.
Convective Lifting	Cloud formed when re-radiation has been strong enough to form an inversion close to the ground. The inversion dissipates as the warm surface air mixes with the higher levels, cooling until it reaches saturation level, forming the cloud.

Convergence	An upward airflow caused by two opposing airstreams meeting and flowing into the area of lowest pressure.
Convergency	The angular difference between two meridians. See further text in the reference section.
COP	Change over Point.
Co-Pilot	A licenced pilot acting in any piloting capacity other than as pilot in command.
COR	Correction. Used in relation to weather reports.
Coriolis Effect	See text in the reference section under Coriolis Effect and Geostrophic Wind.
Coriolis Force	An effect on the Earth's atmosphere deflecting all air movements to the right (in the northern hemisphere with the opposite in the southern hemisphere) due to the Earth's rotation. The force increases in proportion to the sine of latitude and is zero on the equator. See further text in the reference section under Geostrophic Wind.
Coriolis Illusion	An illusion resulting from a prolonged genuine turn that a non-existent turn or acceleration is occurring. See further text in the reference section.
Corposant	Extreme result of a discharge of static electricity resulting in a visual display. Also known as St Elmo's fire. See text in the reference section under Static Electricity.
COSPAS	Russian acronym for search and rescue satellite aided distress tracking.
COT	Coastal. Meteorological.
Coulomb	The unit of electrical charge equal to the quantity of electricity transferred by a current of 1 amp in 1 second.
Coupled Ailerons	Method by which aileron and rudder movements are coupled to reduce adverse yaw.
Course Line	The boundary of points nearest to the runway centre line in any horizontal plane at which there is no difference in depth of modulation.
Cowl Flaps	Flaps that can be adjusted to increase or decrease the cooling effect of an airflow over an engine.
cP	Continental Polar air mass. See Glossary text under Polar Continental Air.
CP	Centre of Pressure, meteorological.
CP	Constant Power.
CP	Operating on reduced power. (NOTAM decode 4th & 5th letters).
CP	Precision approach radar. (NOTAM decode 2nd & 3rd letters). See Glossary text under that heading.
CPA	Closed Point of Approach.
CPF	Complete Power Failure.

CPL	Commercial Pilot's Licence.
CPL	Current flight Plan.
Cpt	Clearance.
CR	Surveillance radar element of a precision approach radar system. (NOTAM decode 2nd & 3rd letters). See Glossary text under Precision Approach Radar.
CR	Temporarily replaced by ..... (NOTAM decode 4th & 5th letters).
CRDF	Cathode Ray Direction Finder.
Creithleag	Irish term for a gentle breeze.
Critical Altitude	The maximum altitude at which it is possible to maintain a specific propeller rpm, power or manifold pressure. See further text in the reference section.
Critical Angle	The angle between the vertical and the angle of transmission of a radio wave. See further text in the reference section under Radio Waves.
Critical Engine	The engine whose failure would most adversely affect the performance or handling qualities of an aircraft. See further text in the reference section.
CRM	Cockpit Resource Management.
Cross Wind Leg	An aerodrome circuit leg at 90° to the take off end of the runway. See the reference section for the purposes and radio calls to be made on each circuit leg under Aerodrome Circuit.
CRS	Course.
CRZ	Cruise.
Cs	Cirrostratus Cloud. See Glossary text under that heading.
C/S	Call Sign.
CS	Communication Station.
CS	Installed. (NOTAM decode 4th & 5th letters).
CS	Secondary surveillance radar. (NOTAM decode 2nd & 3rd letters). See Glossary text under that heading.
CSC	Chief Sector Controller.
CST	Coast.
CSTMS	Customs.
CSU	Constant Speed Unit. Used in engines fitted with a variable pitch propeller.
CT	Continental Tropical air mass. See Glossary text under Tropical Continental Air.
CT	On test, do not use. (NOTAM decode 4th & 5th letters).
CT	Terminal area surveillance radar. (NOTAM decode 2nd & 3rd letters).
CTA	Calculated Time of Arrival.

CTA	Control Area.
CTAM	Climb To And Maintain.
CTC	Contact.
Ctl	Control.
CTLZ	Control Zone.
CTN	Caution.
Ctr	Centre.
CTR	Control zone.
CTZ	Control Zone.
Cu	Cumulus Cloud. See Glossary text under Cumuliform Cloud.
CUF	Cumuliform Cloud. See Glossary text under that heading.
Cumulonimbus Capillatus	Very active high level cumulonimbus cloud peaking with an anvil shaped top.
Cumuliform Cloud	Vertical clouds formed by warm rising air resulting in a formation of domed shaped upper surfaces and a large vertical extent. See further text in the reference section.
Cumulonimbus Cloud	Dark dense cumuliform clouds which if fully developed will form a thunderstorm. See further text in the reference section.
Cumulonimbus Mammatus	Rounded protuberances forming on the underside of a giant anvil top spreading from an active cumulonimbus cloud.
Cumulus	See Glossary text under Cumuliform Cloud.
Cumulus Congestus	Very active cumulus clouds with a strong vertical growth which may reach sufficient size to form altocumulus.
Cumulus Fractus	Wisps of cumulus cloud signalling the formation of larger cumuliform clouds.
Cumulus Granitus	Slang expression used to describe mountain peaks embedded in cumulus clouds.
Cumulus Humilis	Growing cumulus clouds often forming in a line due to rising ground.
Cumulus Mediocris	Active cumulus clouds with a large vertical growth.
Cus	Customs available.
Customs	See text in the reference section for clearances and procedures.
CVFR	Control VFR Flights.
CVR	Cockpit Voice Recorder.
CW	Carrier Wave.
CW	Clockwise.
CW	Continuous Wave.
CWY	Clearway. See Glossary text under that heading.
Cyclogenesis	The process of creation or deepening of a cyclone.
Cyclone	A circular tropical storm around a low pressure system. Anti-clockwise in the northern hemisphere, clockwise in the

southern. Sometimes used as a general term for a depression. See further text in the reference section.

Cyclonic An anti-clockwise airflow in the northern hemisphere, clockwise in the southern hemisphere.

Cyclostrophic Force The force acting upon the winds flowing around curved isobars. The force acts as a centrifugal or centripetal force dependent on the hemisphere and type of pressure area. See further text in the reference section.

Cylinder Head Temperature Gauge Used to indicate the optimum setting for cowl flaps.

CZ Caution Zone.

D

D...	Danger area (followed by identification number).
D	Day.
D	Drag.
DA	Danger Area.
DA	Decision Altitude. See Glossary text under that heading.
DAAC	Director Army Air Corps.
DAAIS	Danger Area Activity Information Service.
DABRK	Daybreak.
DABS	Discrete Address Beacon System.
DACS	Danger Area Crossing Service. See Glossary text under that heading.
DALGT	Daylight.
DALR	Dry Adiabatic Lapse Rate. See Glossary text under that heading.
DaN	DecaNewtons.
D and D	Distress & Diversion.
Danger Areas	See text in the reference section.
Danger Area Crossing Service	A service providing pilots with the activity status of a participating danger area. See further text in the reference section under Danger Area Activity Information Service.
DATCO	Duty Air Traffic Control Officer.
Day	Officially, under the ICAO definition, day means the period half an hour before sunrise and half an hour after sunset. Sunset and sunrise being determined at surface level.
db	Decibels.
d.c.	Direct Current.
DCA	Director(ate) of Civil Aviation.
DCKG	Docking.
DCR	Decrease.
DCT	Direct. Abbreviation used in flight planning or flight plans.
Dead Reckoning	A navigation method by which a heading is estimated and held pending a positive fix.
Dead Side	A positional leg similar to those of an aerodrome circuit. Situated in the opposite position to the downwind leg and in the opposite direction. It is used for descent to circuit height for a crosswind leg join. See the reference section for the purposes and radio calls to be made on each circuit leg under Aerodrome Circuit.
Dead Space	In the context of high frequency transmissions: The area between the end of surface wave cover and the start of the first returning sky wave. See further text in the reference section under Radio Waves.

Dead Stick Landing A landing carried out where all the engines, or the engine if only one is fitted, are inoperative.

DECCA Radio navigation system in which the airborne equipment continuously updates the aircraft's position by receiving signals from two or more ground stations.

Decimetric Frequencies in the ultra high frequency band. See further text in the reference section under Ultra High Frequency.

Decision Altitude The altitude at which, if no visual runway contact is made, the published missed approach procedure must be initiated. See text in the reference section under Decision Height.

Decision Height The height at which, if no visual runway contact is made, the published missed approach procedure must be initiated. See further text in the reference section.

DECR Decrease.

Deep Used as a meteorological expression to describe climacteric low pressure systems.

Deepening Meteorologically used to describe the centre of pressure in a depression that is decreasing.

DEG Degree.

De-ice Systems See text in the reference section.

Delay Infinite Expression used by ATC to advise a pilot that no approach clearance will be given and that a diversion should be instituted.

DENEB Fog Dispersal operations.

Density The mass per unit volume.

Density Altitude The altitude in the standard atmosphere corresponding to a particular value of air density.

Density of Air The International Standard Atmosphere air density value at sea level is 1225 grams per cubic metre. This reduces with height but not at a linear rate. See further text in the reference section.

DEP Departure.

DEPCOM Departure Communication. Common broadcast frequency of 122.950MHZ used by helicopters under 500ft where no ground frequency exists.

Depression Meteorological expression to describe a low pressure system. See further text in the reference section under Depressions.

DES Descend to ...

Designated Operational Coverage The published range of a non-directional beacon in daylight conditions. See text in the reference section under Non Directional Beacons.

DEST Destination.

DETRESFA Distress phase. See Glossary text under that heading.

DEV Deviation or Deviating.

Deviation	An error affecting a magnetic compass resulting from electrical fields and metallic objects in an aircraft. See further text in the reference section under Compass – Magnetic.
Dew	Water vapour forming condensation by cooling on contact with a comparatively cooler surface.
Dewpoint Temperature	The temperature to which air can cool, with no change in pressure, without condensation occuring. See Glossary text in the reference section under Dewpoint.
DF,D/F	Direction Finder or Finding. See Glossary text under that heading.
DFDR	Digital Flight Data Recorder.
DFTI	Distance From Touchdown Indicator.
DFTS	Downdraughts.
DG	Directional Gyro. See Glossary text under that heading.
DGI	Directional Gyro Indicator. See Glossary text under Directional Gyro.
DH	Decision Height. See Glossary text under that heading.
DI	Directional Indicator. See Glossary text under Directional Gyro.
DIF	Diffuse. Meteorological.
Differential Ailerons	An aileron system which increases the drag on the down going wing by increasing the up going aileron's angle of movement in comparison to the down going aileron on the other wing. See text in the reference section under Ailerons for other types.
Diffluence	Meteorologically used to describe diverging streamlines. See Glossary text under Streamline.
Dilution of Precision	An expression used to describe an error of accuracy from a satellite navigation system. See text in the reference section under Global Positioning System.
Dir	Director.
Direct Current	A current in an electrical circuit where the flow has a constant polarity.
Direct Wave	A radio transmission which relies on the transmitter being in line of sight of the receiver. See further text in the reference section under Radio Waves.
Directional Gyro	A gyro driven compass indicator manually or automatically calibrated to the magnetic compass. See further text in the reference section under Directional Indicator.
Directional Indicator	See text in the reference section.
Direction Finding	A method of providing pilots with homing information by the receiving station determining a bearing to the originator of a VHF or UHF transmission. See further text in the reference section.

Direct Radio Waves A basic limitation of high frequency transmissions that restricts the range to the line of sight between transmitter and receiver. See further text in the reference section under Radio Waves.

Displaced Threshold A threshold located at a point on a runway other than at the beginning of the apparent runway area. See further text in the reference section under Runway Markings and Aerodrome – Surface Definitions.

Dissipation Trail A trail of clear air left by an aircraft flying through a very thin cloud layer. The wing tip vortices cause the cloud to descend and warm adiabatically. Also see Condensation Trail in the Glossary text.

Dist Distance.

Dist District.

Distance Measuring Equipment A UHF secondary radar system that enables aircraft equipment to display the distance to or from a DME ground station. If tracking directly to or from the station a ground speed and time estimate may also be obtained. See further text in the reference section.

Distrail See Glossary text under Dissipation Trail.

Distress Message A mayday or emergency message transmitted in the event of the threat of serious and/or imminent danger to the occupants of an aircraft.

Distress Phase A situation where there is reasonable certainty that an aircraft or its occupants are in imminent danger or require immediate assistance. See further text in the reference section.

Diurnal Daily. Meteorologically used in relation to daily temperature or pressure variations. See text in the reference section under Insolation.

DIV Divert or Diverting.

Divergence The moving apart of air masses or currents causing a rise or lowering in air pressure.

DLA Delay or Delayed.

DLI Delay Infinite. See Glossary text under that heading.

DME Distance Measuring Equipment. See Glossary text under that heading.

DME/P Precision Distance Measuring Equipment.

DME/W Distance Measuring Equipment with Wide spectrum characteristics.

DMLS Doppler Microwave Landing System.

DNG Danger or Dangerous.

DNS Dense. In relation to fog, dust or smoke.

DNSL Downslope. Relating to a sloping runway.

DOC	Designated Operational Coverage. The published range of a non-directional beacon in daylight conditions. See text in the reference section under Non Directional Beacons.
DOC	Direct Operating Costs.
Doinionn	An Irish term for wild weather.
DOM	Domestic.
DOP	Dilution of Precision. See Glossary text under that heading.
Doppler Effect	An effect utilised in primary radar to determine the velocity of moving objects by measuring the doppler shift. See further text in the reference section.
Doppler Radar	A radar system exploiting the doppler effect by measuring two or more attributes of a moving target enabling it to calculate the unknowns.
Doppler Shift	The phenomenon in which the frequency of a moving object appears to increase as it approaches and decrease as it departs.
Double Sideband	A amplitude modulated signal with the upper and lower sidebands retained. See further text in the reference section under Radio Waves.
Downburst	Strong gust of descending air associated with an active cumulonimbus cloud. When less than 4km in diameter is referred to as a microburst.
Downwind Leg	An aerodrome circuit leg parallel to the runway and in the opposite direction to that of take off. See the reference section for the purposes and radio calls to be made on each circuit leg under Aerodrome Circuit.
DP	Deep, meteorological. See Glossary text under that heading.
DP	Depart.
DP	Dewpoint Temperature. See Glossary text under that heading.
DPC	Departure Control.
DPNG	Deepening, meteorological. See Glossary text under that heading.
DPT	Depth
DR	Dead Reckoning. See Glossary text under that heading.
DR	Low Drifting snow.
Drag	The resistance of the air as an object moves through it. See further text in the reference section.
DRFT	Drift.
DRG	During.
Drifting	A meteorological term to describe wind blown snow.
Drift (Mechanical)	Refer to the Glossary sections on Apparent Drift & Gyro Drift.
Drift (Wind)	The movement of an aircraft off the desired track caused by wind.
Drizzle	Precipitation with a droplet size of 0.2mm or less reducing visibility to between 500 and 3,000 metres. See further text in the reference section under Visibility.

Drooping Ailerons	Ailerons designed to droop as the flaps are lowered increasing lateral control. See text in the reference section under Ailerons for other types.
Droop Leading Edges	Wing leading edges that automatically extend at low airspeeds increasing lift.
DRSN	Low Drifting Snow.
Dry Adiabatic Lapse Rate	Dry unsaturated air cools at the rate of 3°C for each thousand feet of altitude. See further text in the reference section under Adiabatic Lapse Rates.
Dry Bulb Thermometer	Used in comparison with a wet bulb thermometer to evaluate relative humidity and dewpoint temperature. See further text in the reference section under Wet and Dry Bulb Thermometer.
DS	Dust Storm, meteorological.
DSB	Double Sideband. See Glossary text under that heading.
DSIPT	Dissipate, meteorological.
DST	Daylight Saving Time.
DTAM	Descend and Maintain.
DTG	Date Time Group.
DTRT	Deteriorate or Deteriorating, meteorological.
DU	Widespread Dust, meteorological. See Glossary text under Dust.
DUA	Dedicated User Area.
DUC	Dense Upper Cloud.
DUR	Duration.
Dust	Minute solid particles suspended in the atmosphere reducing visibility to between 1,000m and 10Km. See further text in the reference section under Visibility.
Dust Devils	Intense spiralling vortices of air which form over very hot surfaces and usually under clear skies. See further text in the reference section.
Dust Storms	Resulting from strong winds and/or thermal activity lifting dust from arid areas and reducing visibility to less than 1,000m. See further text in the reference section under Visibility.
DVOR	Doppler Very high Frequency Omni-directional Range.
DWN	Downdraughts.
DWPNT	Dewpoint. See Glossary text under Dewpoint Temperature.
Dynamic Microphone	A modern evolution of the carbon granule based microphone with design and circuitry to provide automatic noise cancellation. See text in the reference section under Headsets.
Dynamic Pressure	An increase in air pressure caused by a moving object passing through an air mass or an air mass impacting upon a fixed object. See further text in the reference section.
DZ	Drizzle. See Glossary text under that heading.
DZ	Dropping Zone. Normally relating to parachutists or glider towing cables.

E	
E	East.
E	Emergency (frequency or lighting).
E	Estimated.
EAC	Expect Approach Clearance. See Glossary text under Expected Approach Time.
Earth	An oblate spheroid inhabited by pilots and other people. See more sensible text in the reference section.
Earth Tied Gyro	A gyroscope which retains its rigidity in relation to the Earth's vertical.
EAS	Equivalent Airspeed. See Glossary text under that heading.
EAT	Expected Approach Time. See Glossary text under that heading.
EB	Eastbound.
ECA	Emergency Controlling Authorities.
ECAC	European Civil Aviation Conferences.
ED	Emergency Distance. See Glossary text under that heading.
EET	Estimated Elapsed Time. See Glossary text under that heading.
EFAS	Electronic Flash Approach light System.
EFAS	En-route Flight Advisory Service.
EFATO	Engine Failure After Take Off.
EFC	Expect Further Clearance.
EFF	Effective.
EGT	Exhaust Gas Temperature.
EHF	Extremely High Frequency. Frequencies in the 30,000 - 300,000 MHz range.
EL	Elevation.
EL	Runway End Lights.
ELBA	Emergency Location Beacon – Aircraft. See Glossary text under Emergency Locator Transmitter.
Electret Microphone	Modern type of microphone unaffected by electromagnetic interference with a wide frequency response and dynamic range. See further text in the reference section under Headsets.
ELEV	Elevation. Height above sea level.
Elevator	Horizontal control surface hinged to the rear of the tailplane providing longitudinal control in pitch. See further text in the reference section.
Elevator Trim Tab	A section located on the trailing edge of the elevator and used to increase or reduce its lift resulting in the reduction of the pressure required on the control column. See further text in the reference section under Trim Tabs.

Elevon	A control surface on the wing of a tailless aircraft which acts as elevator and aileron.
ELR	Environmental Lapse Rate. See Glossary text under that heading.
ELR	Extra Long Range.
ELT	Emergency Locator Transmitter.
EM	Emission.
EMBD	Embedded. Meteorological, as in cumulonimbus embedded in stratus clouds.
EMERG	Emergency
Emergency Ceiling	The highest altitude at which a multi-engined aircraft can maintain a rate of climb of 50 feet per minute with one engine inoperative.
Emergency Distance	The length of the declared take off run plus the length of the stopway. For other distances and areas see text in the reference section under Aerodrome – Surface Definitions.
Emergency Locator Transmitter	An independently powered transmitter fitted to an aircraft and designed to transmit a Morse group automatically on 121.5Mhz, 243Khz or both, following impact. See further text in the reference section.
Emergency Phase	In relation to a distress or mayday call and describes a condition of uncertainty, alert or distress.
Emergency Triangle	A procedure adopted in VMC conditions when radio failure is compounded by the pilot being lost. The pattern has three 2 minute legs. Right hand for transmitter failure and left hand for transmitter and receiver failure. See further text in the reference section.
Encoding Altimeter	An altimeter used in conjunction with the transponder passing information to a SSR screen whilst the transponder is set to Mode C. The system uses a pneumatic altimeter with a parallel coded output of 9 to 11 bits representing the aircraft's height above the 1013.25 datum to the nearest 100 feet.
END	Stop-end, in relation to a runway visual range report.
ENG	Engine.
En-Route Hold	Flight patterns in the shape of a an oval racetrack. The hold takes 4 minutes to complete, 1 minute for each leg and 1 minute for each turn. All turns are right hand at rate one. The same procedure applies for instrument approach procedure holds. See further text in the reference section under Holding Procedures.
ENRT	En-Route.
ENTR	Entire.
Entrainment	The mixing of air from surrounding areas drawn towards the core of a thermal updraft.

Environmental Lapse Rate	The actual rate at which the ambient temperature changes with an increase in height. See further text in the reference section.
EOBT	Estimated Off Block Time. See Glossary text under that heading.
EPIRB	Emergency Position Indicating Radio Beacon.
EPNdB	Effective Perceived Noise decibel. A unit of noise intended to represent its duration and perceived annoyance value.
EPR	Engine Pressure Ratio.
EPROM	Erasable Programable Read Only Memory.
Equisignal Area	An area identified by a localiser receiver where there is no modulation difference in the transmitted signal. See further text in the reference section under Instrument Landing System.
Equivalence Charts	Charts where the representation of an area in correct proportion to that on the earth.
Equivalent Air Speed	Rectified airspeed corrected for compressibility error. Compressibility is always a subtracted quantity.
EQPT	Equipment.
ERS	En Route Supplement.
ERTS	Earth Resources Technology Satellite.
ESSA	Environmental Sciences and Services Authority.
EST	Estimate or Estimated.
Estimated Elapsed Time	The estimated time required to proceed from one significant point or flight information region to another.
Estimated Off Block Time	The estimated time at which an aircraft will commence to move under its own power. Associated with a departure.
Estimated Time of Arrival	The estimated time that an aircraft will arrive at a pre-designated point from where an instrument approach will be commenced or is expected to commence. For visual flights it is the time the aircraft expects to arrive overhead the aerodrome.
ETA	Estimated Time of Arrival. See Glossary text under that heading.
ETD	Estimated Time of Departure.
ETE	Estimated Time En-route.
ETO	Estimated Time over significant point.
ETOPS	Extended range Twin Operations.
ETP	Estimated Time of Penetration.
EUR	European region.
ev	Every.
Evaporation	See text in the reference section.
Evaporation Fog	See Glossary text under Arctic Sea Smoke.
EVE	Evening.
EX	Expect.

EXC	Except.
EXCP	Except.
EXER	Exercises, Exercising, Exercise.
Exhaust Gas Temperature Gauge	An instrument which indicates the temperature of released exhaust gases.
EXP	Expect, Expected, Expecting.
Expected Approach Time	The time at which air traffic control expects that a holding aircraft, following a delay, will leave the hold to commence its approach to land.
EXTD	Extend or Extending.
Extended Centre Line	An imaginary line infinitely extending the centreline of an airfield runway.
Extended Over Water Operations	An operation over water at a horizontal distance of more than 50 nautical miles from the nearest shoreline. See further text in the reference section.
EXTN	Extension.
Extremely High Frequency	Frequencies in the 30,000 – 300,000 MHz range. See further text in the reference section.
EXTRM	Extreme.
EXTSV	Extensive.

F

f	Acceleration.
f	Frequency.
F	Degrees Fahrenheit. See Glossary text under Fahrenheit.
F	Fixed.
F	Aerodrome Forecast. See Glossary text under Terminal Aerodrome Forecast.
F	Friday, when associated with hours of operation.
F	Sequenced Flashing lights.
F1/F2 Layers	See Glossary text under Appleton Layers.
FA	Area meteorological Forecast.
FA	Aerodrome. (NOTAM decode 2nd & 3rd letters).
FAC	Facilities.
FAC	Final Approach Course.
Facilitation	The provision of facilities for arriving and departing aircraft passengers.
FAF	Final Approach Fix. See Glossary text under that heading.
Fahrenheit	Temperature scale with the freezing point of water at 32°F and boiling point at 211°F. See further text in the reference section under Temperature.
FAL	Facilitation of international air transport. A section of the Air Pilot.
Fallstreaks	Synonym for virga. See Glossary text under that heading.
False Horizon	A meteorological situation where an obscured real horizon, a dark surface, stars and geometric ground light patterns, are mistaken for a real horizon.
Fan Marker	See Glossary text under Marker Beacons.
FAP	Final Approach Point. See Glossary text under that heading.
FAT	Final Approach Track. See Glossary text under that heading.
FAX	Facsimile machine used for document transfer by telephone line. Aeronautical applications are for filing flight plans (use lighter back copy) and obtaining METFAX information.
FB	Braking action measurement equipment. (NOTAM decode 2nd & 3rd letters). See Glossary text under Mu-Meter.
FBL	Light, in relation to icing or turbulence.
FBO	Fixed Base Operator.
FBW	Fly by Wire.
FC	Ceiling measurement equipment. (NOTAM decode 2nd & 3rd letters). Used in relation to the upper levels of cloud.
FC	Forecast. Used to replace the code TAF where a bulletin consists of forecasts for one or more aerodromes.
FC	Fracto-stratus cloud. See Glossary text under that heading.

FC	Funnel Cloud, Tornado or Waterspout. See Glossary text under those individual headings.
FCL	Flight Crew Licensing.
FCRS	Flight Crew Record System.
FCST	Forecast, meteorological.
FCU	Flight Control Unit.
FCU	Fuel Control Unit.
FD	Docking system. (NOTAM decode 2nd & 3rd letters).
FDP	Flying Duty Period.
FDR	Flight Data Recorder.
Feathered Propeller	In engines fitted with a variable pitch propeller, a procedure where the blades are rotated so that the leading and trailing edges are nearly parallel with the aircraft's flight path.
FETO	Free Estimated Time of Overflight.
FF	Fire fighting and rescue. (NOTAM decode 2nd & 3rd letters).
FFH	For Further Headings.
FFPS	Free Fall Parachute Site. See text in the reference section.
FG	Fog. See Glossary text under that heading.
FG	Ground movement control. (NOTAM decode 2nd & 3rd letters).
FH	Helicopter alighting area/platform. (NOTAM decode 2nd & 3rd letters).
FI	Fuel Idle
FIBS	Flight Information Billing System.
FIC	Flight Information Centre.
FIC	Flying Instructor's Course.
FIDS	Flight Information and Display System.
Filling	Meteorologically used to describe the centre of pressure in a depression increasing.
Fin	The fixed vertical surface which affects the lateral stability of an aircraft.
Final Approach Fix	The last navigational fix, designated on the published approach plate, which an aircraft will make in a standard instrument approach procedure, before the final instrument approach is commenced.
Final Approach Point	The point designated on the published approach plate where final approach descent may be commenced providing the aircraft is within pre-defined limits. See further text in the reference section.
Final Approach Track	The track designated on the published approach plate where final approach descent may be continued providing the aircraft is within pre-defined limits.

Final Leg	The final leg of an aerodrome circuit at 90° to the base leg and in the direction of landing. See the reference section for the purposes and radio calls to be made on each circuit leg under Aerodrome Circuit.
Final	A radio call made by an aircraft to confirm that it has turned onto the final approach leg of the circuit. In the case of a straight in approach the call should be made at 4nm. See further text in the reference section under Aerodrome Circuit.
FIND	Flight and Information System.
FIR	Flight Information Region. See Glossary text under that heading.
First Returning Sky Wave	Where HF frequency transmissions are angled so that they are refracted off the ionosphere it is the radio wave that returns to Earth closest to the transmitter. See further text in the reference section under Radio Waves.
FIS	Flight Information Service. See further text in the reference section.
FISA	Automated Flight Information Service.
FIW	Flight Input Workstation.
Fixed Balance Tabs	See Glossary text under Balance Tabs.
Fixed Distance Marker	See text in the reference section under Runway Markings.
Fixed Pitch Propeller	See text in the reference section under Propeller.
FJ	Fuel – Jet. See Glossary text under turbine fuel.
FL	Flight Level. See Glossary text under that heading.
FL	Landing direction indicator. (NOTAM decode 2nd & 3rd letters). Normally located in a signals square. See text in the reference section text under Aerodrome Signals.
Flags (Failure)	A flag provided on ILS and VOR display to advise the pilot that any displayed information should be ignored. See further text in the reference section under Omni-Bearing Indicator.
Flags (To & From)	A flag provided on a VOR display to advise the pilot as to whether the aircraft is tracking a *to* or *from* radial. See further text in the reference section under Omni-Bearing Indicator.
Flaps	See text in the reference guide for the types and uses of flaps.
FLD	Field.
FLG	Flashing.
Flight Envelope	The limiting accelerations and speeds that an aircraft may safely fly within.
Flight Information Region	An area controlled by an air traffic control centre which will provide a flight information service to participating aircraft outside controlled airspace.

Flight Information Service	A service offered by an ATCC to provide participating aircraft with any information or assistance they may require except for issuing clearances, collision avoidance advice or positive control of the flight. See further text in the reference section.
Flight Level	The height displayed on an altimeter with 1013mb set on the sub-scale. 4,500 feet displayed would equate to FL45. See further text in the reference section.
Flight Level Ridiculous	Originally a military slang expression for upper atmospheric flights. Now adopted by private pilots to describe flights over 10,000 feet.
Flight Plan	A flight plan form CA48 filed before departure via an air traffic control unit linked to the AFTN or by telephone to a participating unit. The filing of a flight plan is compulsory for certain flights. See further text in the reference section.
Flight Plan Cancellation	In flight a flight plan may be cancelled at any time. In the event of a diversion the original destination aerodrome must be separately advised within half an hour of the expected arrival time.
Flight Recorder	The black box fitted to an aircraft to continuously record flight data and cockpit conversations.
Flight Test	A test carried out by a pilot, or student pilot, to prove their abilities at a specified level of competence.
Flight Visibility	The average forward horizontal distance, from the cockpit of an aircraft in flight, at which prominent unlit objects may be seen and identified by day. See further text under Visibility in the reference section.
Flo	Floodlights.
FLR	Flares.
FLRY	Flurry, meteorological, as in snow flurries.
FLT	Flight.
FLTCK	Flight Check.
Flutter	An unstable oscillation of an aerofoil section.
Fly by Wire	A flight control system using electronic controls to operate electrical circuits and servos which mechanically operate control surfaces. See further text in the reference section.
FM	Fan Marker. See Glossary text under Marker Beacons.
FM	Frequency Modulation. See Glossary text under that heading
FM	From, meteorological.
FM	Meteorological service. (NOTAM decode 2nd & 3rd letters).
FMGS	Flight Management and Guidance System.
FMS	Flight Management System.
FM/Z	Inner/Fan Marker. See Glossary text under Marker Beacons.
FNA	Final Approach. See Glossary text under Final Approach Fix, Point and Track.

FO	Fog dispersal system. (NOTAM decode 2nd & 3rd letters).
FOB	Fuel on Board.
FOD	Flight Operations Department.
FOD	Foreign Object Damage.
Foehn Wind	A warm, dry wind that blows on the leeward side of a mountain range. See further text in the reference section.
Fog	Water droplets with a diameter of less than 0.2mm reducing visibility to less than 1,000 metres. See further text in the reference section under Visibility.
Fog (Advection)	Fog forming over land when a mass of warm air moves over a colder surface causing the air's temperature to drop so increasing its relative humidity.
Fog (Frontal)	Cloud which descends to the surface close to a weather front.
Fog (Hill)	Cloud which descends to the surface over high ground. See Glossary text under Hill Fog.
Fog (Radiation)	Fog forming over low lying, moist, inland areas caused by the radiation of heat from the surface into the atmosphere.
Fohn Wind	See Glossary text under Foehn Wind.
FOQHN	Forecast Regional QNH. See Glossary text under QNH (Regional).
Force 0	Calm. Wind speed not registering
Force 1	Light air. Wind speed between 1 & 3 knots (2 & 6km per hour).
Force 2	Light breeze. Wind speed between 4 & 6 knots (7 & 11km per hour).
Force 3	Gentle breeze. Wind speed between 7 & 10 knots (13 & 18km per hour).
Force 4	Moderate. Wind speed between 11 & 15 knots (20 & 28km per hour).
Force 5	Fresh. Wind speed between 16 & 21 knots (30 & 39km per hour).
Force 6	Strong. Wind speed between 22 & 27 knots (41 & 50km per hour).
Force 7	Near gale. Wind speed between 28 & 33 knots (52 & 61km per hour).
Force 8	Gale. Wind speed between 34 & 40 knots (63 & 74km per hour).
Force 9	Severe gale. Wind speed between 41 & 47 knots (76 & 87km per hour).
Force 10	Storm. Wind speed between 48 & 55 knots (89 & 102km per hour).
Force 11	Violent storm. Wind speed between 56 & 63 knots (104 & 117km per hour).

Force 12	Hurricane. Wind speed 64 knots or greater (119 km per hour).
Forecast Regional QNH	See Glossary text under QNH (Regional).
Form Drag	Drag caused when an airflow becomes so turbulent it lifts away from the aircraft surface causing further air disturbances resulting in further drag. See text in the reference section under Drag for other types.
FORNN	Forenoon.
Fowler Flaps	Flaps that when lowered, move backwards and down increasing the wing area and aerofoil shape. See text in the reference section under Flaps for other types.
FP	Heliport. (NOTAM decode 2nd & 3rd letters).
FP#	Fuel – Petroleum (1=100LL or 100/130).
FPL	Filed Flight Plan.
FPM	Feet Per Minute.
FPPS	Flight Plan Processing System.
FPR	Flight Plan Route.
FPS	Flight Progress Strip.
FPS	Foot/Pound/Second.
FPX	Fuel – Petroleum, octane unspecified.
FQT	Frequent.
FR	Flight Refuelling.
FR	Route Forecast.
Fracto-Stratus Cloud	Broken stratiform cloud. Used to describe 5 – 7 Oktas, or eighths, of cloud cover.
FRC	Flight Route Clearance.
FRC	Full Route Clearance.
Free Call	An expression used by air traffic control to advise a pilot that he/she is free to change frequency when ready.
Free Fall Parachute Sites	See text in the reference section.
Freezing Level	The altitude above mean sea level where the temperature is 0°C.
Freezing Rain	See text in the reference section.
FREQ	Frequency. See text in the reference section under Frequencies.
Frequencies	See text in the reference section.
Frequency Modulation	The result of combining a low frequency with a higher frequency resulting in a signal of an efficiently transmittable level. See further text in the reference section under Radio Waves.
Fresh Wind	Wind speed between 16 & 21 knots (30 & 39km per hour). Force Five.

Friction Layer	A vertical wind layer caused by the mixing effect of the wind meeting surface obstacles. Usually quoted as being measured in comparison to the 2,000 foot geostrophic wind. See further text in the reference section under Surface Winds.
FRMN	Formation.
FRNG	Firing.
FRONT	Front, meteorological. The term used to describe the line where one classification of air mass ends and another starts. See further text in the reference section under Fronts.
Frontal Fog	See text in the reference section.
Frontal Lifting	The lifting of a warm air mass by a cold front. See text in the reference section under Fronts.
Frontal Thunderstorms	Thunderstorms caused by a cold front undercutting a warm front forcing the occluded air upwards. See further text in the reference section.
Fronto-genesis	The formation of a front. See further text in the reference section under Fronts.
Fronto-lysis	The process or state where a front ceases to be active.
Fronts	See text in the reference section.
FROPA	Frontal Passage. See Glossary text under Front.
FROSFC	Frontal Surface. See Glossary text under Front.
Frost	See Glossary text under Hoar Frost.
Frost Smoke	See Glossary text under Arctic Sea Smoke.
FRQ	Frequent. Meteorological, as in frequent thunderstorms.
FRST	Frost.
FRTO	Flight Radio Telephony Operator.
FRZ	Freeze.
FRZN	Frozen.
FS	Fracto-Stratus Cloud. See Glossary text under that heading.
FS	Snow removal equipment. (NOTAM decode 2nd & 3rd letters).
FSL	Full Stop Landing. See Glossary text under that heading.
FST	First.
FT	Feet, Foot.
FT	Forecast. Used to replace the code TAF where bulletin consists of forecasts for one or more aerodromes.
FT	Transmissometer. (NOTAM decode 2nd & 3rd letters). See text in the reference section under Runway Visual Range.
FTD	Flight Training Device.
FTE	Flight Technical Error.
FTL	Flight Time Limitations.
FU	Forecast Upper winds.

FU	Fuel availability. (NOTAM decode 2nd & 3rd letters).
FU	Smoke, meteorological. Derived from the french *fume*. See Glossary text under Smoke.
Fuel 100LL	Light aircraft fuel. LL denotes low lead. The 100 refers to the level of compression that the fuel will take, in comparison to other grades, before it will self detonate.
Fuel Icing	Caused by water held in suspension in fuel freezing and becoming a solid. See further text in the reference section under Icing – Carburettor.
Fuel Injection	A fuel metering and the delivery system providing increased performance and economy in comparison to a normally aspirated, carburettor, system. See further text in the reference section.
Full Stop Landing	A landing which results in the aircraft leaving the runway or landing area and the engine(s) being shut down. See further text in the reference section under Touch and Go.
Funnel Clouds	Formed within very large cumulonimbus clouds. They are intense vortices of circulating air which lower towards the surface. See further text in the reference section under Tornadoes.
Funnel Wind	See Glossary text under Valley Wind.
Fusion	See Glossary text under Latent Heat of Fusion.
FW	Wind direction indicator. (NOTAM decode 2nd & 3rd letters).
FWA	Flight Watch Area.
FWC	Flight Watch Centre.
FZ	Customs. (NOTAM decode 2nd & 3rd letters).
FZ	Freezing.
FZ	Supercooled, meteorological. Relating to water droplets. See Glossary text under Supercooled Water Droplets.
FZDZ	Freezing Drizzle.
FZFG	Freezing Fog.
FZRA	Freezing Rain.
FX	Fuel Unspecified.

G

g	Acceleration due to the Earth's gravity.
G	Green. The colour of a light. Usually shown on airfield approach charts or in relation to aerodrome lighting.
G	Ground control.
G	Gust. Meteorological. See Glossary text under that heading.
GA	General Aviation.
G/A	Ground to Air.
G/A/G	Ground to Air and Air to Ground.
Gale	Wind speed of 34 – 40 knots (63 – 74 km per hour). Force 8.
GAMTA	General Aviation Manufacturer's & Trader's Association.
GAPAN	Guild of Air Pilots and Air Navigators.
GASIL	General Aviation Safety Information Leaflet.
GAT	General Air Traffic.
GATCO	Guild of Air Traffic Control Officers.
GCA	Ground Controlled Approach.
GCA	Ground Controlled Approach system.
GCI	Ground Controlled Interception.
GDOP	Geometric Dilution Of Precision. See Glossary text under that heading.
GDOP	Global Dilution of Precision. See Glossary text under Dilution of Precision.
GEN	General.
Gentle Breeze	Wind speed between 7 & 10 knots (13 & 19km per hour). Force Three.
GEO	Geographic or true.
Geometric Dilution of Precision	A datum by which known errors are multiplied in order to calculate the accuracy of a satellite navigation system position fix. See further text in the reference section under Global Positioning System.
Geostrophic Departure	The vector difference between the geostrophic wind and an actual wind.
Geostrophic Force	A force affecting wind flow around curved isobars due to the Coriolis effect. See further text in the reference section under Geostrophic Wind.
Geostrophic Wind	The wind that blows parallel to straight isobars. See further text in the reference section.
GFDEP	Ground Fog estimated, Deep.
G-Force	Gravity Forces created by centrifugal force generated by the changes in direction of an aircraft.
Gigahertz	1,000,000,000 Hertz or 10^9 cycles per second.

Gimbal	A mounting used to contain a gyroscope allowing un-restricted or restricted movement regardless of an aircraft's movement. See further text in the reference section under Gyroscopes.
Glazed Frost	Icing caused by super cooled water droplets coming into contact with any surface of sub zero temperature. See further text in the reference section under Icing – Airframe – On Ground.
Glaze Ice	Ice formed on aircraft flying through sub zero temperatures in rain. Also known as clear ice. See further text in the reference section under Icing – Airframe – In Flight.
GLD	Glider.
Glidepath	An extended runway centreline final approach track.
Glidepath Indicator	A display used in the ILS to indicate the correct height during an instrument approach. See further text in the reference section under Omni-Bearing Indicator.
Glider Launching Sites	See text in the reference section.
Glideslope	The descent angle required to reach the surface at the runway threshold from a specific height and position. See further text in the reference section under Instrument Landing System.
Glideslope Angle Calculation	The descent angle required to reach the surface at the threshold is calculated by the aircraft's height in feet multiplied by 60 and divided by the distance to run in feet. See further text in the reference section under Instrument Landing System.
Glideslope Transmitter	The UHF descent element of an instrument landing system. See further text in the reference section under Instrument Landing System.
Global Positioning System	See text in the reference section.
GMC	Ground Movement Control.
GMDSS	Global Maritime Distress and Safety Systems.
GMP	Ground Movement Planning.
GMR	Ground Movement Radar.
GMT	Greenwich Mean Time. See Glossary text under that heading.
Gn	Green. The colour of a light. Usually shown on airfield approach charts or in relation to aerodrome lighting.
GND	Ground, earth surface, water or land.
GNDCK	Ground Check.
GND CON	Ground Control.
GNDFG	Ground Fog.
GNSS	Global Navigation Satellite Systems. See Glossary text under Satellite Navigation System.

Go Around	A landing aborted whilst on final approach where the aircraft intends to make a further approach to land. See further text in the reference section under Touch and Go.
Goosenecks	Paraffin flares used as runway lights.
GOS	Gate Operating Systems.
GP	Glidepath. See Glossary text under that heading.
GPS	Global Positioning System. See Glossary text under Satellite Navigation System.
GPU	Ground Power Unit.
GPWS	Ground Proximity Warning System.
Gr	Green. The colour of a light. Usually shown on airfield approach charts or in relation to aerodrome lighting.
GR	Hail or soft hail, derived from the German *graupel*.
GRAD	Gradient.
Gradient Force	See Glossary text under Pressure Gradient Force.
Gradient Wind	The wind that blows parallel to curved isobars from high to low pressure or temperature. See further text in the reference section. Also see text in the reference section under Geostrophic Wind.
GRADU	Gradual or Gradually, meteorological.
Granular Snow	See Glossary text under Snow.
Graupel	(German word). Frozen cloud droplets that clump together to form pellets.
GRASS	Grass landing area.
GRDL	Gradual.
GRE	Ground Run up Enclosure.
Great Circle	A line drawn on the surface of the Earth, with a radius equal to that of the Earth, with a plane that passes through the centre of the Earth.
Greenwich	The location of the Greenwich Observatory. See further text in the reference section.
Greenwich Mean Time	The datum for world time. The time differential for other longitudes being based on the difference in degrees east or west of the Greenwich meridian.
Greenwich Meridian	See Glossary text under Prime Meridian.
Grenoble Wind	A south westerly wind in southern France, normally associated with heavy rain.
GRN	Ground, meteorological.
Ground Clutter	The permanent echo of high ground or substantial fixed objects showing a return on primary radar. See further text in the reference section under Radar – Primary.

Ground Effect	The positive interference upon the upwash, downwash and wingtip vortices causing a reduction in induced drag. See further text in the reference section.
Ground Loop	An effect where an aircraft pivots about the axis of a wing tip. See further text in the reference section.
Ground Speed	The speed of an aircraft over the surface of the Earth. See further text in the reference section.
GRVL	Gravel.
GS	Glideslope. See Glossary text under that heading.
GS	Ground Speed. See Glossary text under that heading.
GS	Small hail or snow pellets of less than 5mm diameter. Derived from the German *graupel*.
GSO	Geostationary Orbit.
GST	Gust. See Glossary text under that heading.
Gust	A temporary increase in wind speed of at least 10 knots. See further text in the reference section.
Gust Front	A well marked area of cold air that causes a down draught in the line of movement of a thunderstorm. See further text in the reference section under Windshear.
GWT	Gross Weight.
GWVSS	Ground Wind Vortex Sensing System.
Gyrocompass	See Glossary text under Directional Gyro.
Gyro Drift	Drift or wander of the axis of a horizontally mounted gyro affecting the accuracy of a gyroscope linked display. See further text in the reference section under Gyroscopes.
Gyroscope	A rotating mass spinning about a movable axis exhibiting properties of precession and rigidity in space. See further text in the reference section.
Gyro Topple	Drift or wander of the axis of a gyroscope in the vertical plane affecting the accuracy of a gyro linked display. See further text in the reference section under Gyroscopes.
Gyro Wander	Any movement of a gyro spin axis away from its predominant direction. See further text in the reference section under Gyroscopes.

H

h	Height.
H	High altitude.
H	Non-directional radio beacon. See Glossary text under Non Directional Radio Beacon.
H+...	Hour plus ... minutes past.
H24	Operates 24 hours a day.
HA...	Braking action is ... 1) Poor 2) Medium/Poor 3) Medium 4) Medium/Good 5) Good. (NOTAM decode 4th & 5th letters). See Glossary text under Mu-Meter.
HAA	Height Above Airport.
Haar	Indigenous name used in parts of England and Scotland for sea fog.
Hail	Balls of ice formed in active cumulonimbus clouds where small ice nuclei are progressively coated with supercooled water droplets to an extent that their weight can no longer be supported by the updrafts. See further text in the reference section.
HAT	Height Above Touchdown.
Haystorms	Intense spiralling vortices of air which form over very hot surfaces, usually under clear skies during anticyclonic conditions. They may rise to several hundred feet and are visible due to cut hay from fields sucked up by the low pressure area in the centre of the system.
HAZ	Hazard.
Haze	Minute solid particles suspended in the atmosphere reducing visibility to between 1,000m and 10Km. See further text under Visibility.
HB...	Braking coefficient is ... (NOTAM decode 4th & 5th letters). See Glossary text under Mu-Meter and BRAF.
HBN	Hazard Beacon.
HC...	Covered by compacted snow to a depth of ... (NOTAM decode 4th & 5th letters).
HC	Critical Height.
HD...	Covered by dry snow to a depth of ... (NOTAM decode 4th & 5th letters).
HDEP	Haze layer Estimated, Deep.
HDF	High frequency Direction Finding station. See Glossary text under Direction Finding.
HD FRZ	Hard Freeze.
HDG	Heading.
HDWND	Head Wind.
HE...	Covered by water to a depth of ... (NOTAM decode 4th & 5th letters).

Headsets	A legal requirement for all public transport flights under flight level 150. See further text in the reference section.
Heat Sink	The segment of a thermodynamic system that absorbs unused heat.
Heaviside Layer	Synonym for the D and E layers of the ionosphere. See further text in the reference section under Ionosphere.
Hectopascal	Pressure unit equivalent to one millibar and 0.02953 inches of mercury. See text in the reference section under Millibar.
Height	The vertical distance above aerodrome or ground level.
HEL	Helicopter.
Helm Wind	A strong north easterly wind indigenous to the Pennines, usually accompanied by helmet shaped clouds over the peaks.
Hemispheric Rule	American flight rule equivalent to the UK and European semi-circular rule.
Hertz	Cycles of frequency per second.
HF	High Frequency. Frequencies in the 3,000 to 30,000KHz range.
HF	Totally free of snow or ice. (NOTAM decode 4th & 5th letters).
HG	Grass cutting in progress. (NOTAM decode 4th & 5th letters).
HGT	Height. See Glossary text under that heading.
HI	High.
HI	High altitude.
HI	High Intensity.
HI	High Intensity directional lights.
HIALS	High Intensity Approach Light System.
High	See Glossary text under High Pressure Area.
High Frequency	Frequencies in the 3,000 to 30,000KHz range.
High Intensity Radio Transmission Area	Prohibited or restricted airspace within which radio equipment and persons health may be damaged. See further text in the reference section.
High Level Thunderstorms	Short lived active cumulonimbus clouds which tend to renew after the dissipating stage. See further text in the reference section under Cumulonibus Clouds.
High Pressure Area	An anticyclonic area formed when an air mass is subject to divergence and moves away from the centre of pressure. See further text in the reference section under Anticyclone.
High Speed Taxiway	A taxiway designed to accept large aircraft turning off a main runway at speeds of up to 60 knots.
Hill Fog	Low cloud drifting over high ground or valley fog rising uphill due to orographic lifting. See further text in the reference section.

HIRL	High Intensity Runway edge Lights.
HIRTA	High Intensity Radio Transmission Area. See text in the reference section.
HISL	High Intensity Strobe Light.
HJ	Launch planned. (NOTAM decode 4th & 5th letters).
HJ	Sunrise to sunset.
HJ+...	Sunrise to ... minutes after sunset.
HK	Bird migration in progress. (NOTAM decode 4th & 5th letters).
HL	Height Loss.
HL	Snow clearance completed. (NOTAM decode 4th & 5th letters).
HLDG	Holding.
HLSTO	Hailstones. See Glossary text under Hail.
HLYR	Haze Layer aloft. See Glossary text under Haze.
HM	Her Majesty's, as in HM Customs, HM Coastguard.
HM	Marked by. (NOTAM decode 4th & 5th letters).
Hmr	Homer, a VHF or HF direction finding station. See Glossary text under Direction Finding.
HMR	Helicopter Main Route.
HN...	Covered by wet snow or slush to a depth of ... (NOTAM decode 4th & 5th letters).
HN	Sunset to sunrise.
HND	Hundred.
HO	Obscured by snow. (NOTAM decode 4th & 5th letters).
HO	Operates during times to meet operational requirements.
Hoar Frost	Formed when moderately dry air is cooled to 0°C without reaching its dewpoint and comes into contact with a sub zero surface. See further text in the reference section under Icing – Airframe – In Flight and On Ground.
HOL	Holiday.
Holding Procedure	See text in the reference section.
Homer	A VHF or HF direction finding station.
Horizontal Situation Indicator	A radio magnetic indicator which can also display ILS and VOR information. See further text in the reference section.
Horizontal Stabilizer	See Glossary text under Tailplane.
HOSP	Hospital Aircraft.
Howler	Slang expression for strong westerly winds in the fifties latitudes.

HP	Horsepower.
HP	Snow clearance in progress. (NOTAM decode 4th & 5th letters).
HPA	Hectopascal. Unit equivalent to one millibar and 0.02953 inches of mercury.
HPBW	Half Power Beam Width.
HPZ	Helicopter Protected Zone.
HQ	Operation cancelled. (NOTAM decode 4th & 5th letters).
HRL	High intensity Runway edge Lighting.
hr/s	Hour/s.
HR	Standing water. (NOTAM decode 4th & 5th letters).
HRCN	Hurricane. See Glossary text under that heading.
HRZN	Horizon.
HS	Operates for Schedules services.
HS	Sanding in progress. (NOTAM decode 4th & 5th letters).
HSI	Horizontal Situation Indicator. See Glossary text under that heading.
HST	High Speed Taxiway turn off. See Glossary text under that heading
HT	Approach according to signals area only. (NOTAM decode 4th & 5th letters). See Glossary text under Aerodrome Signals.
HT	High Tension (cables).
HU	Launch in progress. (NOTAM decode 4th & 5th letters).
HUD	Head Up Display.
Humidity Mixing Ratio	The ratio of the mass of water vapour in comparison to the mass of dry air.
HURCN	Hurricane. See Glossary text under that heading.
Hurricane	Circular tropical storm indigenous to the Caribbean and North Atlantic. Wind speeds in excess of 64 knots (119 km per hour). Storm force 12.
HV	Work completed. (NOTAM decode 4th & 5th letters).
HVAC	Heating, Ventilation and Air Conditioning.
HVDF	Co-located High & Very high frequency Direction Finding stations. See Glossary text under Direction Finding.
HVY	Heavy.
HW	Work in progress. (NOTAM decode 4th & 5th letters).
HX	Concentration of birds. (NOTAM decode 4th & 5th letters).
HX	Operates at no specific Hours/irregular service.
HY	Snow banks exist. (NOTAM decode 4th & 5th letters).
Hydrometeor	Water, in liquid or frozen form, re-introduced into the atmosphere by the wind.

Hygrometer	An instrument for measuring humidity.
Hygroscopic	The ability to absorb or attract moisture, such as condensation nuclei.
Hypersonic	A speed equal to around five times the speed of sound or greater.
Hypoxia	The effect of a lack of oxygen on the human body caused by high altitude. Usually quoted as being above 10,000 feet. See further text in the reference section.
HYR	Higher.
Hysteresis	An expression used to describe the lag between an action and re-action in pressure controlled aircraft instruments. See further text in the reference section under Altimeter.
HZ	Covered by frozen ruts and ridges. (NOTAM decode 4th & 5th letters).
HZ	Haze, meteorological. See Glossary text under that heading.
HZ	Hertz. Cycles of frequency per second.

I

I	Initial Approach.
I	Unit length on a mercator chart. See Glossary text under Mercator Projection.
IAC	Instrument Approach Chart. See Glossary text under that heading.
IAF	Initial Approach Fix. See reference section under that heading.
IAL	Instrument Approach and Landing chart. See Glossary text under Instrument Approach Chart.
IAO	In And Out of clouds.
IAOPA	International council of Aircraft Owners & Pilot Associations.
IAP	Initial Approach Procedures. See reference section under Initial Approach.
IAP	Instrument Approach Procedure. See Glossary text under Instrument Approach Chart.
IAR	Intersection of Air Routes.
IAS	Indicated Airspeed. See Glossary text under that heading.
IB	Inbound.
IBN	Identification Beacon. See Glossary text under Aerodrome Identification Beacon.
IC	Diamond dust, meteorological. See Glossary text under Dust.
IC	Instrument landing system. (NOTAM decode 2nd & 3rd letters). See Glossary text under that heading.
ICAO	International Civil Aviation Organisation.
ICE	Icing. See Glossary text under Carburettor, Impact and Fuel Icing and full text in the reference section.
Ice Nuclei	Minute mineral fragments such as particles of paint, rubber, asphalt and minerals suspended in the atmosphere which if encountered by a supercooled water droplet will enable it to freeze. See Glossary text under Schaefer Point and further text in the reference section under Icing – Airframe.
ICF	Initial Contact Frequency.
ICGIC	Icing In Clouds.
ICGICIP	Icing In Clouds In Precipitation.
ICGIP	Icing in precipitation.
Icing	See Glossary text under Carburettor, Impact and Fuel Icing and full text in the reference section.
ID	Distance measuring equipment associated with instrument landing system. (NOTAM decode 2nd & 3rd letters). See Glossary text under both headings.
ID	Identifier/Identity.

IDENT	Abbreviation for Identification. A button on a transponder which when pressed highlights the aircraft's radar return. See further text in the reference section under Transponder.
Identification Manoeuvre	A turn requested by ATC to confirm a radar contact. See further text in the reference section.
Idle Cut Off	The method used to shut down aircraft piston engines by setting the throttle to idle and the mixture to fully lean, starving the engine of fuel.
IF	Intermediate approach Fix.
IF	Intermediate Frequency.
IFF	Identification Friend or Foe.
IFPS	Initial Flight Plan processing System.
IFR	Instrument Flight Rules. See Glossary text under that heading.
IFTA	Instrument Flight Training Area.
IG	Glide path for an instrument landing system. (NOTAM decode 2nd & 3rd letters). See Glossary text under either heading.
IGA	International General Aviation.
IGS	Instrument Guidance System.
II	Inner marker. (NOTAM decode 2nd & 3rd letters). See text in the reference section under Marker Beacons.
ILS	Instrument Landing System. See Glossary text under that heading.
IM	Inner Marker. See text in the reference section under Marker Beacons.
IM	Middle marker. (NOTAM decode 2nd & 3rd letters). See text in the reference section under Marker Beacons.
IMC	Instrument Meteorological Conditions. See text in the reference section.
IMDT	Immediate.
IMG	Immigration.
IMO	International Maritime Organisation.
Impact Icing	Precipitation impacting upon air intakes and filters in a frozen form causing a blockage. See further text in the reference section under Icing – Carburettor.
IMPR	Improve or Improving, meteorological.
IMPT	Important.
IMT	Immediate.
IMTA	Intensive Military Training Area.
in(s)	Inch(es).
INA	Initial Approach. See text in the reference section.
INBD	Inbound.
INC	In Cloud.

INCERFA	Uncertainty phase. See Glossary text under that heading.
INCL	Include.
INCR	Increase.
IND	Wind or landing direction Indicator.
INDC	Indicate.
INDEF	Indefinite.
Indicated Airspeed	The uncorrected airspeed indicated by the airspeed indicator and only accurate as a true airspeed under ISA conditions. See further text in the reference section under Airspeed Definitions.
Induced Drag	Drag produced as a result of vortices at the wing tips and trailing edges. See text in the reference section under Drag for other types.
Induction System Icing	The more accurate name for the more commonly used expression, carburettor icing. See text in the reference section under Icing – Carburettor.
Inertial Navigation System	A computer linked system utilizing three accelerometers which continuously measure an aircraft's speed and direction enabling it to calculate a precise position.
In Flight Refuelling Area	Restricted airspace used for military refuelling at unspecified altitudes and headings. See further text in the reference section.
INFO	Information.
Infrasonic Waves	Frequency range of less than 20Hz, below range of the human ear.
Initial Approach Fix	The stage of an instrument approach where the aircraft arrives at the first navigational facility associated with the procedure.
Initial Approach Area	The stage of an instrument approach where the aircraft arrives at the designated area associated with the procedure. See further text in the reference section.
Inner Marker	A beacon located between the outer marker and the runway threshold. See text in the reference section under Marker Beacons.
INOP	Inoperative.
INP	If Not Possible.
INPR	In Progress.
Ins	Inches.
INS	Inertial Navigation System. See Glossary text under that heading.
Insolation	The heating of the Earth's surface by the Sun. See further text in the reference section.
INST	Instrument.
Instability Line	A row of non-frontal, active cumulonimbus clouds producing heavy showers or thunderstorms.
INSTBY	Instability, meteorological.

INSTL	Install, Installed, Installation.
INSTR	Instrument.
Instrument Approach Charts	Published charts detailing heights, headings and procedures to be followed when making an instrument approach to an airfield.
Instrumented Runway Visual Range	The distance over which, a pilot of a landing aircraft, can expect to see centreline or runway edge lights on touchdown. The range being measured by a transmissometer. See further text in the reference section under Runway Visual Range.
Instrument Flight Rules	Flight rules which are compulsory in IMC conditions and certain types of airspace but voluntary for VMC in open flight information region areas.
Instrument Landing System	A pilot interpreted radio approach aid providing heading and descent information which enables an aircraft to make an approach to land without external visual reference. See further text in the reference section.
Instrument Meteorological Conditions	Weather conditions which prohibit flight under visual flight rules. Such flights are required to comply with the semi-circular rules and terrain clearance minimas. See further text in the reference section.
Instrument Rating	A rating enabling the holder to fly in all types of airspace under any meteorological flight conditions.
Instrument Runway	A runway equipped with electronic navigation aids for which a precision or non-precision approach procedure exists. See text in the reference section under Instrument Landing System - The Runway.
Instrument Runway Visual Range	See text in the reference section under Runway Visual Range.
INT	Intersection.
INTCP	Intercept.
INTER	Intermittent.
Interception Procedures	A set of published and internationally agreed procedures to be followed by intercepted and intercepting aircraft. See further text in the reference section.
International Standard Atmosphere	The main items are: Pressure at mean sea level 1013.25 millibars, temperature at mean sea level +15°C, density at mean sea level 1225 gm/cubic metre, temperature lapse rate of 1.98°C/1000 feet. See further text in the reference section.
Inter-tropical Convergence Zone	The zone enclosing the inter-tropical front.
Inter-Tropical Front	The division line between the wind systems of the northern southern hemispheres, known as the Doldrums.

INTL	International.
INTMT	Intermittent.
INTRG	Interrogator.
INTRP	Interrupt, Interrupted, Interruption.
INTS	Intense.
INTSF	Intensify or Intensifying.
INTST	Intensity.
Inversion	A layer of the atmosphere where the temperature increases with height. See further text in the reference section.
INVOF	In the Vicinity Of.
INVRN	Inversion, meteorological. See Glossary text under that heading.
I/O	Input/Output.
IO	Outer marker. (NOTAM decode 2nd & 3rd letters). See text in the reference section under Marker Beacons.
Ionosphere	The layer of atmosphere surrounding the stratosphere starting at around 50km and extending to approximately 500km. See further text in the reference section.
Ionospheric Interference	An error affecting the accuracy of a satellite navigation system receiver. As the signal passes through the ionosphere charged particles affect the speed of sound and consequently radio signals. See text in the reference section under Global Positioning System.
IOVC	In the Overcast.
IPV	Ice on the runway.
IPV	Improve.
IR	Ice on the Runway.
IR	Infra-Red.
IR	Instrument Restricted controlled airspace.
I/R	Instrument Rating. See Glossary text under that heading.
IRE	Instrument Rating Examiner.
IRVR	Instrumented Runway Visual Range. See text in the reference section under Runway Visual Range.
IS	Instrument landing system category I. (NOTAM decode 2nd & 3rd letters). See Glossary text under Instrument Landing System.
ISA	International Standard Atmosphere. See Glossary text under that heading.
Isallobar	A line on a pressure chart joining points experiencing the same rate of change of pressure.
Isallobaric Wind	The term used to describe the inertial effect caused by a pressure gradient of such strength that it delays the effect of the coriolis force.

ISB	Independent Sideband.
Isobars	Lines on a synoptic chart that join points of equal barometric pressure.
Isochrone	Lines on a chart used to show the progressive positions of frontal or pressure systems over particular time intervals.
Isoclinal Line	A line on a chart joining points experiencing equal magnetic dip.
Isogonal	A line joining points of equal magnetic variation.
Isogriv	A line joining points of equal angular difference between magnetic north and the north of a navigational grid.
Isoheight	A line drawn on a weather chart joining points of equal height.
ISOL	Isolated, meteorological.
ISOLD	Isolated, meteorological.
Isopleth	Generic term for any line joining points of equal value.
Isoshear	A line joining points of equal wind shear.
Isotach	A line joining points of equal wind speed.
Isotherm	A line joining points of equal temperature.
Isothermal Layer	A layer of the atmosphere where the temperature remains constant throughout a height of several thousand feet.
ISWL	Isolated Single Wheel Load.
IT	Instrument landing system category II. (NOTAM decode 2nd & 3rd letters). See Glossary text under Instrument Landing System.
ITTF	Integrated initial flight plan processing system Tests Task Force.
IU	Instrument landing system category III. (NOTAM decode 2nd & 3rd letters). See Glossary text under Instrument Landing System.
I/V	Instrument/Visual controlled airspace.
IVFRC	In Visual Flight Rules Conditions.
IVR	Instrumental Visual Range. See text in the reference section under Runway Visual Range.
IW	Microwave landing system. (NOTAM decode 2nd & 3rd letters). See Glossary text under that heading.
IX	Locator, outer. (NOTAM decode 2nd & 3rd letters). See text in the reference section under Marker Beacons.
IY	Locator, middle. (NOTAM decode 2nd & 3rd letters). See text in the reference section under Marker Beacons.

J

JAA	Joint Airworthiness Authority.
JAR	Joint Airworthiness Requirements.
JAS	Joint Airmiss Section.
JAWG	Joint Airmiss Working Group.
JB	Jet Barrier.
JET	Jet stream. See text in the reference section.
Jet Standard Atmosphere	Standards are the same as the International Standard Atmosphere with the exception of the temperature lapse rate which is 2°C per 1,000 feet with no tropopause. See further text in the reference section.
Jet Streak	Exceptionally strong winds within a jet stream. See text in the reference section under Jet Streams.
Jet Stream	A wind classified as being in excess of 80 knots caused by a steep thermal gradient. See further text in the reference section.
Jet Turbine Fuel	See text in the reference section.
Jolly or Jollies	Slang term to describe a pleasure flight. Usually to another airfield for no justifiable reason except pleasure.
JSA	Jet Standard Atmosphere. See Glossary text under that heading.
JTST	Jet Stream. See text in the reference section.

K

K	Kelvin. See Glossary text under that heading.
K	Kts.
Katabatic Wind	Downdrafts occuring on a mountain side where the air nearest the surface cools quicker than the air above it and flows down the slope. See further text in the reference section.
Katafront	A warm front where the air sinks down the frontal surface weakening or impeding the frontal activity.
Kc/s	Kilocycles, 1,000 cycles.
KDEF	Smoke layer Estimated, deep. Meteorological.
Kelvin	A temperature scale measured from absolute zero of -273°C. Also known as absolute temperature. See text in the reference section under Temperature.
Kerosene	See text in the reference section under JET A-1.
Kg(s)	Kilogram(s), 1,000 grammes.
KHz	KiloHertz. 1,000 Hertz or 10^3 cycles per second.
KIAS	Knots Indicated Air Speed. See Glossary text under Indicated Air Speed.
KiloHertz	1,000 Hertz or 10^3 cycles per second.
KLYR	Smoke Layer aloft, meteorological.
Km	Kilometre, 1,000 metres.
Km/h	Kilometres, 1,000 metres, per hour.
KOCTY	Smoke Layer Over City.
Kpa	Kilo Pascal, equivalent to 0.145 pounds per square inch.
Kt(s)	Knot(s).
Kw(h)	Kilowatt, 1,000 watts (hour).

L

L	Cleared to Land.
L	Compass Locator. See text in the reference section under Marker Beacons.
L	Left (runway identification).
L	Licenced (air traffic control).
L	Lighted.
L	Locator beacon. See text in the reference section under Marker Beacons.
LA	Approach lighting system (NOTAM decode 2nd & 3rd letters).
LA	Operating on auxiliary power only. (NOTAM decode 4th & 5th letters).
Labile	A term used to describe an environmental lapse rate that is equal or less than the dry adiabatic lapse rate. See text in the reference section under Adiabatic Lapse Rates.
Lag	See Glossary text under Hysteresis.
Lambert Projection Chart	Conformal charts where the lines approximately follow great circles. Scale distances are accurate.
LAME	Licensed Aircraft Maintainance Engineer.
Laminar Flow	The smooth, non-turbulent flow of a gas or liquid.
LAMS	Light Aircraft Maintenance Schedule.
LAN	Inland/overland, meteorological.
Land Breeze	Formed after sunset when the Earth's surface is cooler than that of the sea causing a drift of air from land to sea. See further text in the reference section.
Landing Distance Available	The length of the runway which is suitable for the landing run of an aircraft commencing at the visual threshold marking or threshold lights. For other distances and areas see text in the reference section under Aerodrome – Surface Definitions.
Landlash	Scottish name for a gale.
Lapse Rate	The decrease in temperature with height. The rate is dependent on the moisture content of the air. See text in the reference section under Adiabatic Lapse Rates.
LARS	Lower Airspace Radar Service. See Glossary text under that heading.
Lat	Latitude. See Glossary text under that heading.
LATCC	London Air Traffic Control Centre. See Glossary text under Low Level Civil Aircraft Notification Procedure.
Latent Heat of Condensation	When saturated air is cooled to a temperature below its dewpoint, condensation will occur. As this happens the latent heat stored in the vapour is released and slows the rate of cooling. See text in the reference section for other types of heat transfer under Latent Heat.

Latent Heat of Evaporation	For an air mass to absorb water from a moist source, energy is required to convert the water to water vapour. The latent heat energy is stored in the vapour until a further change take place. See text in the reference section for other types of heat transfer under Latent Heat.
Latent Heat of Fusion	The heat released during the change from water to ice or the amount absorbed in the change from ice to water. See text in the reference section for other types of heat transfer under Latent Heat.
Latent Heat of Sublimation	The heat released during the change from water vapour to ice or released in the change from ice to water vapour. There is no liquid stage. See text in the reference section for other types of heat transfer under Latent Heat.
Latent Heat of Vapourisation	Synonym for latent heat of evaporation. See Glossary text under that heading.
Lateral Separation	Aircraft division expressed as a horizontal distance.
Latitude	Imaginary lines drawn around the Earth to the north or south of the equator. They are measured in degrees and minutes, 1 minute of latitude is equal to 1 nautical mile.
Latr	Locator (Compass). See text in the reference section under Marker Beacons.
Layer Cloud	Synonym for a stratus cloud formation.
lb(s)	Pound(s) (weight).
LB	Aerodrome beacon. (NOTAM decode 2nd & 3rd letters). See Glossary text under that heading.
LB(s)	Pound(s) (weight).
LB	Reserved for aircraft based therein. (NOTAM decode 4th & 5th letters).
L Band	Group of radio frequencies in the 390Mhz to 1550Mhz range.
LBCM	Locator Back Course Marker. See text in the reference section under Marker Beacons.
LBM	Locator Back Marker. See text in the reference section under Marker Beacons.
LC	Closed. (NOTAM decode 4th & 5th letters).
LC	Runway centreline lights. (NOTAM decode 2nd & 3rd letters).
LCD	Liquid Crystal Display.
LCG	Load Classification Group.
LCL	Lifting Condensation Level.
LCL	Local.
LCN	Load Classification Number.
Lctr	Locator, non-directional beacon. See text in the reference section, under Marker Beacons.

LD	Landing direction indicator lights. (NOTAM decode 2nd & 3rd letters).
LD	Unsafe. (NOTAM decode 4th & 5th letters).
LDA	Landing Distance Available. See Glossary text under that heading.
LDA	Localiser type Directional Aid. See Glossary text under Localiser.
LDG	Landing. In relation to windshear on the approach path. At present it is not an abbreviation used for UK aerodromes.
LDI	Landing Direction Indicator.
LDIN	Sequenced flashing Lead-In light system.
LD-SVR	Slant Visibility meter. See Glossary text under Slant Visibility.
LE	Operating without auxiliary power supply. (NOTAM decode 4th & 5th letters).
LE	Runway edge lights. (NOTAM decode 2nd & 3rd letters).
Leading Edge	The front edge of a wing.
Leading Edge Slats	Slats which extend automatically at low airspeeds increasing lift and lateral stability.
LED	Light Emitting Diode.
Lee	Downwind, usually quoted in the context of the lee side of a range of hills or mountains.
Lee Depression	See Glossary text under Orographic Depression.
Lee Waves	Also known as standing waves and mountain waves. Air wave formations that are effectively static in position in relation to the mountain they are passing over. See text in the reference section under Standing Waves.
LEN	Length.
Lenticular Cloud	Formed in mountain waves and on the leeward side of a large range of hills. The clouds may show as a dotted line decreasing in size downwind or a pile of lens shaped clouds piled upwards. See text in the reference section under Standing Waves.
LF	Interference from ..... (NOTAM decode 4th & 5th letters).
LF	Low frequency. Frequencies in the 30 – 300KHz range.
LF	Sequenced flashing lights. (NOTAM decode 2nd & 3rd letters).
LFA	Local Flying Area.
LFA	Low Flying Area.
LFC	Level of Free Convection.
LFC	Low Flying Chart.
LFMU	London Flow Management Unit.
LFR	Low Frequency radio Range.
LFS	Low Flying System.

LG	Operating without identification. (NOTAM decode 4th & 5th letters).
LGT	Light or Lighting.
LGTD	Lighted.
LH	High intensity runway lights. (NOTAM decode 2nd & 3rd letters).
LH	Left Hand.
LH...	Unserviceable for aircraft heavier than ... (NOTAM decode 4th & 5th letters).
LHS	Left Hand Seat.
LI	Closed to instrument flight rules operations. (NOTAM decode 4th & 5th letters). See Glossary text under Instrument Flight Rules.
LI	Low Intensity omni-directional lights.
LI	Low intensity runway lights. (NOTAM decode 2nd & 3rd letters).
LI	Inner Locator. See text in the reference section under Marker Beacons.
Licence	See text in the reference section under Licence – Pilot's.
LIFR	Low Instrument Flight Rules.
Lift	The force generated by an aerofoil at right angles to the flow of air around it.
Lift Dumper	A section raised from the upper surface of a wing used to disturb the airflow and reduce lift.
Light Air	Wind speed between 1 – 3 knots (2 – 6km per hour). Force 1.
Light Breeze	Wind speed between 4 & 6 knots (7 & 11km per hour). Force 2.
Lightning	An electrical discharge between two clouds or between a cloud and the ground. The charge is generated by friction of the molecules in the up and downdraughts of a thunderstorm, most commonly occurring where the temperature is between +/- 10°C. See further text in the reference section.
Lightning Strike	A lightning strike on an aircraft can cause, amongst other electrical damage, the corrector and main magnets of a magnetic compass to drain. A compass swing is a mandatory requirement after a lightning strike. See further text in the reference section under Lightning.
Lights (Aircraft)	The basic lights are specified in the reference section under Rules Of The Air.
Light Signals	Signals used as a reserve in the event of radio failure or for communicating to non-radio aircraft. See further text in the reference section for a full listing of the signals.
Light Speed	300 x 106, or 300,000,000 metres per second.

LIL	Light Intensity Low.
LIM	Light Intensity Medium.
LIM	Locator Inner Marker. See text in the reference section under Marker Beacons.
Line Squall	Cumuliform clouds formed in a continuous line along a cold front producing heavy but short lived rain showers and possibly hail and thunder.
LIRL	Low Intensity Runway Lights.
LITAS	Low Intensity Two-colour Approach Slope system.
LJ	Runway alignment indicator lights. (NOTAM decode 2nd & 3rd letters).
LK	Category II components of approach lighting system. (NOTAM decode 2nd & 3rd letters).
LK	Operating as a fixed light. (NOTAM decode 4th & 5th letters).
LKLY	Likely.
LL	Low intensity runway lights. (NOTAM decode 2nd & 3rd letters).
LL...	Usable for a length of ... and width of ... (NOTAM decode 4th & 5th letters).
LLWS	Low Level Wind Shear. See Glossary text under Windshear.
LLZ	Instrument landing system Localiser. See Glossary text under Localiser.
LM	Locator middle Marker. See text in the reference section under Marker Beacons.
LM	Medium intensity runway lights. (NOTAM decode 2nd & 3rd letters).
LMM	Locator Middle Marker. See text in the reference section under Marker Beacons.
LMT	Limit.
LMT	Local Mean Time.
LN	Closed to all night operations. (NOTAM decode 4th & 5th letters).
LNDG	Landing.
LNG	Long.
LO	Locator, Outer. See text in the reference section under Marker Beacons.
LOC	Localiser. Part of the instrument landing system. See Glossary text under Localiser.
LOC	Locally, Local, Location, Located.
LOC	Locator. See text in the reference section under Marker Beacons.

Localiser	The VHF component of an instrument landing system used to guide an aircraft onto the runway centreline. It transmits a beam usable up to an altitude of 6,250 feet and a distance of 25 nautical miles. See further text in the reference section under Instrument Landing System.
Local Winds	Synonym for the friction layer or wind from the surface to 2,000 feet. See further text in the reference section under Surface Winds.
Locator	Synonym for marker beacon. See text in the reference section under Marker Beacons.
Log Books	Documents legally required under the articles of the Air Navigation Order in respect of an aircraft, engine and propeller. See further text in the reference section.
LOM	Compass Locator Outer Marker or Locator Outer Maker. See text in the reference section under Marker Beacons.
Lombarde	Usually warm but occasionally cold wind found in the French Wind Alps.
LONG	Longitude. See Glossary text under that heading.
Long Final	Aircraft flying a final approach of greater than 4nm should report *long final* when beyond 4nm as soon as established and *final* when 4nm is reached. Aircraft flying a straight in approach should call *long final* at 8nm and *final* at 4nm. See further text in the reference section under Aerodrome – Circuit.
Longitude	Imaginary lines drawn from the true north pole to the true south pole. Also known as meridians. They are measured in degrees and minutes and 1 minute is equal to 1 nautical mile only at the equator. See further text in the reference section.
Longitudinal Separation	Aircraft division expressed in terms of height. See further text in the reference section under Radar Separation.
LOP	Line Of Position.
LORAN	Long Range Air Navigation system. Loran determines an aircraft's position by the relative travel time of pulse signals from two or more radio stations. See further text in the reference section.
Low	Abbreviation for an area of low pressure. Also known as a depression. See further text in the reference section under Depressions.
Lower Airspace Radar Service	A service offering an information or advisory service to aircraft in UK controlled airspace up to FL 95 and within 30nm of each unit. See further text in the reference section under Radar Services.

Lower Sideband Frequencies	When a frequency is amplitude modulated the resultant carrier wave will consist of the superimposed frequency plus two side band frequencies. The lower sideband is at a frequency of the superimposed frequency less the original frequency. See further text in the reference section under Radio Waves.
Low Flying Rules	The Air Pilot specifies various rules particularly that no aircraft shall fly closer than 500ft to any person, vessel, vehicle or structure. Other rules relate to flight over towns, cities, settlements and an assembly of persons. See further text in the reference section.
Low Frequency Band	Frequencies in the 30 – 300KHz range. See further text in the reference section.
Low Level Civil Aircraft Notification Procedures	A system where civil traffic involved in aerial work at or below 1,000 feet agl notify the Tactical Booking Cell of the London Air Traffic Control Centre (Military) by freephone before commencing work. See further text in the reference section.
Low Pressure Areas	Atmospheric areas also referred to as depressions or cyclones. They are caused either by a localised phenomenon or more commonly by disrupted waves in the polar front. See further text in the reference section under Depressions.
LP	Precision approach path indicator. (NOTAM decode 2nd & 3rd letters). See Glossary text under that heading.
LP...	Prohibited to ... (NOTAM decode 4th & 5th letters).
LR	Aircraft restricted to runways and taxiways. (NOTAM decode 4th & 5th letters).
LR	All landing area lighting facilities. (NOTAM decode 2nd & 3rd letters).
LRC	Long Range Cruise.
LRF	Low Frequency radio Range.
LRG	Long Range.
LRL	Low intensity Runway edge Lighting.
LS	Stopway lights. (NOTAM decode 2nd & 3rd letters). See Glossary text under Stopway.
LS	Subject to interruption. (NOTAM decode 4th & 5th letters).
LSALT	Lowest Safe Altitude.
LSAS	Longitudinal Stability Augmentation System.
LSQ	Line Squall, meteorological. See Glossary text under that heading.
LT...	Limited to ... (NOTAM decode 4th & 5th letters).
LT	Threshold lights. (NOTAM decode 2nd & 3rd letters). See Glossary text under Threshold.
LTD	Limited, meteorological.
LTMA	London Terminal control Area.

Lull	A temporary decrease in wind speed. The opposite to a gust. Reported to pilots when the difference is at least 10 knots.
LUS	London Upper Sector.
LV	Closed to visual flight rules operations. (NOTAM decode 4th & 5th letters). See Glossary text under Visual Flight Rules.
LV	Light and Variable, in relation to wind.
LV	Visual approach slope indicator system. (NOTAM decode 2nd & 3rd letters). See Glossary text under that heading.
LVE	Leave or Leaving.
LVL	Level.
LW	Heliport lighting. (NOTAM decode 2nd & 3rd letters).
LW	Will take place. (NOTAM decode 4th & 5th letters).
LX...	Operating but caution advised due to ...
LY	Taxiway edge lights.
LYR	Layer or Layered, in relation to cloud.
LZ	Runway touchdown zone lights. (NOTAM decode 2nd & 3rd letters). See Glossary text under Precision Approach Runways.

M

m	Mass.
m	Metre(s).
m	Minutes.
M...	Mach (followed by number). See Glossary text under Mach Number
M	Magnetic.
M	Measured ceiling.
M	Missing.
M	Monday.
Ma	Mass flow of air.
MA	Movement area. (NOTAM decode 2nd & 3rd letters). See Glossary text under that heading.
MAA	Maximum Authorized Altitude.
Mach Meter	A device capable of directly displaying the true airspeed of an aircraft as a Mach number.
Mach Number	An aircraft's true airspeed converted to a Mach number by taking into account the ambient temperature and pressure. See further text in the reference section.
Mackerel Sky	A regular fish scale like pattern of altocumulus or cirrocumulus clouds.
MAD	Magnetic Anomaly, affecting the magnetic compass.
MADGE	Microwave Automatic Digital Guidance Equipment. See Glossary text under Microwave Landing System.
Mag	Magnetic.
Magma	The moulten core at the centre of the Earth. Its movement is considered by some theories to be the reason for the annual change in magnetic variation.
Magnetic Bearing	A radio bearing based on magnetic tracks. Referred to as a QDM or QDR dependent on whether the bearing is to or from a ground station.
Magnetic Equator	The aclinal line of zero magnetic dip. See further text in the reference section.
Magnetic Poles	See text in the reference section.
MAINT	Maintenance.
MALS	Medium intensity Approach Light System.
MALSF	Medium intensity Approach Light System with sequenced Flashing lights.
MALSR	Medium intensity Approach Light System with Runway alignment indicator lights.

Manoeuvring Area	The part of the aerodrome provided for the take off and landing of aircraft and for the movement of aircraft on the surface. It excludes the apron and any part of the aerodrome provided for aircraft maintenance. For other areas see text in the reference section under Aerodrome – Surface Definitions.
MAP	Aeronautical maps and charts section of the Air Pilot.
MAP	Missed Approach Procedure. See text in the reference section under Missed Approach Point.
MAPt	Missed Approach Point. See text in the reference section.
MAR	At sea/over the sea. Derived from maritime.
MARAS	Middle Airspace Radar Advisory Service. See Glossary text under that heading.
Mares Tails	A streaky pattern of cirrus clouds.
Maritime Radio Beacons	Non-directional beacons provided for maritime use but the signal and bearing information is usable by aircraft equipped with an ADF receiver. See further text in the reference section.
Marker Beacons	Locator or fan marker beacons that emit a narrow, vertical, coned shaped beam which can only be received by an aircraft flying within the area of the beam. They are used for positive position fixing. See further text in the reference section.
Marker Receiver	Audio/visual display equipment fitted in an aircraft illuminating a blue, orange or white light together with its respective discrete tone, dependent on the type of beacon being over-flown. See text in the reference section under Marker Beacons.
MARS	Aeronautical information Retrieval System.
Matiniere Wind	Mountain wind occuring in the Alps, often very violent in the mornings.
MATO	Military Air Traffic Operations.
MATS	Manual of Air Traffic Services.
MATZ	Military Air Traffic Zone. See text in the reference section.
MAX	Maximum.
Maximum Elevation Figure	Figures over printed on the ICAO, 1:500,000 visual navigation charts, showing the height, amsl, of the highest known object in each half a degree of latitude and longitude box. The height provides for no element of safe clearance.
Mayday	A distress or emergency message transmitted in the event of serious and/or imminent danger to the occupants of an aircraft. See further text in the reference section.
MB	(Surface) bearing strength. (NOTAM decode 2nd & 3rd letters). See Glossary text under Pavement Classification Number.
Mb(s)	Millibar(s). Unit of pressure equal to 1 hectopascal and 0.02953 inches of Mercury.

MBOH	Minimum Break Off Height. See Glossary text under Decision Height.
MC	Clearway. (NOTAM decode 2nd & 3rd letters). See Glossary text under that heading.
MCA	Minimum Crossing Altitude.
Mc/s	Megacycles per second.
MCW	Modulated Continuous Wave.
MD	Declared distances. (NOTAM decode 2nd & 3rd letters).
MDA	Master Diversion Aerodrome.
MDA	Minimum Descent Altitude. See Glossary text under Minimum Descent Height.
MDF	Medium frequency Direction Finding station.
MDH	Minimum Descent Height. See Glossary text under that heading.
MDT	Moderate, meteorological, See Glossary text under that heading.
MEA	Minimum En-route Altitude.
Mean Camber Line	A line drawn halfway on the cross section of the upper and lower wing surfaces.
Mean Sea Level	The average height of the surface of the sea for all stages of tide.
Mechanical Turbulence	Interference caused to any horizontally flowing air mass as it encounters an obstacle. See further text in the reference section under Surface Winds.
MEDA	Military Emergency Diversion Aerodrome. See Glossary text under that heading.
MediumFrequency	Frequencies in the 300 – 3,000Khz range.
MEF	Maximum Elevation Figure. See Glossary text under that heading.
Megahertz	1,000,000 Hertz or 106 cycles per second.
MEHT	Minimum pilot Eye-Height over Threshold, quoted in respect of visual approach slope indicator systems.
MEL	Minimum Equipment List.
MEL	Multi-engine, Land.
Melamboreas Wind	A Northerly wind similar to the Mistral but occuring in Provence, France.
Melting Band	A bright primary radar return caused by snowflakes melting within a vertical section of a cloud.
MER	True height above Mean sea level.
Mercator Projection	Used for nautical and long range military charts. Conformal projection rhumb lines are represented by straight lines and great circles by curved lines.

Meridian Chart	A great circle joining the true north and south poles and used to define points of longitude.
MET	Meteorological/Meteorological office.
METAR	Meteorological Aerodrome Report. See text in the reference section under Meteorological Aerodrome Report.
Meteorological Aerodrome Forecast	See text in the reference section under Terminal Aerodrome Forecast or Meteorological Forecast - Personalised.
Meteorological Aerodrome Report	Also referred to as an actual and METAR. Used to advise pilots of the actual weather at an aerodrome. They are compiled at half-hourly or hourly intervals. See further text in the reference section.
METFAX	TAF, METAR, Airmet, satellite, wind, and weather charts available to the public by means of a facsimile machine. Index page on 0336 400 501.
Metform 214	UK spot wind and temperature chart issued at 0400, 1000, 1600 and 2150 hours and valid for 0900, 1500, 2100 and 0300 hours respectively.
Metform 215	UK low level weather chart issued at 0400, 1000, 1600 and 2150 hours and valid for 0900, 1500, 2100 and 0300 hours respectively. See further text in the reference section.
Metform 216	Decode listing for Metform 215.
MEW	Mean Equivalent Wind.
MF	Mandatory Frequency.
MF	Medium Frequency. Frequencies in the 300 – 3,000Khz range.
MFA	Minimum Flight Altitude.
MFD	Malfunctioning Display.
MFT	Manufacturer.
MFV...	Forward Visibility more than ... Miles.
MG	Taxying guidance system. (NOTAM decode 2nd & 3rd letters).
MGIR	Motor Glider Instructor Rating.
MH	Runway arresting gear. (NOTAM decode 2nd & 3rd letters). See Glossary text under Runway Arrester Gear.
MHA	Minimum Holding Altitude.
MHDF	Co-located Medium and High frequency Direction Finding station. See text in the reference section under Co-Located Navigation or Approach Equipment.
MHVDF	Co-located Medium, High and Very high frequency Direction Finding stations. See text in the reference section under Co-Located Navigation or Approach Equipment.
MHZ	Megahertz. 1,000,000 Hertz or 10^6 cycles per second.
MI	Medium Intensity lighting.
MI	Mile(s).

MI	Shallow, meteorological. Used to describe fog, See Glossary text under Fog.
MIA	Minimum Instrument flight rules Altitude.
MIALS	Medium Intensity Approach Light System.
Microburst	Small localised downburst. See Glossary text under Downburst.
Microwave	Any frequency over 1,000MHz. See Glossary text in the reference section under Super High Frequency.
Microwave Landing System	An instrument landing system where a microwave beam scans a large area of sky enabling several aircraft to utilize different approach paths.
MID	Middle.
MID	Mid-point, in relation to runway visual range.
Middle Airspace Radar Advisory Service	Service given by military ATC radar units to all aircraft flying outside controlled airspace in UK FIR (except those on ADRs) and transponder equipped between FL 100 and FL 240. See further text in the reference section under Radar Services.
Middle Marker	See text in the reference section under Marker Beacons.
MIDN	Midnight.
MIFG	Shallow Fog. See Glossary text under Fog.
MIL	Military.
Military Air Traffic Zone	An additional zone is established around a military ATZ. It comprises of the airspace in a radius of 5nm from the surface to 3,000 feet aal. See further text in the reference section.
Military Emergency Diversion Aerodrome	Aerodromes which offer any distressed aircraft radar vectoring (if required) and landing facilities on a 24 hour basis.
Military Middle Airspace Radar Service	See Glossary text under Middle Airspace Radar Advisory Service.
Military Training Area	Prohibited or restricted area. The areas are marked on navigational maps, normally with a reference to the base and upper height limits. See further text in the reference section.
Millibar	Unit of pressure equal to 1 hectopascal and 0.02953 inches of Mercury. See further text in the reference section.
MIM	Minimum.
Min	Minimum.
Min DH	Minimum Descent Height. See Glossary text under that heading.
min/s	Minute/s.
Minimum Descent Height	The height in a non-precision approach below which the pilot should not descend unless it is safe to do so by visual reference.

Minimum Safe Altitude	Minimas shown on radio navigation charts to provide adequate terrain clearance. The altitudes give a clearance of 1,000 feet in areas with obstacles up to and including 5,000ft, increasing to 2,000 feet above 5,000ft. See further text in the reference section.
Minimum Sector Altitude	Altitudes shown on standard instrument arrival and departure charts giving a safe altitude figure based on 10nm either side of the approach or departure track.
MIRL	Medium Intensity Runway edge Lights
Missed Approach Point	A point marked on an instrument approach chart at which the standard, published, missed approach procedure must be carried out. See further text in the reference section.
Missed Approach Procedure	A procedure published on an instrument approach chart showing the action to be taken by a flight that is unable to make visual contact on an approach. See text in the reference section under Missed Approach Point.
Mist	Water droplets with a diameter of less than 0.2mm reducing visibility to not less than 1,000 metres. See further text in the reference section under Visibility.
Mistral Wind	North westerly, cold, dry and often violent wind affecting in the Rhone valley and extending as far south as northern Sardinia.
Mixture Control	A device for adjusting the air/fuel ratio of an engine to obtain the most efficient setting for various heights. See further text in the reference section.
Mizzle	Meteorological slang for a mixture of mist and drizzle.
MK	Parking area. (NOTAM decode 2nd & 3rd letters). See Glossary text under Apron.
MKR	Marker. See text in the reference section under Marker Beacons.
MLG	Main Landing Gear.
Mlnd	Maximum landing weight.
MLS	Microwave Landing System. See Glossary text under that heading.
MLW	Maximum certificate Landing Weight.
MLWA	Maximum Landing Weight Authorized.
MLZ	Microwave Landing system receiver. See Glossary text under Microwave Landing system.
MM	Daylight markings. (NOTAM decode 2nd & 3rd letters).
MM	Middle Marker. See text in the reference section under Marker Beacons.
MMO	Maximum Operating Mach number.
MN	Apron. (NOTAM decode 2nd & 3rd letters). See Glossary text under that heading.

MNE	Never Exceed Mach number.
MNLD	Mainland.
MNM	Minimum.
MNO	Normal Operating Mach number.
MNP(S)	Minimum Navigation Performance (Specifications).
MNR	Minimum Noise Route.
MNT	Monitor, Monitored, Monitoring.
MNTN	Maintain.
MOA	Military Operations Area.
MOC	Minimum Obstruction Clearance (required).
MOCA	Minimum Obstruction Clearance Altitude.
MOD	Ministry of Defence.
MOD	Moderate, meteorological. See Glossary text under that heading.
Mode A	Transponder option which displays the selected discrete aircraft identification on a SSR screen. See text in the reference section under Transponder, Radar-Secondary and page 271 for specific transponder codes.
Mode B	Not used for UK or European operations.
Mode C	Transponder option which displays the selected discrete aircraft identification and altitude on a SSR screen. See Glossary text under Pneumatic Altimeter and the reference section under Transponder, Radar-Secondary and page 271 for specific transponder codes.
Moderate	Meteorological intensity in relation to icing, turbulence or static.
Moderate Breeze	Wind speed between 11 & 15 knots (20 & 28km per hour). Force 4.
Mode S	Transponder option which contains a 24 bit address of the installation together with a capability report in its message file. See further text in the reference section under Transponder, Radar-Secondary and page 271 for specific transponder codes.
Modulation	A method where low frequencies are combined with a higher frequency to allow for efficient transmission. See further text in the reference section under Radio Waves.
MOGAS	Motor Gasoline. See text in the reference section under MOGAS.
MOGR	Moderate or Greater.
Molan	Term used to describe a downdraft in the French Alps.
MON	Above Mountains.
MON	Monday.

Monsoon	A wind that reverses its direction with the seasons, blowing from continent to sea in winter and opposite in summer.
Montagnere Wind	A land breeze found on the southern slopes of the Alps.
MOPS	Minimum Operational Performance Standards.
MOR	Mandatory Occurrence Report
MORA	Minimum Off-Route Altitude.
MORS	Mandatory Occurrence Reporting Scheme.
MOTNE	Meteorological Operational Telecommunications Network Europe.
Mountain Waves	See text in the reference section under Standing Waves
MOV	Moving, meteorological.
Movement Area	Runways, taxiways and other areas that are used for taxying, take off and landing of aircraft excluding loading ramps and parking areas. For other areas see text in the reference section under Aerodrome – Surface Definitions.
Moving Target Indicator	Intelligence circuits in a primary radar system which are able to distinguish between clutter and moving targets. See further text in the reference section under Radar - Primary.
Motor Glider	An aircraft equipped with one or more engines. With the engines inoperative having the characteristics of a glider. For sub-categories see Glossary text under Touring Motor Glider, Self-Launching Glider and Self-Substaining Glider.
MP	Aircraft stands. (NOTAM decode 2nd & 3rd letters).
MP	Maintenance Period.
MP	Manifold Pressure.
MP	Maritime Polar air mass. See Glossary text under Polar Maritime Air.
MPH	Statute Miles Per Hour.
MPS	Metres per Second.
MPS	Minimum Performance Specification.
MR	Runway. (NOTAM decode 2nd & 3rd letters).
MRA	Minimum Reception Altitude.
MRCC	HM Coastguard Maritime Rescue Co-ordination Centre.
MRG	Medium Range.
MRGL	Marginal.
MRL	Medium intensity Runway edge Lighting.
MRNG	Morning.
MRP	Air traffic service Meteorological Reporting Point.
MRS	Medical Records System.
MRSC	HM Coastguard Maritime Rescue Sub-Centre.
MRTM	Maritime.

m/s	Metres per second.
MS	Stopway. (NOTAM decode 2nd & 3rd letters). See Glossary text under that heading.
MS	Maintenance Schedule.
MS	Minus.
MSA	Minimum Safe Altitude. See Glossary text under that heading.
MSA	Minimum Sector Altitude. See Glossary text under that heading.
MSAW	Minimum Safe Altitude Warning.
MSD	Minimum Separation Distance.
MSG	Flight plan and associated update message.
MSG	Message.
MSL	Mean Sea Level.
MSSR	Monopulse Secondary Surveillance Radar.
MSTR	Moisture.
mt	Metric tonne.
MT	Threshold. (NOTAM decode 2nd & 3rd letters). See Glossary text under that heading.
MT	Maritime Tropical air. See Glossary text under Tropical Maritime Air.
MT	Mountain.
MTA	Military Training Area. See Glossary text under that heading.
MTBF	Mean Time Between Failures.
MTCA	Minimum Terrain Clearance Altitude.
MTI	Marked Temperature Inversion. See Glossary text under Temperature Inversion.
MTI	Moving Target Indicator. See Glossary text under that heading.
MTMA	Military Terminal control Area.
MTN	Mountain.
MTU	Metric Units.
MTW	Mountain Waves. See text in the reference section under Standing Waves.
MTWA	Maximum Total Weight Authorized.
MU	Runway turning bay. (NOTAM decode 2nd & 3rd letters).
Mu-Meter	Device used to access runway braking action by measuring the co-efficient of friction and verify the possibility of slush-planing.
MVDF	Co-located Medium & Very high frequency Direction Finding stations. See text in the reference section under Co-Located and Direction Finding.
MVFR	Marginal Visual Flight Rules.

MW	Strip. (NOTAM decode 2nd & 3rd letters).
MWE	Manufacturers Weight Empty.
MWO	Meteorological Watch Office.
MX	Mixed types of ice (white & clear).
MX	Taxyway(s). (NOTAM decode 2nd & 3rd letters).
MXD	Mixed.

N	
n	Load factor.
N	Engine rotational speed.
N	Night. See text in the reference section.
N	North.
N/A	Not Applicable.
NA	All radio navigation facilities (except...). (NOTAM decode 2nd & 3rd letters).
NA	Not Authorized.
NAA	National Airports Authority.
NAPS	Noise Abatement Procedures.
NAS	Naval Air Station.
NATCS	National Air Traffic Control Services.
NATO	North Atlantic Treaty Organisation – when shown on approach charts denotes standard military system.
NATS	National Air Traffic Services.
NATSU	Nominated Air Traffic Service Unit.
NAV	Navigation.
NAVAID	Navigation Aid.
NAV/COM	Navigation & Communication aids.
NB	Northbound.
NB	Non directional radio beacon. (NOTAM decode 2nd & 3rd letters). See text in the reference section under Non Directional Beacons.
NBFM	Narrow Band Frequency Modulation.
NC	Decca navigation system. (NOTAM decode 2nd & 3rd letters). See Glossary text under DECCA.
NC	No Change.
NCWX	No Change in Weather.
ND	Non directional radio beacon. (NOTAM decode 2nd & 3rd letters). See text in the reference section under Non Directional Beacons.
NDB	Non Directional radio Beacon. See text in the reference section under Non Directional Beacons.
NDB/L	Non Directional radio Beacon or Locator. See text in the reference section under Non Directional Beacons.
NE	North East.
Near Continent	Term used to describe airfields near the English Channel in France or the Netherlands.
Near Gale	Wind speed between 28 – 33 knots. (52 – 61 km per hour). Force 7.

NEB	North Eastbound.
NEG	No, Negative, permission not granted, not correct.
Nephoscope	An instrument used to measure the direction and angular velocity of clouds.
Neutral Stability	Atmospheric state which exists when the environmental lapse rate is equal to that of a parcel of air that is being lifted through it. See further text in the reference section under Adiabatic Lapse Rates.
NF	Fan Marker. (NOTAM decode 2nd & 3rd letters). See text in the reference section under Marker Beacons.
NFBR	Not Before.
NFT	Navigation Flight Test.
NGT	Night. See Glossary text under that heading.
Night	(ICAO) Night means the time between half an hour after sunset and half an hour before sunrise. Sunset and sunrise being determined at surface level. See Glossary text under Night Flight.
Night Effect	Error affecting ADF systems where due to the change of the ionosphere at night, LF and MF signals may become returned to the aircraft as sky waves giving a fluctuating and unreliable needle indication. See text in the reference section under Non Directional Beacons.
Night Flight	Flights carried out when the depression of the sun's centre is not less than 12 degrees below the horizon.
Night Rating	Extension of a pilot's licence which allows a pilot to act as pilot in command providing he/she has, within the preceding 13 months, carried out as pilot in command not less than 5 take-offs and 5 landings at a time when the depression of the Sun's centre was not less than 12 degrees below the horizon.
Nimbostratus Cloud	Grey, dark, layer cloud associated with continuous falling rain or snow.
NINST	Non-Instrument Runway. See Glossary text under that heading.
NL	Locator. (NOTAM decode 2nd & 3rd letters). See text in the reference section under Non Directional Beacons.
NLG	Nose Landing Gear.
NM	Nautical Mile(s).
NM	VOR/DME. (NOTAM decode 2nd & 3rd letters). See Glossary text under Very High Frequency Omni-Directional Range and Distance Measuring Equipment.
NMI	Nautical Mile(s).
NML	Normal.
NMRS	Numerous.
NN	TACAN. (NOTAM decode 2nd & 3rd letters). See Glossary text under Tactical Air Navigator.

NO	OMEGA navigation system. (NOTAM decode 2nd & 3rd letters). See Glossary text under that heading.
No Delay Expected	ATC phraseology used to advise an expected approach time and means: *Do not anticipate being required to remain in a holding pattern for longer than 20 minutes before commencing an approach.*
No Gyro Approach	Radar approach procedure adopted in the event of gyrocompass or directional gyro failure.
No Gyro Vectors	Headings passed to an aircraft suffering gyro compass or directional gyro failure by passing left, right and stop turn instructions.
Nominated Air Traffic Service Unit	A unit providing a danger area activity service giving pilots an airborne update of the activity status of a participating danger area.
NON	Unmodulated Carrier Wave. See Glossary text under Modulation and Carrier Wave.
Non Directional Radio Beacon	LF and MF transmitters used by aircraft equipped with automatic direction finding equipment. Beacons are used for tracking to, from and for homing purposes. See further text in the reference section under Non Directional Beacons.
Non Instrument Runway	Runway intended for use by aircraft using visual approach procedures.
NONP	Non-Precision approach Runway. See Glossary text under Non-Instrument Runway.
NoPR	No Procedural turn to be instigated without air traffic control clearance. See Glossary text under Procedure Turn.
NoPT	No Procedure Turn without air traffic control authorization. See Glossary text under Procedure Turn.
Normally Aspirated Engine	An engine whose fuel supply is fed via a carburettor(s). See further text in the reference section.
NOSIG	No Significant change. Meteorological information included in a report indicating a likely weather tendency. See further text in the reference section under TREND.
NOTAM	Notice to Airmen. See Glossary text under that heading.
Notice to Airmen	Information issued by a telephone system or by post dependent on its urgency, and relating to the establishment, condition or change of a facility, procedure or hazard. See further text in the reference section under NOTAM.
NOZ	No Operating Zone.
NPRs	Noise Preferential Routes.
NR	Number.
NRW	Narrow.
NS	Nimbostratus cloud. See Glossary text under that heading.
NSW	No Significant Weather, meteorological.

NT	VORTAC. (NOTAM decode 2nd & 3rd letters). Very high frequency omni-directional range and tactical air navigator. See Glossary text under both headings.
NTE	Not To Exceed.
NTIS	National Technical Information Service (USA).
NTP	Temperature & Pressures Normal.
NV	VOR. (NOTAM decode 2nd & 3rd letters). See Glossary text under Very High Frequency Omni-Directional Range.
NW	North West.
NWB	North Westbound.
NX	Direction finding station. (NOTAM decode 2nd & 3rd letters). See Glossary text under Direction Finding.
NX	Next.
NXT	Next.
NYO	Not Yet Operating.

O

(o)	Omni-directional.
OA	Aeronautical information service. (NOTAM decode 2nd & 3rd letters).
OB	Obstacle. (NOTAM decode 2nd & 3rd letters).
OB	Outbound.
OBI	Omni-Bearing Indicator. See text in the reference section.
Oblique Visibility	The distance on the ground between a point directly below an aircraft and the most distant object the pilot can see.
OBS	Omni-Bearing Selector. See text in the reference section under Omni-Bearing Indicator.
Obs	Obstacle lights.
OBS	Observe, Observed, Observation.
OBSC	Obscure, Obscured, Obscuring. Meteorological.
OBST	Obstruction.
Obstacle Clearance Altitude	A published altitude used for obstacle clearance procedures.
Obstacle Clearance Height	A published height used for obstacle clearance procedures based on a height above aerodrome level.
Obstacle Clearance Limit	The height above the aerodrome elevation below which the prescribed safe clearance cannot be maintained.
Obstn	Obstruction.
OCA/H	Obstacle Clearance Altitude/Height. See Glossary text under Obstacle Clearance Height.
OCA/H$_{fm}$	Obstacle Clearance Altitude/Height for the final approach and straight missed approach.
OCA/H$_{ps}$	Obstacle Clearance Altitude/Height for the precision segment.
OCC	Occulting. A light beam deflected or reflected off, a cloud.
Occluded Front	See Glossary text under Occlusion.
Occlusion	The point at which two fronts meet. See further text in the reference section.
Occulting	A light beam deflected by, or reflected off a cloud.
Occurrences & Accidents	Such incidents as defined in the Air Pilot that require a mandatory report. See further text in the reference section.
OCFNT	Occluded Front. See Glossary text under Occlusion.
OCH	Obstacle Clearance Height. See Glossary text under that heading.
OCL	Obstacle Clearance Limit. See Glossary text under that heading.
OCL	Obstruction Clearance Limit. See Glossary text under Obstacle Clearance Limit.
OCL	Occlude.

OCLN	Occasional or Occasionally.
OCLN	Occlusion. See Glossary text under that heading.
Oculogyral Illusion	An optical illusion where a steady light appears to develop a movement. See further text in the reference section.
ODALS	Omni-Directional sequenced flashing lead in Light System.
ODL	Opposite Direction Level.
OE	Aircraft entry requirements. (NOTAM decode 2nd & 3rd letters).
Off Shore Installations	Installations which have helicopter landing sites have an air traffic zone from mean sea level to 2,000 feet amsl with a 1.5nm radius.
OFP	Occluded Front Passage. See Glossary text under Occlusion.
OFSHR	Offshore.
OFZ	Obstacle Free Zone.
OGE	Out of Ground Effect. See Glossary text under Ground Effect.
OHD	Overhead.
Ohms Law	States that the current flowing in a circuit is directly proportional to the applied voltage and inversely proportional to the resistance. See further text in the reference section.
OJTI	On-the-Job Training Instructor.
Oktas	The unit used to describe cloud cover based on eighths. Overcast being eight oktas.
OL...	Obstacle lights on ... (NOTAM decode 2nd & 3rd letters).
OM	Outer Marker. See Glossary text in the reference section under Marker Beacons.
Omega	Very low frequency navigation system based on 8 transmitters covering the whole world.
Omni Bearing Indicator	A needle used in a VHF omni-directional range receiver display to indicate which radial an aircraft is on. See further text in the reference section.
Omni-Bearing Selector	A knob fitted to a VHF omni-directional range receiver bearing display which is used to rotate a compass rose and select a specific radial. See further text in the reference section under Omni-Bearing Indicator.
OMTNS	Over Mountains. Meteorological.
One in Sixty Rule	A rule used for visual navigation flights to calculate the distance off track and required closing angle. See the reference section under Track Error for the formula.
ONSHR	Onshore.
On Top	Meteorologically used to describe flight in visual conditions above a layer of cloud.
OPA	Opaque, a white type of ice formation.
Opacus	A cloud thick enough to totally obscure the sun.
Op hrs	Operational hours.

OPMET	Operational Meteorological (information).
OPN	Open, Opening, Opened.
OPR	Operator, Operate, Operative, Operating, Operating.
Oprn	Operations.
OPS	Operations.
OPT	On Top. See Glossary text under that heading.
OPT	Operational Testing Phase. Test phases of the integrated initial flight plan processing system.
O/R	On Request.
OR	Operational Requirements.
OR	Over-Run. See Glossary text under Stopway.
OR	Rescue co-ordination centre. (NOTAM decode 2nd & 3rd letters).
Orographic Cloud	Cloud formed on the windward side of a range of mountains or hills.
Orographic Depression	A localised low pressure area formed on the lee side of a mountain range.
Orographic Lifting	The lifting effect on a horizontal air flow as it encounters a range of mountains or hills.
Orographic Low	See Glossary text under Orographic Depression.
Orthormorphic Chart	The European term for the conformal class of charts.
OT	Other Times.
OT	On Top. See Glossary text under that heading.
OTS	Out of Service.
OUBD	Outbound.
Outer Marker	A marker beacon provided as a position fix in an instrument landing system approach. See text in the reference section under Marker Beacons.
OVC	Overcast. See Glossary text under that heading.
Overcast	8 oktas or eight eights of cloud cover.
Over-run	See Glossary text under stopway.
Overseeding	A meteorological state where such a high concentration of cloud condensation or ice nuclei exist that all available moisture is attached to the nuclei before they become large enough to fall as precipitation. See Glossary text under Ice Nuclei.
Ovrn	Over-run. See Glossary text under Stopway.
OVRN	Over-Run standard approach lighting system.
OVRNG	Over-Running.
OWE	Operating Weight Empty.
Owners Manual	A handbook containing performance statistics and operational procedures for the operation of a particular aircraft.

P

p	Paved surface.
P	Port (left).
P	Pressure.
P	Primary frequency.
P	Private aerodrome.
P...	Prohibited area, followed by an identification number.
P1	Pilot in command.
P2	Co-pilot.
PA	Standard instrument arrival. (NOTAM decode 2nd & 3rd letters).
PA	Precision Approach Lighting System.
PA1	Precision Approach Runway category I. See Glossary text under Precision Approach Runways.
PA2	Precision Approach runway category II. See Glossary text under Precision Approach Runways.
PA3	Precision Approach Runway category III. See Glossary text under Precision Approach Runways.
PALS	Precision Approach Lighting System.
PAM	Pulse Amplitude Modulation. See Glossary text under Pulse Modulation.
Pan Call	An urgency message transmitted by an aircraft to notify a ground station of a situation affecting the safety of the aircraft, a person on board or a third party in sight of the aircraft. See further text in the reference section.
PANS OPS	Procedures for Air Navigation Services Operations.
PAPA	Parallax Aircraft Parking Aid.
PAPI	Precision Approach Path Indicators. See Glossary text under that heading.
PAR	Parallel.
PAR	Precision Approach Radar. See Glossary text under that heading.
PAR	Preferential Arrival Route.
Parallax Error	The reading error resulting from interpreting an instrument display at an angle other than head on. Also referred to as slant error.
Parallel Runways	Where aerodromes have two or more runways with the same magnetic direction. They are suffixed L – left, R – right and C – centre.
Parasite Drag	Created as a result of the airflow passing over parts of the aircraft. The greater the eddies and turbulence created, the greater the parasite drag. See text in the reference section under Drag for other forms.

PARL	Parallel.
PATWAS	Pilot Automatic Telephone Weather Answering Service.
Pavement Classification Number	A number expressing the load bearing strength of a runway.
PAX Number	Passengers.
PBDI	Position, Bearing & Distance Indicator.
PBL	Probable.
PCA	Positive Control Area.
PCD	Proceeding or Proceed.
PCN	Pavement Classification Number. See Glossary text under that heading.
P Code	Precise or Protected Code, in respect of a satellite navigation system. See text in the reference section under Global Positioning System.
PCPN	Precipitation. See Glossary text under that heading.
PD	Period.
PD	Standard instrument departure. (NOTAM decode 2nd & 3rd letters).
PDAR	Preferential Departure and Arrival Route.
PDR	Pre-Determined Routing.
PDR	Preferential Departure Route.
PE	Ice Pellets, meteorological.
PE	Position Error.
PEC	Position Error Correction.
PER	Performance.
PERM	Permanently.
Permanent Echo	Radar signals reflected from fixed objects on the Earth's surface. Being in fixed locations they are sometimes used to check radar alignment. See text in the reference section under Radar – Primary.
PF	Flow control procedures. (NOTAM decode 2nd & 3rd letters).
PFA	Popular Flying Association.
PFL	Practice Forced Landing.
PFR	Permitted Flying Route.
PH	Holding procedure. (NOTAM decode 2nd & 3rd letters). See Glossary text under En-Route Holds.
PH	Public Holidays.
Phantom Station	A waypoint created by an area radio navigation system with data received from a co-located VOR & DME station. The system to gives heading, distance and time information of the

	track to the waypoint. See text in the reference section under Area Navigation System.
Phonetic Alphabet	A system of allocating words to letters of the alphabet so that messages may be spelt out clearly by radio telephony. The full phonetic alphabet is listed on page 270.
PI	Instrument approach procedure. (NOTAM decode 2nd & 3rd letters). See Glossary text under Instrument Approach Charts.
PIBAL	Pilot Balloon.
PIC	Pilot in Command.
PIC	Potential Icing Category.
Pilot's Licence	See text in the reference section under Licence – Pilot's. See Glossary text under Owner's Manual.
Pinch Hitter	An American expression for a safety or second pilot. See text under Safety Pilot.
PINS	Pipeline Inspection Notification System.
Piston Engine Induction System Icing	Technically correct phrase used to describe carburettor icing. See further text in the reference section under Icing - Carburettor.
Pitch Hitter	Corruption of pinch hitter. See Glossary text under that heading.
Pitot Head	See Glossary text under Pitot Tube.
Pitot Heat	An electrical heating element fitted to a pitot tube to prevent an ice build up from blocking the air flow.
Pitot Pressure	A combination of dynamic and static pressure fed to the air speed indicator via a pitot tube.
Pitot Tube	A air collection device designed to point directly into the airflow, whilst in cruise configuration, to feed pitot pressure to the air speed indicator. See further text in the reference section.
PJA	Parachute Jumping exercise.
PJE	Parachute Jumping Exercise.
PL	Obstacle clearance limit. (NOTAM decode 2nd & 3rd letters). See Glossary text under that heading.
PLA	Practise Low Approach.
PLASI	Pulse Light Approach Indicator System.
PLN	Flight Plan.
PLVN	Present Level.
PM	Aerodrome operating minima. (NOTAM decode 2nd & 3rd letters). See Glossary text under that heading.
PM	Phase Modulation.
PN	Part Number
PN	Prior Notice required.
PNdB	Perceived Noise decibel. A unit of noise that takes into account the annoyance value of frequencies as heard from the ground.

Pneumatic Altimeter	A system used in an encoding altimeter operated in conjunction with the transponder passing information to ATC whilst the transponder is set to Mode C. The system uses a parallel coded output of 9 to 11 bits representing the aircraft's height above the 1013.25 datum to the nearest 100 feet.
PNL	Perceived Noise Level. Measured in PNdB.
PNR	Point of No Return. See Glossary text under that heading.
PNR	Prior Notice Required.
PO	Dust devil, dust/sand whirls, meteorological.
PO	Obstacle clearance altitude. (NOTAM decode 2nd & 3rd letters). See Glossary text under that heading.
POB	Persons On Board.
POH	Pilot's Operating Handbook. See Glossary text under Owner's Manual.
Point of No Return	The point at which an aircraft has insufficient fuel to return to the point of departure.
Polar Continental Air	At source, very cold dry air. On reaching the UK very cold, stable and hazy. For more information and classifications See text in the reference section under Air Masses.
Polar Depressions	Lows occuring in winter when cold air moves over a warm sea surface. The comparatively cold upper air usually results in several days of bad weather. See further text in the reference section under Depressions.
Polar Front	The dividing line between the northern polar air and warmer sub-tropical air. The front generally lies between Newfoundland and the North of Scotland in winter and between Florida and the South West of England during the summer.
Polarisation	The direction or plane of an electrical field. A vertically polarised signal is one who's electrical field is vertical to the Earth's surface. See further text in the reference section.
Polar Maritime Air	At source, stable, cold and moist. On reaching the UK unstable, cool and moist bringing cumulus cloud, rain showers and possible thunderstorms interrupting good visibility. For more information and classifications see text in the reference section under Air Masses.
Pooley's	A VFR flight guide pilots giving details of airfields and associated flight planning information.
Port	Nautical and aviation term for left.
Portable Telephones	See text in the reference section.
POSN	Position.
Potential Temperature	Meteorologically, the temperature that a parcel of air would be at 1,000 millibars using the dry (3°C per 1,000 feet) adiabatic lapse rate.
Powered Sailplane	See Glossary text under Motor Glider.

PP	Obstacle clearance height. (NOTAM decode 2nd & 3rd letters). See Glossary text under that heading.
PPI	Plan Position Indicator.
PPL	Private Pilots Licence. See Glossary text under that heading.
PPL	Pulse Position modulation.
PPL(A)	Private Pilot's Licence (Aeroplanes). See Glossary text under that heading.
PPL(AS)	Private Pilot's Licence (Airships).
PPL(B)	Private Pilot's Licence (Balloons).
PPL(GR)	Private Pilot's Licence examiner authorized to conduct ground examinations and sign certificates of experience.
PPL(H)	Private Pilot's Licence (Helicopters).
PPLIR	Private Pilot's Licence with an Instrument Rating.
PPL(R)	Private Pilot's Licence examiner authorized to sign certificates of experience.
PPL(X)	Private Pilot's Licence examiner authorized to conduct flight tests, ground examinations and sign certificates of test and certificates of expedience.
PPL(XMG)	Private Pilot's Licence examiner authorized to conduct flight tests and examinations and sign certificates of test for self launching motor gliders and sign certificates of experience.
PPO	Prior Permission Only.
PPR	Prior Permission Required.
PPS	Precise Positioning System (P Code – military satellite navigation system). See text in the reference section under Global Positioning System.
PPSN	Present Position.
posn	Position.
PR	Primary Radar. See Glossary text under that heading.
PR	Radio failure procedure. (NOTAM decode 2nd & 3rd letters).
PRDS	Processed Radar Display System.
Precession	If a force is applied to the spin axis of a giro the reaction will be as if the force had been applied at a point 90° onwards in the direction of rotation. See text in the reference section under Gyroscopes.
Precipitation	Meteorological. Water in any form, liquid or frozen, falling upon the surface or moving between vertical bands of air. See further text in the reference section.

Precision Approach Path Indicators	A system of angled lights, red in the lower half, white in the top, and visible to a pilot on final approach. They have sharp transition characteristics, meaning that they will either show red or white. A combination of two red and two white lights confirms the aircraft is on the correct approach slope. See further text in the reference section.
Precision Approach Radar	A radar service where precise heading and height check instructions are passed from controller to pilot enable the flight to complete a visual landing. The service terminates no less than 400 metres from the end of the runway. See further text in the reference section under Radar Services.
Precision Approach Runways	Runways with touchdown zone markings up to a distance of 600 metres, placed 150 metres apart. These are the threshold marker, fixed distance marker and runway markers. The threshold and fixed distance markings bracket the optimum touchdown area.
PRES	Pressure.
PRESFR	Pressure Falling Rapidly.
PRESRR	Pressure Rising Rapidly.
Pressure Altitude	Coded as QNE. With the altimeter subscale set to 1013mb it is the height the altimeter will indicate upon landing. The setting is used for landings at high altitude airfields where the pressure reading is too low for a QFE to be set.
Pressure Gradient	The rate of change of pressure with distance. It is measured at right angles to the isobars, usually at 100 nautical mile intervals.
Pressure Gradient Force	The force created by the difference between high and low pressure systems. The force moves from high to low as it attempts to equalise the atmospheric pressure. See further text in the reference section.
PRI	Primary.
Primary Radar	A radar system transmitting a continuous train of pulses from a revolving parabolic aerial. By using the doppler effect it is able to identify moving objects and display them as a light blip on a screen. See text in the reference section under Radar – Primary.
Prime Meridian	Also known as the Greenwich Meridian. It passes through Greenwich, London and has a value of zero degrees. It is used as the datum for positions east and west of this line.
Private Pilot's Licence	A licence issued when a pilot has reached the required standard of competence. To remain valid a minimum of 5 hours must be flown as pilot in command within 13 months of the last certificate of experience, or issue of the original licence. See further text in the reference section under Licence – Pilot's.
PRF	Pulse-Recurrence Frequency.
PRKG	Parking.

PROB	Probability, shown as a percentage, meteorological.
PROC	Procedure.
Procedure Turn	A standard left turn of 45° to the reciprocal of an inbound track. Banking within the turn is at 3° per second.
Prohibited Area	See text in the reference section.
Prognostic	A premonition, meteorologically a synonym for forecast.
Proj	Projection.
PROM	Programable Read Only Memory.
Promulgated Range	The range for non directional beacons published in the COM section of the UK Air Pilot. It is based on a daytime protection ratio of wanted and unwanted signals of not less than three to one. This limits bearing errors to +/- 5° or less. See further text in the reference section under Non Directional Beacon.
PROP	Propeller. See text in the reference section.
Propeller	See text in the reference section.
PROV	Provisional.
PRP	Pulse Repetition Period.
PRST	Persist.
PS	Plus.
PS	Positive value.
PSBL	Possible.
Pseudo Random Code	A method used in a satellite navigation system where the receiver is synchronized with the satellites ensuring that the period calculation of the transmission time to the receiver time is as exact as possible. See text in the reference section under Global Positioning System.
PSG	Passage.
PSG	Passing.
PSGR	Passengers.
Psi	Pounds per square inch.
PSN	Position.
PSR	Packed Snow on Runway.
PSR	Point of Safe Return.
PSR	Primary Surveillance Radar. See Glossary text under Primary Radar.
Psychrometer	A pair of similar thermometers, one wet bulb, one dry bulb. See Glossary text under Wet Bulb Thermometer.
PT	Procedure Turn. See Glossary text under that heading.
PT	Public Transport.
PT	Transition altitude. (NOTAM decode 2nd & 3rd letters). See text under that heading.
PTCHY	Patchy, meteorological.

PTN	Procedure Turn. See Glossary text under that heading.
PTT	Press to Transmit switch.
PU	Missed approach procedure. (NOTAM decode 2nd & 3rd letters). See Glossary text under that heading.
Pulse Light Approach Slope Indicator	A light based glideslope indicator which shows a steady white light when on the glideslope and a steady red if just below. See further text in the reference section.
Pulse Modulation	A short burst of pulses, normally around one microsecond, followed by a equivalently long pause, conventionally of around one millisecond, before a further burst. See further text in the reference section under Radio Waves.
Pulse Repetition Frequency	A unique pulse repetition code used by airborne distance measuring equipment to enabling it to calculate its distance from a DME ground station. See text in the reference section under Distance Measuring Equipment.
Purple Airway	A temporary airway established for a royal flight. Notice of the restricted airspace is promulgated by Royal Flight NOTAM.
PWR	Power.
PX	Minimum holding altitude. (NOTAM decode 2nd & 3rd letters).
Pyrotechnics	Firework type flares used by ground based personnel to warn pilots of an airspace infringement or possible danger. See further text in the reference section.
PZ	Air defence identification zone procedure. (NOTAM decode 2nd & 3rd letters).

Q

Q	For a full listing of ICAO Q Codes refer to DOC 8400/4 available from CAA Stationery
Q	Engine torque.
Q	Meteorological, indicating that QNH is given in millibars.
Q	Squall, meteorological.
QAM	What is the latest meteorological observation for ......
QAO	What is the wind direction (°True) for flight level/altitude.
QBA	What is the horizontal visibility at ..... (place).
Q-Band	Nomenclature for the 35,000Mhz microwave band.
QBB	What is the cloud amount, type and height (above aerodrome level) at ...... (place).
QBC	Report meteorological conditions observed from your aircraft at ..... (position) at ..... (time).
QBF	I am flying in cloud at flight level/altitude .....
QBG	I am flying above cloud at flight level/altitude .....
QBH	I am flying below cloud at flight level/altitude .....
QBN	I am flying between two layers of cloud at flight level/altitude .....
QBP	I am flying in and out of cloud at flight level/altitude .....
QBT	What is the runway visual range at ..... (place).
QBI	Compulsory instrument flight rules apply from .... to ....
Q Codes	Codes developed during the last world war to abbreviate requests, instructions and information.
QCX	My full call sign is .....
QDM	Magnetic heading to steer to reach ..... with zero wind is ..... degrees.
QDR	Magnetic bearing from aircraft to ..... with no wind.
QDT	I am flying in visual meteorological conditions.
QFA	Meteorological forecast for (flight, route, section of route or zone) for the period ..... until .....
QFE	If the altimeter subscale is set to read ..... millibars (hectopascals) the instrument will indicate the height above aerodrome elevation (above threshold R/W No..).
QFF	The QFE reduced to a mean sea level value by using actual temperature and pressure conditions. It is used by meteorological units for plotting synoptic charts.
QFT	Icing has been observed at ..... (position) at heights above..... (datum).
QFU	Magnetic orientation or number of the runway in use.
QFZ	What is the aerodrome forecast for the period .....

QGH	May I land using ..... (procedure or facility). (Normally only used by military traffic for VDF approaches.)
QMI	The vertical distribution of cloud observed from my aircraft at ..... (hours) is ..... (oktas), base ....., tops .....
QMU	What is the dewpoint and temperature at ..... (place).
QMW	At ..... (position) what is the freezing level.
QMX	What is the air temperature at ..... (position) at ..... (hours) at ..... (flight level/altitude).
QNE	What height will my altimeter indicate if I land at ..... at ..... hours with my altimeter subscale set to 1013mb. [Also referred to as pressure altitude.]
QNH	If the altimeter subscale is set to read ..... millibars the instrument will read the elevation of the airfield if the aircraft was on the ground. [It is calculated by reducing the QFE to mean sea level by using ISA constants.]
QNH (Regional)	The lowest QNH value forecast by the meteorological office for a particular altimeter setting region. It is issued for the current hour and for the hour ahead.
QNI	Turbulence has been observed at .....(position) with an intensity of ..... at heights above .....
QNT	What is the maximum speed of the surface wind at ..... (place).
QNY	What is the present weather at .....
QSY	Request a change of frequency to ..... (Now officially discouraged in the UK but still used in some European countries).
QTE	What is my true bearing from you or, what is my true bearing from ..... (call sign).
QTH	What is your position/my position is .....
QTL	What is your true heading.
QTM	What is your magnetic heading.
QUAD	Quadrant.
Quadrantal Error	An error affecting the accuracy of ADF equipment caused by the effect of radio waves upon a metallic airframe.
Quadrantal Rule	Compulsory for all flights in instrument meteorological conditions outside controlled airspace below 24,500 amsl. See further text in the reference section.
Quasi-Stationary Front	Any front that is moving at less than 5 knots. Also referred to as a stationary front.
QUH	What is the current barometric pressure at sea level.
QUJ	What is the true track to reach ...../the true track to reach ..... is .....

R

R	Radar.
R	Radial.
R	Radius.
R	Rate of turn.
R	Red. The colour of a light. Usually shown on airfield approach charts or in relation to aerodrome lighting.
R	Resistance.
R	Right, suffixed after a runway identification number.
R	Runway. See Glossary text under that heading.
R	Runway lighting.
R...	Restricted area, followed by identification number.
RA	Airspace reservation. (NOTAM decode 2nd & 3rd letters).
RA	Radio Altimeter. See Glossary text under that heading.
RA	Rain. See Glossary text under that heading.
RA	Resolution Advisory, airborne collision avoidance.
RAC	Rules of the Air and air traffic services section of the Air Pilot.
Race Track Procedure	Synonym for a hold. See Glossary text under En-Route Hold.
RAD	Radar.
RAD	Radar Approach aid.
Radar	See text in the reference section under Radar – Primary, Radar – Secondary Surveillance and Radar Services.
Radar Advisory Service	A service where a flight information service is provided and in addition instructions will be passed with radar vectors or flight level allocations for avoidance of other traffic. See further text in the reference section under Radar Services.
Radar Altimeter	A narrow beam radar system aimed directly below the aircraft. The time taken for the returning pulses to be received is used to display the actual height above terrain or sea.
Radar Control Service	A service granted in controlled airspace and special rules zones. It provides radar separation and monitoring of arriving, departing and en-route aircraft, together with radar vectoring, assistance with navigation and customary information services.
Radar Information Service	Similar to a radar control service but traffic information will be limited to range and bearing with no avoidance action offered. See further text in the reference section under Radar Services.
Radar Point Out Procedure	A procedure where the current radar controller retains RT communication with an aircraft whilst it penetrates another controller's airspace.
Radar Separation	The separation, lateral and horizontal, provided by a radar controller. See further text in the reference section.

Radar Service Terminated	The message passed to a flight when it has reached the the limits of the controller's area or because of terrain, the required service can no longer be provided
RadarVectoring	A procedure where a radar controller will pass headings and height instructions to an aircraft for positioning, navigation or collision avoidance. See further text in the reference section under Radar Services.
Radial	An imaginary line with a magnetic orientation drawn from a ground based radio navigation aid.
Radiation Fog	Fog caused by the radiation of heat from the surface into the atmosphere. See further text in the reference section.
Radio Altimeter	A constantly updated display of an aircraft's QFE without any pilot input. See further text in the reference section under Radar Altimeter.
Radio Magnetic Indicator	A display with a rotating compass card which is slaved to the magnetic compass so that the magnetic heading of the aircraft is shown at the top of the card. The apparatus can display ADF and VOR information with a dual needle display or dual ADF and dual VOR needles. See further text in the reference section.
Radiosonde	An electronic weather station carried aloft by balloon with equipment that is able to record the humidity, pressure and temperature, plus other information dependent on type, and transmit the information to a ground station.
Radio Waves	See text in the reference section.
RAFC	Regional Area Forecast Centre.
RAF F2919	Flight plan form also known as a CA48.
RAFL	Rainfall.
RAFSC	Royal Air Force Support Command.
RAG	Runway Arrester Gear. See Glossary text under that heading.
RAI	Runway Alignment Indicator.
RAIL	Complimentary Runway Alignment Indicator Lights.
Rain	Drops of water with a diameter of greater than 0.5mm. 2.9mm to 5.4mm is classed as moderate. Above 5.5mm as heavy. See further text in the reference section under Precipitation.
RAL	Runway Alignment beacon, at distance from threshold indicated.
RAM	Random Access Memory.
RAPID	Rapid or Rapidly, meteorological.
RAR	Radar Arrival Route.
RAREP	Radar weather Report.
RAS	Radar Advisory Service. See Glossary text under that heading.
RAS	Rectified Airspeed. See Glossary text under that heading.

RASA	Radar Advisory Service Area. See Glossary text under Radar Advisory Service.
RASH	Rain Showers. See Glossary text under Rain.
RASN	Rain & Snow. See Glossary text under both headings.
Rate Gyro	A gyroscope with movement, by utilizing one gimbal, about two axis. Used in the rate of turn indicator. See text in the reference section under Gyroscope and Turn and Slip Indicator.
Rate of Turn Indicator	An instrument display based on an electrically driven rate gyro used to represent the angle of bank of an aircraft's wings. It is a safety back-up in the event of a failure of the artificial horizon. See further text in the reference section under Turn & Slip Indicator.
Rate One Turn	A turn made at 3° a second, 180° in one minute. See further text in the reference section.
Ravine Wind	See Glossary text under Valley Wind.
R.B.	Relative Bearing. See Glossary text under that heading.
RB	Rescue Boat.
RBI	Relative Bearing Indicator. See Glossary text under that heading.
RBN	Radio Beacon. See Glossary text under Marker Beacons.
r/c	Rate of climb.
RCA	Reach Cruising Altitude.
RCC	Rescue Co-ordination Centre.
RCF	Radio Communications Failure.
RCH	Reach or Reaching.
RCL	Runway Centreline.
RCLL	Runway Centreline Light.
RCLM	Runway Centreline Markings.
RCLS	Runway Centreline Lighting System.
RCO	Remote Communication Outlet.
RCR	Route Contingency Reserve.
RCR	Runway Condition Reading.
R-CRS	Report on Course.
RCV(S)	Receive(s).
R/D	Rate of Descent.
Rd	Red. The colour of a light. Usually shown on airfield approach charts or in relation to aerodrome lighting.
RD	Danger area. (NOTAM decode 2nd & 3rd letters).
RD	Relative Density.
RD	Report Departing.
RDG	Ridge, meteorological. See Glossary text under that heading.

RDH	Reference Datum Height, with regard to an instrument landing system.
RDL	Radial. See Glossary text under that heading.
RDO	Radio.
RDR	Radar Departure Route.
RDT	Requested Departure Time.
RE	Recent, as in rain ...RERN, meteorological.
Real Wander	Any movement of the spin axis of a gyroscope caused by a force, generally caused by instrument imperfections. These can be imperfections in the balance of the gyro wheel itself or unequal friction at the spin axis or gimbal bearings. See further text in the reference section under Gyroscopes.
REC	Receive or Receiver.
Rectified Airspeed	The indicated airspeed corrected for pressure error due to inherent instrument and position errors. See text in the reference section under Airspeed Definitions.
REDL	Runway Edge Light(s).
REDZ	Recent Drizzle.
REF	Reference.
Reference Humidity	ISA standards defined as a percentage humidity for spot temperatures with the relative humidity linear between those temperatures. See further text in the reference section.
Reference Signal	Terminology for a carrier wave used in a VOR. The allocated signal frequency is modulated at 30Hz and transmitted omni-directionally so that all receiving aircraft will receive the same phase of the signal regardless of their bearing to the beacon. See further text in the reference section under Very High Frequency Omni-Directional Range.
REFRA	Recent Freezing Rain.
Refractive Surgery	Laser surgery used to remove the need for wearing glasses. See further text in the reference section.
REG	Registration
Regional Pressure Setting	See Glossary text under QNH (Regional).
Regional QNH	See Glossary text on QNH (Regional).
REGR	Recent hail, GR is derived from The German *graupel*
Regs	Regulations.
REIL	Runway End Identifier Lights.
REL	Relative, direction or bearing.
Relative Bearing	The bearing of a ground position or another aircraft in relation to an aircraft's heading being 0°, regardless of its actual heading.

Relative Bearing Indicator	A needle display with a fixed or rotating compass card. The needle displays the bearing to the beacon relative to the fore-aft axis of the aircraft. See further text in the reference section.
Relative Humidity	The ratio between the actual amount of water present in a parcel of air, in comparison to the amount of water that parcel could hold at that temperature, expressed as a percentage. See further text in the reference section.
RENL	Runway End Light(s).
REP	Report, Reporting, Reporting Point.
Repetitive Flight Plan	A flight plan related to a series of regularly repeated flights with identical basic features. The plan is submitted and retained by air traffic services for retrieval and activation as required.
REQ	Request or Requested.
RERA	Recent Rain.
RESH	Recent Showers.
RESN	Recent Snow.
RESTR	Restricted or Restrict.
Restricted Area	See text in the reference section under prohibited and restricted areas.
RET	Rapid Exit Taxiway. See Glossary text under High Speed Taxiway.
RETS	Recent Thunderstorm.
Returning Polar Maritime Air	At source, stable cold, moist air. Dependent on how far south it travelled before returning to the UK either warm, stable, moist air bringing stratocumulus with fog, or cumulus with possible thunderstorms. For more information and classifications See text in the reference section under Air Masses.
Reverse Pitch	A variable pitch propeller that can be rotated to produce a backwards thrust for braking or positioning of an aircraft.
Revolving Storm	See Glossary text under Tropical Cyclone.
REVS	Revolutions.
RFI	Radio Frequency Interference.
RFNOTAM	Royal Flight Notice to Airmen. See Glossary text under Royal Flight and Notice to Airmen.
RFP	Repetitive Flight Plan. See Glossary text under that heading.
RG	Range (lights).
RGN	Region.
RH	Relative Humidity. See Glossary text under that heading.
RH	Right Hand.
RHI	Range-Height Indicator, (radar).
RHS	Right Hand Seat.
Rhumb Line	A regularly curved line on the surface of the Earth that cuts through all of the meridians it passes at the same angle.

Ridge	Meteorological term for an elongated area of high pressure.
Riesengebirg Wind	Designation given to the fall wind in East Germany.
RIF	Re-clearance In Flight.
RIF	Route Information.
Right Hand Rule	Refer to the text in the reference section under Rules of the Air.
Rigidity	In relation to a spinning gyro. The rigidity in space is proportional to its speed of rotation and the radius at which the mass is concentrated. See further text in the reference section under Gyroscopes.
Rime Frost	Frost layer formed when fog drifts over frozen or snow covered surfaces. The deposit is of an uneven, white, opaque appearance composed of droplets containing small air pockets. See further text in the reference section under Icing – Airframe – On Ground.
Rime Ice	A milky and opaque granular deposit of ice formed by the rapid freezing of supercooled water droplets as they strike an airframe or sub-zero object. See further text in the reference section under Icing – Airframe – In Flight.
RIS	Radar Information Service. See Glossary text under that heading.
RL	Report Leaving, in respect of a flight level, altitude or height.
RL	Runway (edge) Lights.
RLCE	Request Level Change En-route.
RLLS	Runway Lead in Light System.
RMI	Radio Magnetic Indicator. See Glossary text under that heading.
RMK	Remark.
RMN	Remain.
RMS	Precision approach system, eastern European – non International Civil Aviation Organisation designation.
RNAS	Royal Naval Air Station.
RNAV	Area Radio Navigation System. See Glossary text under Area Navigation System.
RNG	Range (radio).
RNLI	Royal National Lifeboat Institution.
RNT	Return, Returned, Returning.
RO	Overflying of. (NOTAM decode 2nd & 3rd letters).
RO	Report Over or Overhead.
Roaring Forties	Prevailing westerly winds below the 40° south latitude.
ROC	Rate Of Climb.
Rocketsonde	An electronic weather station launched by rocket and returns to Earth by parachute. The equipment is able to transmit to a

	ground station values for humidity, pressure and temperature as well as other information dependent on type.
ROD	Rate Of Descent.
ROFOR	Route Forecast, meteorological.
Roll Cloud	Formed in areas of marked mountain wave activity, below the peak on the leeward side. The cloud is created by extreme up and downdrafts known as rotor zones and will mark the area of most turbulence. See further text in the reference section under Standing Waves.
ROM	Read Only Memory.
RON	Receiving Only.
RON	Remain Overnight.
Rope Cloud	A modern expression used to describe the satellite view of a squall line or similar cloud display.
Rotate	The action of pulling up the nose of an aircraft on takeoff.
Rotor Cloud	See Glossary text under Roll Cloud.
Royal Flight	A flight transporting a royal person requiring the establishment of a purple airway. See Glossary text under Purple Airway.
RP	Prohibited area. (NOTAM decode 2nd & 3rd letters).
RP	Reporting Point.
RP	Report Passing.
RPD	Rapid, meteorological.
RPL	Repetitive Flight Plan. See Glossary text under that heading.
RPM	Revolutions Per Minute.
RPRT	Report.
RPS	Radar Position Signal.
RPS	Regional Pressure Setting. See Glossary text under QNH (Regional).
RQMNTS	Requirements.
RQP	Request flight Plan.
RQRD	Required.
RQS	Request Supplementary flight plan.
RR	Low/medium frequency Radio Range station.
RR	Report Reaching, a height, altitude or flight level.
RR	Restricted area. (NOTAM decode 2nd & 3rd letters).
RRP	Runway Reference Point.
RSC	Runway Surface Condition.
RSCD	Runway Surface Condition.
RSG	Rising, meteorological.
RSPT	Report Staring Procedure Turn.
RSR	En-route Surveillance Radar.

RSTD	Restricted.
RT, R/T	Radio Telephony. A conversation by radio.
RT	Temporary restricted area. (NOTAM decode 2nd & 3rd letters).
RTA	Required Time of Arrival.
RTD	Delayed.
RTE	Route.
RTF	Radiotelephony.
RTHL	Runway Threshold Light(s).
RTO	Rejected Take Off
RTZL	Runway Touchdown Zone Lights.
Rudder	A foot pedal operated section attached to the trailing edge of the fin used for directional control in yaw. See further text in the reference section under Rudder and Trim Tabs.
Rules of the Air	Extracts from the Air Pilot RAC section are quoted in the reference section under Rules of the Air.
Runway	A rectangular area prepared for the landing and takeoff run of aircraft along its length. Runways are identified by a two number code relating to the nearest 10° of its magnetic heading. For of other areas refer to the reference section under Aerodrome – Surface Definitions.
Runway Arrester Gear	Equipment provided at some naval air stations and used by aircraft equipped with hooks to simulate carrier landings.
Runway Braking Action	When runways are contaminated by water or snow a Mu-Meter is used to assess the possibility of slush-planing. A Tapley meter is used to assess braking action on ice and dry snow. This information is then passed to an incoming flight as to the likely effect on a landing aircraft.
Runway Categories	Runways with approved instrument approach procedures are categorised as to their operating minimas. See further text in the reference section, under Instrument Landing System - The Runway - Precision Operation Categories (UK)
Runway Markings	All CAA runways have a centreline, threshold and runway designator markings. Non-instrument runways more than 1,100 metres without VASIS have fixed distance markers 300 metres from the threshold. See Glossary text under Precision Approach Runway and reference section under Runway Markings.
Runway Usage	Under certain criteria more than one aircraft may use the active runway. See further text in the reference section
Runway Visual Range	The visual distance, in metres, over which the pilot of a landing aircraft can expect to see centreline or runway edge lights on touchdown. Suffix codes are U = increasing, D = decreasing and N = no change. See further text in the reference section.

RVR	Runway Visual Range. See Glossary text under that heading.
R/W	Runway.
RW	Runway.
Rwy	Runway.
rx.	Receiver (or reception only).

S

(S)	Summer time.
S	Secondary frequency.
S	Seconds.
S	South.
S	Strobes (lights).
S	Supplementary frequency.
S	Wing area.
S/A	Selective Availability, (satellite navigation system). See Glossary text under that heading.
SA	Automatic terminal information service. (NOTAM Decode 2nd & 3rd letters). See Glossary text under that heading.
SA	Safety Altitude.
SA	Simple Approach lighting system.
SA	Duststorm, Sandstorm, rising dust or rising sand. See Glossary text under Sandstorm.
Safe Clearance Altitude	See Glossary text in the reference section under Minimum Safe Altitude.
Safety Pilot	A second qualified pilot sat in the right hand seat during simulated IMC conditions or a non-licenced pilot who has been trained under a safety or second pilot's course to be competent to fly and land an aircraft under ATC instruction.
SAIT	Stand-Alone Integration testing. Test phases of the integrated initial flight plan processing system.
SAL	Supplementary Approach Lighting.
SALS	Short Approach Light System.
SALSF	Short Approach Light System with Sequenced lights.
SALR	Saturated Adiabatic Lapse Rate. See Glossary text under that heading.
SALSR	Short Approach Light System with Runway alignment indicator lights.
Sandstorm	Strong winds and possibly thermal activity lifting sand into the atmosphere and reducing visibility to less than 1,000 metres. See further text in the reference section under Visibility.
SAP	Simulated Attack Profile.
SAR, S&R	Search & Rescue.
SARSAT	Search & Rescue Satellite Aided Tracking system.
Sat	Saturday.
SATCO	Senior Air Traffic Control Officer.

Satellite Navigation System	A navigation system based on a constellation of satellites orbiting the Earth at an altitude of around 11,000 miles, each satellite completing an orbit every 12 hours. See further text in the reference section under Global Positioning System.
SATNAV	Satellite Navigation system. See Glossary text under that heading.
Saturated Adiatatic Lapse Rate	When air has reached a stage when it can no longer hold water in vapour form, condensation takes place. This causes the release of latent heat which reduces the rate of cooling. The lapse rate averages at 1.5°C for each 1,000 feet. See further text in the reference section under Adiabatic Lapse Rates.
Saturation	When an air mass reaches a stage when it cannot hold water in vapour form it is said to be saturated, or at saturation point with 100% relative humidity.
SB	Air traffic services reporting office. (NOTAM Decode 2nd & 3rd letters).
SB	Southbound.
SBO	Sideband Only, (instrument landing system).
SBTs	Self Briefing Terminals.
SC	Area control centre. (NOTAM Decode 2nd & 3rd letters).
SC	Sector Controller.
SC	Stratocumulus Cloud. See Glossary text under that heading.
SCA	Safe Clearance Altitude. See text in the reference section under Minimum Safe Altitude.
SCAN	Surface Condition Analyzer.
ScATTC	Scottish and oceanic Air Traffic Control Centre.
Scattered Cloud	1 - 4 oktas, or eights, of cloud.
Sch	Schedule.
Schaefer Point	The temperature of -40°C at which ice crystals will form without the need of ice nuclei.
SCN	Slot Cancellation message, in relation to air traffic flow control.
SCOB	Scattered Cloud Or Better.
Scotch Mist	Scottish expression for a mixture of mist and drizzle.
SCT	Scattered Cloud. 1 - 4 oktas or eighths.
Sctr	Sector.
Scud	Small detached stratus fractus clouds below a layer of higher stratiform or nimbostratus clouds.
SCWD	Supercooled Water Droplets. See Glossary text under that heading.
Sd	Sodium, (lighting).
SD	Standard Deviation.
SDAU	Safety Data and Analysis Unit.

SDBY	Standby.
SDF	Simplified Direction Facility.
SDF	Step Down Fix.
SE	Flight information Service. (NOTAM Decode 2nd & 3rd letters). See Glossary text under that heading.
SE	South East.
Sea Breeze	A localised effect rarely extending further than 15 miles inland and 1,000 feet vertically with a wind strength not normally exceeding 10 knots. See further text in the reference section.
Sea Smoke	See Glossary text under Arctic Sea Smoke.
SEB	South Eastbound.
SEC	Seconds.
SEC	Section.
SEC	Special Event Charter flight.
Secondary Depression	Formed at the point of an occlusion and prolonging the poor weather associated with the primary depression.
Secondary Surveillance Radar	A radar system where a ground transmitter emits a train of pulses recognised by an aircraft receiver. The receiver, or transponder, sends a reply from its transmitter and signal is plotted on a radar screen. The display can include identification and height data. See further text in the reference section under Radar - Secondary Surveillance and Transponder.
Second Critical Engine	The critical engine is the one whose failure would most adversely affect the performance or handling qualities of the aircraft. The Second critical engine is named on the basis that the critical engine has not failed.
Second Pilot	See Glossary text under Safety Pilot.
SECT	Sector.
Sector Safety Altitude	Altitudes shown on standard instrument arrival and departure charts giving a safe altitude figure for each quadrant in a 25nm radius around an aerodrome. See further text in the reference section under Minimum Safe Altitude.
Sectors of Ambiguity	An error of received signals from a VOR when at close range and whilst passing through the radials of up to 10° either side of the radials which are at 90° to that selected on the OBS. See further text in the reference section under Omni-Bearing Indicator.
Seeding	A method of attempting to produce rain by dropping solid carbon dioxide particles into cloud in the hope that they will act as icing or condensation nuclei.
SEL	Single Engine, Land.
SEL	Abbreviation for selective calling system when used in a flight plan. See Glossary text under that heading.
SELCAL	Selective Calling system. See Glossary text under that heading.

Selective Availability	Used to describe the deliberate degradation of a satellite navigation system's accuracy. This is designed to deny hostile forces the full tactical advantage of the system and was implemented during the Gulf War. See further text in the reference section under Global Positioning System.
Selective Calling System	A high frequency speech system with an allocated call code. This discrete code is noted on filed flight plans and is used to contact the aircraft on long range flights. See further text in the reference section.
Semi-Circular Rule	Compulsory rule for flights in airways at any height and for all flights above 24,500 feet amsl outside controlled airspace in IFR. See further text in the reference section for specific rules.
Self-Launching Glider	A motor glider capable of taking off under its own power and fitted with a fully or partially retractable engine. See Glossary text under Motor Glider.
Self-Sustaining Glider	A motor glider incapable of taking off under its own power and fitted with a fully or partially retractable engine. See glossary text under Motor Glider.
SER	Service, Servicing, Served.
SET	Situation Emergency Training.
SETD	Scheduled Estimated Time of Departure.
SEV	Severe, in relation to icing & turbulence.
Severe Gale	Wind speed of 41 - 47 knots (76 - 87 km per hour). Force 9.
SF	Aerodrome flight information service. (NOTAM Decode 2nd & 3rd letters). See Glossary text under that heading.
SFC	Specific Fuel Consumption.
SFC	Surface of the Earth.
Sferics	The location of lightning flashes determined by radio triangulation.
SFLOC	Sferic Location. See Glossary text under Sferics.
s.g.	Specific gravity.
SG	Snow Grains. See Glossary text under Snow.
SGL	Signal.
SH	Showers, meteorological.
SHF	Super High Frequency. Frequencies in the 3,000 - 30,000Mhz range. See further text in the reference section.
SHLW	Shallow, meteorological, as in fog.
Short Field Take Offs/Landings	Method of taking off or landing using the minimum possible ground run. See further text in the reference section for general guidance. Refer to the owner's manual for the operation of individual aircraft.

Short Final	A radio call made by aircraft making a late call on finals or when turning onto the final approach of a shortened circuit pattern. In the case of a straight in approach the call is made at 2nm. See further text in the reference section under Aerodrome - Circuit.
Shower	Intermittent precipitation.
SHWR	Shower, meteorological. See Glossary text under that heading.
SI	Straight In approach. See Glossary text under that heading.
SIAPS	Standard Instrument Approach Procedures.
SID	Standard Instrument Departure. For safety altitude information see text in the reference section under Minimum Safe Altitude.
Side Band Frequencies	The result of a radio signal being amplitude modulated by a carrier wave. See further text in the reference section under Radio Waves - Modulation.
SIF	Selective Identification Feature.
SIGMET	Significant Meteorological information. See Glossary text under that heading.
Significant Meteorological Information	A warning message passed by ATC to aircraft at subsonic cruising levels liable to be affected by adverse meteorological conditions. See further text in the reference section.
SIGWX	Significant Weather.
Simple Flaps	A flap system that lowers a section of the wing increasing the aerofoil shape for the inner section of the wing. See text in the reference section under Flaps for other types.
SIMUL	Simultaneous or Simultaneously.
Simulated Instrument Flight	A flight during which mechanical or optical devices are used in order to reduce the field of vision or the range of visibility from the cockpit of the aircraft. See further text in the reference section.
Single Sideband Transmission	A amplitude modulated signal with either the upper or lower sideband removed. See further text in the reference section under Radio Waves.
SITA	Société Internationale de Telecommunications Aéronautique. A data processing system used by airlines.
SKC	Sky Clear.
SKED	Schedule or Scheduled.
Sky Waves	The name given to a high frequency transmission when directed towards the ionosphere and subjected to refraction within the inonospheric layer. See further text in the reference section under Radio Waves.
SL	Flow control centre. (NOTAM Decode 2nd & 3rd letters).
SL	Sea Level.
Slant Error	An optical error that occurs by reading an instrument from a side angle.

Slant Visibility	A decrease in visibility in haze, mist or fog as a result of looking through a greater amount of particles in observations at any other angle than directly down. See further text in the reference section.
SLAP	Slot Allocation Procedures.
Slat	See Glossary text under Leading Edge Slats.
Sleet	See text in the reference section under Precipitation.
SLGT	Slight.
Sling Psychrometer	A revolving version of a normal psychrometer which is considered to test a more average sample than the static system. See Glossary text under Psychrometer.
Slip Indicator	An instrument used to indicate yaw. Simply a steel ball inserted in a curved glass tube. In balanced flight the ball responds to gravity but if the aircraft enters a skidding turn centrifugal force throws the ball away from the centre showing that rudder input is required. See further text in the reference section under Turn & Slip Indicator.
Slipstream	The current of air thrown back by a propeller.
SLMG	Self Launching Motor Glider.
SLO	Slow.
Slotted Flaps	A flap type which, when extended, exposes a slot through which air from below the wing flows out over the flap, increasing lift. See text in the reference section under Flaps for other types.
SLP	Slope.
SLP	Speed Limiting Point.
SLR	Slush on Runway.
SLT	Sleet. See text in the reference section under Precipitation.
SLW	Slow.
s.m.	Statute miles.
Small Circle	An imaginary circle drawn on the surface of the Earth with a radius that is not the same as that of the Earth and with a plane that does not pass through the centre of the Earth.
SMC	Surface Movement Control.
SMF	Separation Monitoring Function
SMK	Smoke. See Glossary text under that heading.
Smog	An abridgment of smoke and fog. A weather phenomenon where both are combined. See Glossary text under both headings.
SMOH	Since Major Overhaul.
Smoke	Solid particles in the atmosphere reducing visibility to less than 1,000 metres. See text in the reference section under Visibility.
SMR	Surface Movement Radar.
SMTH	Smooth.

SN	Snow. See Glossary text under that heading.
SNFLK	Snowflakes. See Glossary text under snow.
SNOCLO	Message relating to aerodrome closure due to snow added to VOLMET and OPMET messages.
Snoplan	An annually published plan relating to the proposed action to be taken by an individual aerodrome in the event of significant snow fall. See further text in the reference section under SNOTAM.
Snow	Small ice crystals which build into individual crystalline snowflakes. Granular snow is classified as being comprised of small grains of less than 1mm diameter. See further text in the reference section under Precipitation and Visibility.
SNOWTAM	Special Notices to Airmen regarding the presence or removal of hazardous conditions due to snow, ice, slush or standing water and issued in a specific standard format. See further text in the reference section.
SNSH	Snow Showers. See text in the reference section under precipitation.
SNW	Snow. See Glossary text under that heading.
SNWFL	Snowfall.
SO	Oceanic area control centre. (NOTAM Decode 2nd & 3rd letters).
SOC	Start of Climb.
Soft Field Take Offs/Landings	Method of taking off or landing when operating from soft surface or high friction runways. Refer to the reference section for general guidance. Refer to the owner's manual for the operation of individual aircraft.
Somatogravic Illusion	An illusion that during rapid acceleration the pilot has a high nose-up attitude, and, during rapid de-acceleration, a steep nose down attitude. Pilot action taken based on the illusion will induce control input where none is required. See further text in the reference section.
Souledre Wind	Cold north easterly wind in France.
Source Regions	Regions covered by an air mass which is allowed to remain stationary for several days. The mass takes on the region's characteristics with uniform temperature and humidity. As the masses move and reach the UK they bring relatively predictable weather. See text under in the reference section under Air Masses for classifications.
SP	Approach control service. (NOTAM Decode 2nd & 3rd letters).
Space Gyro	A spinning mass mounted within two gimbals allowing freedom of movement in all planes. See further text in the reference section under Gyroscopes.
Span	See Glossary text under Wingspan.

SPAR	Slight Precision Approach Radar, mobile equipment.
Spatial Disorientation	A loss of pilot control capability caused by a single or combination of natural illusions resulting in contradictory sensual information.
SPECI	Aviation selected Special weather report (in meteorological code). Not used in the UK.
SPECIAL	Special meteorological report, in plain language.
Special Rules Area	See Glossary text under Special Rules Zone.
Special Rules Zone	Zones and areas established around an air traffic zone with rules applying during the periods of operation of the ATZ. Special clearance is required before the airspace may be entered. See further text in the reference section.
Special Visual Flight Rules	A clearance granted to a pilot entering a special rules zone. It does not absolve the pilot of complying with all other rules regarding visibility, terrain clearance and low flying. See text in the reference section under Special Rules Zones.
Specific Heat	The quantity of heat required to raise the temperature of a unit mass by one degree.
Specific Humidity	The ratio of the mass of water vapour in comparison to the total mass of air.
Speechless Code	Used in distress situations where an aircraft's transmission is weak, distorted or unintelligible but received signals are audible. Refer to text in the reference section under Mayday or the quick reference section on page 276 for codes only.
Speed of Light	300×10^6, or 300,000,000 metres per second.
Speed of Propogation	The speed of a travelling radio wave, equal to the speed of light.
SPL	Supplementary flight plan.
Split Flap	A design which lowers a flap from the lower trailing edge of the wing without any change to the upper surface area. See text in the reference section under Flaps for other types.
Spoilers	See Glossary text under Lift Dumper.
SPOT	Spot Wind. The wind at a specified location.
Spot Wind Charts	Metform 214 used by the UK meteorological office. See further text in the reference section for validity and availability times.
SPRD	Spread.
SPS	Standard Positioning Service, satellite navigation system.
SQ	Squall(s). See Glossary text under that heading.
SQ	Squawk. See Glossary text under that heading.
SQAL	Squall. See Glossary text under that heading.
SQLN	Line Squall. See Glossary text under that heading.

Squall	A strong gusting wind that rises and falls quickly. It is classified as a squall if the wind increases by at least 16 knots with a mean speed of 22 knots lasting for one minute or more.
Squall Line	See Glossary text under Line Squall.
Squawk	The discrete number selected on a transponder and displayed on a secondary surveillance radar screen. See text in the reference section under Transponder and the quick reference section on page 271 for a listing of transponder codes.
SR	Sunrise.
SRA	Special Rules Airspace.
SRA	Special Rules Area. See Glossary text under Special Rules Zone.
SRA	Surveillance Radar Approach. See Glossary text under that heading.
SRE	Surveillance Radar Element of precision approach radar system.
SRE	Surveillance Radar Equipment.
SRG	Short Range.
SRP	Slot Reference Point, in relation to air traffic flow control.
SRQ	Slot Request message, in relation to air traffic flow control.
SRR	Search & Rescue Region.
SRV	Surveillance.
SRY	Secondary.
SRZ	Special Rules Zone. See Glossary text under that heading.
SS	Flight service station. (NOTAM Decode 2nd & 3rd letters).
SS	Sand Storm, meteorological.
SS	Sunset.
SSA	Sector Safety Altitude. See text in the reference section under Minimum Safe Altitude.
SSAL	Sequenced flashing Lights.
SSALF	Simplified Short Approach Light system with sequenced Flashing lights.
SSALR	Simplified Short Approach Light system with Runway alignment lights.
SSALS	Simplified Short Approach Light System.
SSB	Single Sideband. See Glossary text under Single Sideband Transmission.
SSR	Secondary Surveillance Radar. See Glossary text under that heading.
SSR Mode A	Secondary Surveillance Radar providing coded aircraft identification.

SSR Mode C	Secondary Surveillance Radar provided coded aircraft identification and altitude. See Glossary text under Pneumatic Altimeter.
SSR Mode S	Secondary Surveillance Radar with selective interrogation capability.
SS-SR	Sunset - Sunrise.
SST	Supersonic Transport.
ST	Aerodrome control tower. (NOTAM Decode 2nd & 3rd letters).
ST	Stratus Cloud. See Glossary text under Stratiform Cloud.
STA	Straight in Approach. See Glossary text under that heading.
Stabilator	The horizontal control surface which also acts as a tailplane, or, dependent on design, a foreplane. Forward or backward movement of the control column changes its attack angle and provides longitudinal control in pitch.
Stability (Aircraft)	An aircraft's resistance to change in its condition of steady flight.
Stability (Meteorological)	Refer to Glossary text under Absolute Instability, Absolute Stability, Conditional Stability and Neutral Stability.
Stall	The condition where an aerofoil section ceases to create lift due to an excessive angle of attack or low airspeed.
Stalling Angle of Attack	An angle at which the streamline flow on the upper surface of a wing will break down. Usually at around 16°.
Standard Atmosphere	See Glossary text under International Standard Atmosphere.
Standard Pressure Setting	The standard setting is 1013 millibars which is the ISA pressure standard. It is used for aircraft flying at flight levels to ensure separation above the transition altitude.
Standing Waves	Also known as mountain waves or lee waves. See text in the reference section.
STAR	Standard Instrument Arrival. For safety altitude information see text in the reference section under Minimum Safe Altitude.
Starboard	Nautical and aviation term for right.
Static Discharger	See Glossary text under Static Wick.
Static Electricity	Term used to describe any form of audio radio interference. It mainly affects MF and HF frequencies. See further text in the reference section.
Static Pressure	The pressure exerted by the weight of air above an object. See further text in the reference section.
Static Vent	A small hole on the outside of an aircraft through which static pressure is fed to various aircraft instruments. See further text in the reference section.

Static Wick	Metal impregnated wicks fitted to the trailing edges to discharge static electricity into the air.
Stationary Front	See Glossary text under Quasi-Stationary Front.
STB	Stopbars.
STBY	Standby.
STC	Strike Command.
STD	Standby.
STD	Standard Time.
STD	Standard. Indication of an Altimeter set to 29.92Hg or 1013.2mb without temperature correction. See Glossary text under Standard Pressure Setting.
STDY	Steady.
Steam Fog	See Glossary text under Arctic Sea Smoke.
St Elmo's Fire	Extreme result of a discharge of static electricity resulting in a visual display. See text in the reference section under Static Electricity.
Steppenwind	Indigenous to Germany. A strong cold north easterly wind.
Stf	Stratiform cloud. See Glossary text under that heading.
ST-IN	Straight In, approach. See Glossary text under that heading.
STM	Storm. See Glossary text under that heading.
STN	Station.
STNR	Stationary. See Glossary text under Quasi-Stationary Front.
STNRY	Stationary. See Glossary text under Quasi-Stationary Front.
STOL	Short Take-off and Landing.
STOL	Slow Take-off and Landing.
Stop & Go	A practice procedure where the aircraft comes to a complete stop after landing before taking off again. See further text in the reference section under Touch and Go.
Stopway	A rectangular area, commencing at the end of the take off run available, which is suitable for the ground run of an aeroplane decelerating after a discontinued take off. For other areas see text in the reference section under Aerodrome – Surface Definitions.
Storm	See Glossary text under Storm Force Winds.
Storm Force Wind	Wind speed between 48 & 55 knots (89 & 102km per hour). Force 10.
STP	Standard Temperature and Pressure 29.92Hg or 1013.2mb and +15° Celsius.
Straight In Approach	An approach within 30° of the centreline where an aircraft does not enter a circuit or traffic pattern before making its final approach to land. For radio call distances see text in the reference section under Aerodrome – Circuit.

Stratiform Cloud	An overcast layer of any type of cloud. See further text in the reference section.
Strato Cumulus Cloud	An overcast layer of cumulus cloud formed by warm rising air resulting in a formation of domed shaped upper surfaces with a relatively level base.
Stratosphere	The atmospheric layer above the tropopause which starts at around 30 miles above the Earth's surface with a constant or increasing temperature.
Stratus Cloud	See Glossary text under Stratiform Cloud.
Streamline	Chart lines used to show the direction of wind flow. They are mainly used for plotting wind directions in equatorial regions where pressure differences are minimal and isobars are too widely spaced to gauge wind flow information.
Strong Wind	Wind speed between 22 & 27 knots (41 & 50 km per hour). Force 6.
Sts	Stratus cloud. See Glossary text under Stratiform Cloud.
STS	Reason for special handling by air traffic (as in flight plan).
STWL	Stopway Light(s).
SU	Upper area control centre. (NOTAM Decode 2nd & 3rd letters).
SUBJ	Subject to.
Sublimation	The process where water vapour turns directly to ice, or vice versa, without passing through the liquid stage.
Subsidence	A phenomenon frequently occurring in polar highs where there is an extensive area of sinking air.
Suckers Gap	Slang expression for a short break of CAVOK within generally dismal flying weather.
Sun	Sunday.
Super-Adiabatic Lapse Rate	A generic phrase used to describe any lapse rate greater than the dry adiabatic lapse rate. See further text in the reference section under Adiabatic Lapse Rates.
Supercell	A mighty version of a large cumulonimbus cloud where the updrafts flow out of the top of the cell and disperse rather than flowing back down inhibiting the upward flow.
Supercooled Water Droplets	Droplets of water in liquid form that can exist in temperatures as low as -40°C. The droplets exist most often between 0°C to -10°C. See further text in the reference section under Icing - Airframe.
Super High Frequency	Frequencies in the 3,000 - 30,000Mhz range. See further text in the reference section.
Super- saturation	An air mass saturated to the extent that it contains more water vapour than that required to produce saturation or more than 100% relative humidity.

Surface Wave	Also known as a ground wave. Frequencies in the LF & MF bands which follow the curvature of the Earth due to diffraction. See further text in the reference section under Radio Waves.
Surface Wind	The wind speed as measured from 10 metres above the ground. See further text in the reference section.
Surveillance Radar Approach	Similar to a precision approach except that no height information is available to the controller. Height checks are given as the aircraft passes various distances from the threshold and headings passed to maintain the centreline. See further text in the reference section under Radar Services.
SV	VOLMET broadcast. (NOTAM Decode 2nd & 3rd letters). See Glossary text under Very High Frequency Meteorological Report.
SVC	Service message.
SVCBL	Serviceable.
SVFR	Special Visual Flight Rules. See Glossary text under that heading.
SW	South West.
SWB	South Westbound.
SWY	Stopway. See Glossary text under that heading.
SY	Upper advisory service. (NOTAM Decode 2nd & 3rd letters).
SYDAC	5,000 MegaHertz instrument landing system installation.
SYNOP	Internationally coded synoptic weather report. See Glossary text under Synoptic Chart.
Synoptic Chart	A weather map covering a fixed time period.
Synoptic Station	A weather station, sea or ground based, which passes fixed time observations to a meteorological centre.
SYRED	Internationally coded synoptic weather report of reduced length.

T	
t	Time.
t	Tonne(s).
t	Trend landing forecast.
T	Temperature, in degrees kelvin.
T	Threshold lighting.
°T	True heading or track in degrees.
TA	Traffic Advisory, airborne collision avoidance.
TA	Transition Altitude. See Glossary text under that heading.
TAC	Tactical Air Navigator. See Glossary text under that heading.
TAC	Terminal Area Charts.
TACAN	Tactical Air Navigator. See Glossary text under that heading.
Tactical Air Navigator	The military equivalent of a co-located civil VOR/DME station. Usually located within military air traffic zones and on the airfield. See further text in the reference section.
Tactical Booking Cell	See text under Low Level Civil Aircraft Notification Procedure.
TAF	Terminal Aerodrome Forecast. See Glossary text under that heading.
TA/H	Turn Altitude/Height.
TAIL	Tailwind.
Tailplane	The horizontal aerofoil at the rear of an aircraft to which the elevator is attached. If the entire rear section is pivoted it is known as a stabilator.
Take-off Distance Available	The length of the declared take off run plus the clearway. For other distances and areas see text in the reference section under Aerodrome – Surface Definitions.
Take-off Run Available	The length of runway available and suitable for the ground run of an aeroplane taking off. For other distances and areas see text in the reference section under Aerodrome - Surface Definitions.
TANS	Tactical Air Navigation System
Tapley Meter	Device used to assess runway braking action on ice and dry snow.
TAR	Terminal Area surveillance Radar.
T&S	Turn and Slip Indicator. See Glossary text under that heading.
TAS	True Air Speed. See Glossary text under that heading.
TAX	Taxying or Taxi.
Tax	Taxiway lights.
TAXI	Taxi and parking facilities charts.
T.B.	True Bearing, not taking into account magnetic variation. See Glossary text under Bearing and True Bearing.
TBO	Time Before Overhaul.

TC	Tropical Cyclone. See Glossary text under that heading.
TCA	Terminal Control Area. See Glossary text under that heading.
TCAS	Airborne Collision Avoidance System.
TCH	Threshold Crossing Height.
TCU	Towering Cumulonimbus Cloud.
TDA	Temporary Danger Area.
TDA	Today.
TDO	Tornado, meteorological. See Glossary text under that heading.
TDR	Terminal Data Record.
TDWR	Terminal Doppler Weather Radar.
TDZ	Touchdown Zone.
TDZE	Touchdown Zone Elevation.
TDZL	Touchdown Zone Lights.
TE	Taxiways Edge lights.
Technical Log	A flight and maintenance record required for some aircraft under the Air Navigation Order. See further text in the reference section.
Tel	Telephone.
TEMP	Temperature.
Temperature	See text in the reference section.
Temperature Inversion	An inversion exists where the temperature increases with height as opposed to the normal situation where it reduces.
TEMPO	Temporary or Temporarily, meteorological. Change expected to last for less than one hour.
TEND	Tend or Tending to, meteorological.
Terminal Aerodrome Forecast	Weather forecasts prepared between one and two hours before their period of validity. For civil aerodromes they are valid for either a 9 or 18 hour period. See further text in the reference section.
Terminal Control Area	Areas normally established at the junction of airways in the vicinity of one or more major aerodromes and used to separate transit traffic from landing and departure traffic.
Terminal Velocity	The maximum speed at which a falling body may move through the air. The pull of gravity being balanced by the friction resisting force.
TERPS	Terminal instrument approach Procedures.
TFC	Traffic.
TGC	Travel Group Charter.
TGL	Touch & Go Landing. See Glossary text under that heading.
TGS	Taxi Guidance System.
Th	Thursday.

THDR	Thunder, meteorological.
Thermal	A localised updraft forming above a warm surface and caused by a vertical thermal gradient.
Thermal Depression	Low pressure areas formed by the air over a heated land mass rising and drawing in cooler, usually maritime, air.
Thermal Gradient (Horizontal)	Wind movement resulting from the steep thermal gradient due to the difference in height of the tropopause. The movement forms tubes of fast moving thermal wind which can reach speeds in excess of 200 knots. See further text in the reference section under Jet Streams.
Thermal Gradient (Vertical)	A localised updraft may formed above a warm surface causing a vertical thermal gradient. The updraft or wind is created as the temperatures attempt to equalise.
Thermal Turbulence	The result of surface heating causing warmed air to rise away from the surface.
Thermal Winds	See text in the reference section.
Thickness	In relation to a wing aerofoil. The greatest distance between the upper an lower surfaces.
Third Engine Critical	The critical engine is the one whose failure would most adversely affect the performance or handling qualities of the aircraft. The second or third critical engine are named on the basis that the critical engine has not failed.
THK	Thick, meteorological.
THLD	Threshold. See Glossary text under that heading.
THN	Thin, meteorological.
Thr	Threshold lights.
THR	Threshold. See Glossary text under that heading.
Three Bar Visual Approach Slope Indicator	See text in the reference section under Visual Approach Slope Indicators.
Threshold	The beginning of that portion of the runway used for landing. See further text in the reference section under Runway Markings and Aerodrome – Surface Definitions.
THRU	Through.
THSD	Thousand.
Thunderstorm	Well developed, active, cumulonimbus clouds. The requirements for a thunderstorm are instability, high moisture and trigger action. The unstable layer must be at least 10,000 feet in depth and the trigger action may be any form of lifting. See further text in the reference section under Cumulonibus Clouds.
TIBA	Traffic Information Broadcast by Aircraft.

Tied Gyro	A gyroscope that has freedom of movement in three planes. Used in the directional indicator and maintains rigidity in line with the yaw axis of the aircraft. See further text in the reference section under Gyroscopes.
TIL	Until.
TIP	Until Past ... (place), meteorological.
TIZ	Traffic Information Zone.
TKOF	Take Off. Usually in relation to windshear on the take off path.
TL	Transition Level. See Glossary text under that heading.
TL	Until, meteorological.
TLS	Target Level of Safety.
TLWD	Tailwind.
TMA	Terminal control Area. See Glossary text under that heading.
TMA	Terminal Manoeuvring Area.
TMC	Terminal Control.
TMG	Track made good.
TML	Terminal.
TMPRY	Temporary.
TN	Turn altitude.
TNDCY	Tendency.
TNH	Turn Height.
T/O	Take-off.
TO	To ... (place).
To & From Flags	Flags provided in an omni-bearing indicator linked to a VOR receiver that verifies which radial an aircraft is tracking. Overhead the beacon neither flag will be visible as the aircraft passes through the cone of confusion. See further text in the reference section under Omni-Bearing Indicator.
TOC	Top of Climb.
TOD	Time of Departure.
TODA	Take-Off Distance Available. See Glossary text under that heading.
TOP	Cloud Top.
TORA	Take-Off Run Available. See Glossary text under that heading.
Tornado	A violent storm which can rotate at speeds up to 300 kph. See further text in the reference section.
TOSA	Take-Off Space Available.
Touch & Go Landing	A landing on a runway followed by a take off without the aircraft stopping. See further text in the reference section.

Touring Motor Glider	A motor glider capable of taking off under its own power and fitted with a non-retractable engine. See Glossary text under Motor Glider.
TOVC	Top of Overcast Cloud.
TOW	Take off weight.
T/P	Teleprinter.
TP	Turning Point.
TR	Track.
TRA	Temporary Reserved Airspace.
Track Error	The distance, calculated in degrees or nautical miles, that an aircraft is off its desired track. See text in the reference section under Track Error for the one in sixty rule formula.
TRACON	Terminal Radar Approach Control.
Trade Winds	Term used to describe the prevailing oceanic winds within 30° of the Equator. North easterly in the northern hemisphere, south easterly in the southern.
Trailing Edge	The back edge of a wing.
TRANS	Transmits or Transmitter.
TRANSALT	Transition Altitude. See Glossary text under that heading.
Transition Altitude	The height above mean sea level, above which instrument flight rules traffic must use flight levels. See further text in the reference section.
Transition Layer	The distance between the transition level and the transition altitude. The depth of this layer varies in accordance with the local barometric pressure. See further text in the reference section.
Transition Level	The lowest available flight level above the transition altitude. See further text in the reference section.
TRANSLEV	Transition Level. See Glossary text under that heading.
Transmissometer	An optical/electronic instrument system for measuring runway visual range.
Transponder	An aircraft secondary surveillance transmitter/receiver which detects ground based emissions and transmits a reply at a different frequency. The aircraft data is then displayed on a radar screen. See further text in the reference section, and page 271 for codes.
Transport Wander	See Glossary text under Real Wander and Apparent Wander.
Traverse Wind	Westerly Alpine wind accompanied by heavy rain.
TRE	Type Rating Examiner.
TREND	Landing forecast of conditions during the two hours after the observation time. See further text in the reference section.
Trim Tab	See text in the reference section.
TRLVL	Transition Level. See Glossary text under that heading.

TrM	Track Magnetic.
TRML	Terminal.
TROF	Trough. See Glossary text under that heading.
TROP	Tropopause. See text under that heading.
Tropical Continental Air	At source, stable, hot, dry air. On reaching the UK, stable warm, dry fine weather with haze and heat wave conditions. For more information and classifications see text in the reference section under Air Masses.
Tropical Cyclone	A circular tropical storm around a low pressure system. Anti-clockwise in the northern hemisphere, clockwise in the southern. Classified as a Tropical Depression, Storm or Hurricane. See Glossary text under these headings.
Tropical Depression	The classification for tropical cyclone with winds of up to 34 knots.
Tropical Hurricane	The classification for tropical cyclone with winds of 65 knots or more. Also referred to as a typhoon.
Tropical Maritime Air	At source, stable, warm and moist air. On reaching the UK warm, very moist with poor visibility, stratus and stratocumulus cloud. For more information and classifications See text in the reference section under Air Masses.
Tropical Storm	The classification for tropical cyclone with winds of 35 to 64 knots. See further text in the reference section.
Tropopause	The layer of atmosphere forming the limits of the troposphere. The height varies according to temperature. See further text in the reference section under Troposphere.
Troposphere	The layer of atmosphere from the Earth's surface to the tropopause where most weather transpires. See further text in the reference section.
Trough	An elongated area of low pressure emanating from the main low pressure area.
TRRN	Terrain.
TRS	Tropical Cyclone. See Glossary text under that heading.
TRSA	Terminal Radar Service Area.
TrT	Track True. See Glossary text under True Track.
True Air Speed	The equivalent airspeed corrected for density error. See text in the reference section under Airspeed Definitions.
True Bearing	A bearing based on the Earth's true north and south poles. Referred to as a QTE or QUJ dependent on whether the bearing is to or from a ground station. See Glossary text under QTE and QUJ.
True Poles	The geographical poles of the Earth that lie in different locations to that of the magnetic poles. The angle of variation between these poles is used to calculate a magnetic heading. See text in the reference section under Variation.

True Track	A track based on the position of the Earth's true poles to which magnetic variation is applied to calculate a magnetic track. See text in the reference section under Variation.
TS	Thunderstorm. See Glossary text under that heading.
TSGR	Thunderstorm with hail. GR is derived from the German *graupel.*
TSHWR	Thundershower.
TSMT	Transmit.
TSMTR	Transmitter.
TSQLS	Thundersqualls, meteorological.
TSSA	Thunderstorm with duststorm or sandstorm Associated.
TST	A Morse identification signal transmitted by a radio navigation aid whilst the equipment is on test. The aid should not be used if this signal is received. See further text in the reference section under Omni-Bearing Indicator.
TSTM	Thunderstorm. See Glossary text under that heading.
T Type Visual Approach Slope Indicator	See text in the reference section under Visual Approach Slope Indicator.
Tu	Tuesday.
TURB	Turbulence, meteorological.
Turbine Fuel	AVTUR, or Kerosene is used in gas turbine engines, (jets). It is straw coloured and has a very distinctive smell. Aircraft filler points are colour coded black (AVGAS is red) to prevent the loading of the incorrect fuel.
Turbofan	A jet engine in which most of the intake air by-passes the combustion chamber and is discharged as a cold jet.
Turbojet	A jet engine in which all of the intake air goes through the combustion chamber.
Turboprop	A gas turbine engine that drives a propeller.
Turbulence	The resultant uneven air flow caused by an air mass flowing horizontally across the surface of the Earth encountering obstructions causing vertical movements.
Turbulence Cloud	Cloud formed by uplifted air rising and being cooled adiabatically.
Turbulence Layer	A layer of air that is compared in thickness to the 2,000 feet geostrophic wind. See further text in the reference section under Surface Winds.
Turn and Slip Indicator	A combination instrument, the turn indicator is more correctly referred to as a rate of turn indicator. The slip indicator verifies any yaw being experienced by the aircraft. See further text in the reference section.

Turn Co-ordinator	Synonym for a rate of turn indicator. See Glossary text under that heading.
TVOR	Terminal Very high frequency Omni-directional Range.
TWEB	Transcribed Weather broadcast.
Twister	Synonym for tornado. See Glossary text under that heading.
TWR	Aerodrome control Tower or aerodrome control.
TWY	Taxiway.
TWYL	Taxiway-Link.
tx	Transmitter or Transmission.
TYP	Type of Aircraft.
TYPH	Typhoon, meteorological. See Glossary text under that heading.
Typhoon	See Glossary text under Tropical Hurricane.
Tyro	Learner or apprentice. Used as a radio telephony code phrase to indicate that the pilot lacks experience in a particular situation. Used as a call sign prefix by the pilot in a distress or urgency situation to ensure that the pilot is not passed complex instructions.

U

(u)	Uni-directional.
u	Unpaved Surface.
U	Frequencies in the ultra high frequency, 300 to 3,000MHz range.
U	Upper. When used as a prefix to an airway.
UA	Air report.
UAA	Upper Advisory Area.
UAB	Until Advised by ...
UACC	Upper Airspace Control Centre.
UAD	Upper Advisory Route.
UAR	Upper Air Route.
u/c	Under construction.
UDA	Upper advisory Area.
UDDF	Up and Down Drafts.
UDE	Speed of vertical gust, meteorological.
UDF	Ultra high frequency Direction Finding station. See Glossary text under Direction Finding.
UFIR	Upper Flight Information Regions. See Glossary text under that heading.
UFN	Until Further Notice.
UHF	Frequencies in the Ultra High Frequency, 300 to 3,000MHz range. See further text in the reference section under Ultra High Frequency Range.
UHMRA	Upper Heyford Mandatory Radio Area. No longer in existence.
UIC	Upper Information Centre.
UIR	Upper flight Information Region. See Glossary text under that heading.
UIS	Upper Information Service.
UK	United Kingdom.
UKLFHB	United Kingdom military Low Flying Handbook.
ULR	Ultra Long Range.
Ultra High Frequency	Frequencies in the ultra high frequency, 300 to 3,000MHz range. See further text in the reference section.
UNA	Unable.
UNAVBL	Unavailable.
Uncertainty Phase	A degree of an emergency situation where a period where uncertainty exists as to the safety of an aircraft and its occupants. See further text in the reference section.

Undershoot Area	The area between an aerodrome boundary and the runway threshold that is clear of obstructions. For further areas see text in the reference section under Aerodrome – Surface Definitions.
UNICOM	Aeronautical advisory service.
Universal Time	Synonym for Greenwich mean time. See Glossary text under that heading.
UNKN	Unknown.
UNL	Unlimited altitude.
UNREL	Unreliable.
UNRSTD	Unrestricted.
Unsaturated Air	Air with a low or negligible moisture content within which the temperature drop with height is at the dry adiabatic lapse rate. See further text in the reference section under Adiabatic Lapse Rates.
Upper Airspace	Airspace at flight level 245 and above.
Upper Flight Information Regions	Upper airspace information regions for flight level 245 and above. The UK is covered by the Scottish and London upper information regions.
Upper Sideband Frequencies	When a frequency is amplitude modulated the resultant carrier wave will consist of the superimposed frequency plus two side band frequencies, the upper sideband will be at a frequency of the superimposed frequency plus the original frequency. See further text in the reference section under Radio Waves.
U/S	Unserviceable, not working.
UTA	Upper control Area.
UTC	Co-ordinated Universal Time.

V	
V	Design diving speed.
V	Speed, true airspeed.
V	Variable.
V	Volt.
V_1	Speed when an engine failure is assumed to be recognised, (decision speed).
V_2	Takeoff safety speed; Initial climb out speed.
V_{2min}	Minimum takeoff safety speed.
V_A	Design manoeuvring speed.
VA	Visual Approach slope indicator system. See Glossary text under that heading.
VA	Volcanic Ash, meteorological.
VAC	Visual Approach Chart.
VAL	In Valleys, meteorological.
Valley Wind	The wind caused by a horizontally moving air mass when confronted with a range of mountains. See further text in the reference section.
VAN	Runway control Van.
Vapourisation	See Glossary text under Latent Heat of Evaporation.
Vapour Trail	A track left by a jet aircraft whose engines have warmed the atmosphere sufficiently for cloud to form.
VAR	Magnetic Variation.
VAR	Visual-Aural radio Range.
Variable Pitch Propeller	A propeller linked to a constant speed unit which enables a constant rpm to be maintained whilst the propeller angle of attack is changed. See further text in the reference section under Propeller.
Variation	The angle of difference between the meridians of the true north and south poles in comparison with the meridians of the magnetic north and south poles. See further text in the reference section.
Variphase Signal	A carrier wave transmitted by a VOR on the discrete frequency that amplitude modulates the signal. The 360° radial is at the same phase as the reference signal. The 180° radial the variphase signal is 180° out of phase. Radial identification is by comparing the phases. See further text in the reference section under Very High Frequency Omni-Directional Range.
VAS	Vortex Advisory System.
VASI	Visual Approach Slope Indicators. See Glossary text under that heading.
VASIS	Visual Approach Slope Indicator System. See Glossary text under that heading.

VAT	Target Threshold speed.
V_B	Design speed for maximum gust intensity.
V_c	Design cruising speed, wind component perpendicular to track.
VC	In vicinity, meteorological.
VCR	Visual Control Room.
VCY	Vicinity.
V_d	Design diving speed.
V_{df}	Demonstrated flight diving speed.
VDF	Very high frequency Direction Finding, (station). See Glossary text under Direction Finding.
VDP	Visual Descent Point.
V_e	Equivalent air speed. See Glossary text under that heading.
Veering Wind	The shifting of the wind across a specific ground point in a clockwise direction.
Velocity Threshold	A value calculated at 1.3 x the indicated stalling speed in the approach configuration at maximum landing weight. It is used to categorize aircraft from A – E dependent upon this speed.
Ventania	Portuguese term used to describe a gale.
Venturi Effect	A venturi is a tube which gently narrows at the centre and broadens at the ends. If air, or any fluid, flows through the tube, the pressure at the narrow section will be less than that at the ends.
VER	Vertical.
Vertical Separation	Aircraft division provided by distance in height. See further text in the reference section under Radar Separation.
Vertical Speed Indicator	An aircraft instrument which uses the principle of differential static pressure to display the rate of descent or climb of an aircraft. See further text in the reference section.
Vertical Stabilizer	See Glossary text under Fin.
VERVIS	Vertical Visibility.
Very High Frequency	Frequencies in the 30 to 300MHz range. See further text in the reference section.
Very High Frequency Meteorological Report	A service referred to as VOLMET and produced on various VHF frequencies to cover weather for selected aerodromes. Each broadcast cycle is preceded by a time announcement stating the time at the end of the observing period. See further text in the reference section.
Very High Frequency Omni-directional Range	A radio navigation system based on a ground station transmitting radials. These are an infinite number of position lines emanating from the station. An aircraft equipped with a receiver and an omni-bearing selector and indicator can determine which radial it is on. By using a co-located DME or taking a cross cut from another VOR an exact location may be established. See further text in the reference section.

Very Low Frequency	Frequencies in the 3 to 30Khz range.
V_f	Design flap speed.
V_F	Design diving speed.
V_{fe}	Maximum flap extended speed.
VFR	Visual Flight Rules. See Glossary text under that heading.
VGS	Visual Guidance System.
V_h	Maximum speed in level flight without maximum continuous power.
VHF	Very High Frequency, frequencies in the 30 to 300MHz range. See text in the reference section under that heading.
VI	Variable Intensity lights.
VI/d	Best lift over drag speed.
Violent Storm	Wind speed of 56 – 63 knots (104 – 117 km per hour. Force 11.
Virga	Precipitation which evaporates before reaching the surface.
VIS	Visibility. See Glossary text under that heading.
Visibility	The distance at which objects of known distance are visible over at least half the horizon during daylight hours. It is reduced by various phenomena. See further text in the reference section.
Visual Approach Slope Indicator	The full system comprises of twelve units arranged to form two lighted wingbars each side of the runway. The alternative, but similar, systems have a reduced number of lights in each wingbar or T on one or both sides of the runway. See further text in the reference section.
Visual Descent Point	The position shown on an approach chart that defines the fix on the final path of a non-precision, straight-in approach from which a descent from the minimum descent altitude may be made. See further text in the reference section.
Visual Flight Rules	A set of minimas required to fly in visual meteorological conditions. See further text in the reference section.
Visual Manoeuvring Area	An area near an aerodrome suitable for visual manoeuvring after an instrument descent. See further text in the reference section.
Visual Meteorological Conditions	Conditions in which flights are able to be made under visual flight rules.
Visual Reporting Point	A visual reference point, being a town, landmark, disused aerodrome or similar, used as a reporting point for aircraft inbound, outbound or passing the airfield to which the point relates.
Vle	Maximum landing gear extended speed.
VLF	Frequencies in the Very Low Frequency, 3 to 30KHz range.
VLNT	Violent, meteorological.

V_{lo}	Maximum landing gear operating speed.
VLR	Very Long Range.
V_{mc}	Minimum control speed with the critical engine inoperative.
VMC	Visual Meteorological Conditions. See Glossary text under that heading.
V_{mca}	Minimum control speed in the air.
V_{mcg}	Minimum control speed on the ground.
V_{mcl}	Minimum control speed during landing with all engines operating.
V_{mcl-1}	Minimum control speed during landing approach with the critical engine inoperative.
V_{mcl-2}	Minimum control speed during landing with two critical engines inoperative.
Vme	Maximum endurance speed, sailplanes.
VMH	Visual Manoeuvring Height.
VMO	Maximum permissible operating speed or Mach number.
V_{mu}	Minimum unstick speed.
V_n	Wind component perpendicular to heading.
V_{ne}	Never exceed speed.
V_{no}	Maximum structural cruising speed.
VOLMET	Very high frequency Meteorological report for aircraft in flight. See Glossary text under that heading.
VOR	Very high frequency Omni-directional Range. See Glossary text under that heading.
VORTAC	Very high frequency Omni-directional Range and combined Tactical Air navigator. See Glossary text under both headings.
Vortices	See Glossary text under wake Turbulence.
VOT	Very high frequency Omni-bearing indicator checkpoint or range Test signal.
VOX	Voice Operated transmit.
V_R	Rotation speed.
VR	Veer. See Glossary text under Veering Wind.
VR	Visual Route.
VRB	Variable, wind.
VRB/L	Variable, landing direction & circuits.
V_{ref}	Reference speed for final approach.
V_{REF}	Reference landing approach speed, all engines operating.
V_{REF-1}	Reference landing approach speed, one engine inoperative.
VRG	Visual Reference Giro.
VRP	Visual Reporting Point. See Glossary text under that heading.

V_S	Stalling speed or minimum steady flight speed at which the aircraft is controllable.
VSA	By Visual Reference to the ground.
VSBY	Visibility. See Glossary text under that heading.
V_{S1}	Stalling speed or minimum steady flight speed with flaps up and no power being applied.
VSI	Vertical Speed Indicator. See Glossary text under that heading.
V_{slg}	Stalling speed at the 1g breakpoint.
VSM	Visual Separation Minima.
V_{so}	Stalling speed with the flaps and undercarriage down and with no power being applied.
VSP	Vertical Speed.
V_{sse}	Minimum safe single engine speed for a multi-engine aircraft.
VSTOL	Very Short Take Off and Landing.
V_{TDM}	Minimum demonstrated threshold speed.
V_{Tmax}	Maximum Threshold speed.
V_{Tmin}	Minimum Threshold speed.
VTOL	Vertical Take-off and Landing.
V/V	Vertical Velocity or speed.
VV	Vertical Visibility. VV/// means sky obscured.
VW	Tailwind component.
VWS	Vortex Wake System.
V_X	Best angle of climb speed.
V_{XSE}	Best single engine angle of climb speed for twin engined aircraft.
V_y	Best rate of climb speed.
V_{yse}	Best single engine rate of climb speed for twin engine aircraft.

W

(W)	Winter term.
w	Watts.
W	Wednesday.
W	Weight.
W	West.
W	Wing bars
WA	Air display. (NOTAM decode 2nd & 3rd letters).
WAC	World Aeronautical Chart, 1:1,000,000.
Waddy	Cornish expression for a small gust of wind.
WAFC	World Area Forecast Centre.
Waff	Scottish expression for a gentle breeze.
Wake Turbulence	The effect caused by wake vortices generated by the wing tips of aircraft and the main rotors of helicopters in forward flight. See Glossary text under Wake Vortices and further text in the reference section under Wake Turbulence.
Wake Turbulence Classifications	Aircraft are classified in relation to wake turbulence for purposes of safe separation. See text in the reference section under Wake Turbulence.
Wake Turbulence Minima Spacings	Certain criteria are set out for spacings in respect of distance and time between aircraft for final approach and departures. See text in the reference section under Wake Turbulence.
Wake Vortices	Wind spirals generated from the wing tips of aircraft or from the main rotors of a helicopter in forward flight. The vortices are made up of two counter rotating cylindrical air masses trailing behind the aircraft. They tend to drift slowly downwards and will be drifted or halted in progress by any local winds. See text in the reference section under Wake Turbulence.
Warm Front	The ground level boundary between warm air and cooler air ahead of it. See text in the reference section under Fronts.
Warm Sector	The area of warm air behind a warm front being pushed along by a further mass of cold air behind it. See text in the reference section under Fronts.
Waterspout	A phenomenon caused by a thunderstorm passing over water or sea during its mature stage. See further text in the reference section under Tornadoes.
Water Vapour	Particles of water suspended in the atmosphere. See further text in the reference section.
Wave Cyclone	A cyclone which forms and moves along a front, deforming the line of the front with wave like cloud formations.
Waypoint	See Glossary text under Phantom Station.
WB	Aerobatics. (NOTAM Decode 2nd & 3rd letters).

WB	Westbound.
WBAR	Wing Bar Lights.
WC	Captive balloon or kite. (NOTAM decode 2nd & 3rd letters).
WCA	Wind Correction Angle.
WD	Demolition of explosives. (NOTAM decode 2nd & 3rd letters).
WDI	Wind Direction Indicator.
WDSPR	Widespread, meteorological.
WE	Exercises. (NOTAM decode 2nd & 3rd letters).
WEA	Weather.
Wed	Wednesday.
Wedge	Synonym for ridge. See Glossary text under that heading.
WEF	With Effect from.
Weight Schedule	All aircraft with a valid certificate of airworthiness must be weighed and its centre of gravity resolved. From this a calculation system is provided for each aircraft so that a pilot can calculate if an aircraft is within safe weight and balance criteria under varying load conditions before flight.
Wet Bulb Thermometer	A thermometer used alongside a dry bulb thermometer. The wet bulb has its bulb covered in a wick which is kept moist by being dipped in water. Evaporation of the water from the wick extracts heat from the bulb and difference in temperatures are used to evaluate relative humidity and dewpoint. See further text in the reference section.
WF	Air refuelling. (NOTAM Decode 2nd & 3rd letters). See Glossary text under Air to Air refuelling area.
WFP	Warm Front Passage, meteorological!
WG	Glider flying. (NOTAM decode 2nd & 3rd letters).
Wh	White.
Whirlwind	See Glossary text under Dust Devils.
Whiteout	Visual condition where no shadows exist to distinguish ground features over a snow covered area due to a solid cloudbase overhead.
WI	Within.
WID	Width.
WIE	With Immediate Effect.
WILCO	Will Comply.
Wind Direction	Wind direction is always given as the bearing *from* which it blows.
Windshear	The change of wind direction and/or speed over a short distance. Variations may be vertical, horizontal or a combination of both. See further text in the reference section.

Wing Loading	The load carried by the wings whilst in straight and level flight or the weight supported for each unit area of wing. See further text in the reference section.
Wingspan	The distance from wingtip to wingtip.
WINTEM	Forecast upper Wind and Temperature for aviation.
WIP	Work in Progress.
WJ	Banner/target towing. (NOTAM decode 2nd & 3rd letters).
WK	Weak, meteorological.
wkd	Weekdays, Monday – Saturday inclusive.
WKN	Weaken or Weakening, meteorological.
WL	Ascent of free balloon. (NOTAM decode 2nd & 3rd letters).
WM	Missile, gun or rocket firing. (NOTAM decode 2nd & 3rd letters).
WMO	World Meteorological Organisation.
WND	Wind.
WO	Without.
W/P	Way-point.
WP	Parachute jumping exercise. (NOTAM decode 2nd & 3rd letters).
WPT	Way-point.
WRDA	Weapons Range Danger Area.
WRM	Warm, meteorological.
WRMFRNT	Warm Front. See Glossary text under that heading.
WRNG	Warning, meteorological.
WS	Burning or blowing gas. (NOTAM decode 2nd & 3rd letters).
WS	Windshear. See Glossary text under that heading.
WSHFT	Windshift, meteorological.
WT	Mass movement of aircraft. (NOTAM decode 2nd & 3rd letters).
WT	Weight.
W/T,WT	Wireless Telegraphy.
WTSPT	Waterspout. See Glossary text under that heading.
W/V	Wind Velocity.
WV	Formation flight. (NOTAM decode 2nd & 3rd letters).
WV	Wave, meteorological.
WW	Significant volcanic activity. (NOTAM decode 2nd & 3rd letters).
WX	Weather.
WZ	Model flying. (NOTAM decode 2nd & 3rd letters).

X	
X	On request.
X	Cross.
XBAR	Crossbar, of approach lighting.
XC	Cross Country.
XM	Extra Marker. See text in the reference section under Marker Beacons.
XNG	Crossing.
XPDR	Transponder. See Glossary text under that heading.
XS	Atmospherics.
XX	Heavy, meteorological, in relation to weather XXRA = heavy rain.
XX	NOTAM decode 4th & 5th letters followed by a plain language message.

Y

Y	Yellow.
Yaw	The effect of an aircraft skidding in its direction of travel.
Ye	Yellow.
YCZ	Yellow Caution Zone, runway Lighting.
YD(s)	Yard(s).

Z	
Z	Suffix indication of Greenwich mean time.
Z	Tower.
Z	Very high frequency station marker at a non-directional beacon.
Zero Thrust	For multi-engined aircraft, a manifold pressure setting that will simulate the reduction in drag experienced when an engine is actually feathered and shut down. See further text in the reference section.
ZFW	Zero Fuel Weight
Zulu Time	Synonym for Greenwich mean time. See further text in the reference section.

THE
AIR PILOT'S
REFERENCE
GUIDE

ABEAM

Abeam is a frequently used radio telephony phrase used for position fixing. An aircraft is abeam a fixed ground point when its track passes at 90° to it. Due consideration must be given to any difference between heading and track to provide an accurate fix.

ABOVE GROUND LEVEL - AGL

An aircraft's height above ground level is also known as **Absolute Altitude**. It may be calculated by subtracting the elevation of the ground below from the flight altitude above mean sea level. In the vicinity of an aerodrome is may be read directly from the altimeter by setting the QFE, or if fitted, by a radio altimeter.

ACCELERATE STOP DISTANCE

Phraseology used for multi-engine aircraft. The Accelerate stop distance is defined as the distance for an aircraft, under the prevailing conditions, to accelerate to V1 (speed when an engine failure is assumed to be recognised, decision speed), with all engines operating and then with one engine failed, to come to a stop with the remaining engines at idle or if available using reverse thrust.

ACLINAL LINE

An aclinal line joins places around the Earth that exhibit forces of equal magnetic dip. These forces affect a magnetic compass. The dip is corrected for as much as possible in the compass design, but any compass is considered to be unreliable if used in latitudes in excess of 70° North or 70° South.

ADIABATIC - Cooling & Heating

The definition of adiabatic is 'without heat entering or leaving the system'. Any parcel of air that is forced to rise will experience a reduction in pressure permitting it to expand. The temperature of the air consequently drops. The drop in temperature caused solely by the reduction in pressure is known as **Adiabatic Cooling**. Where the air temperature increases solely due to increased pressure, i.e. compression, it is known as **Adiabatic Heating**. The most frequent domestic comparison is the bicycle pump which becomes quite hot as it is used to compress air.

ADIABATIC LAPSE RATES

There are two standard temperature/height lapse rates used for meteorological calculations. The temperature lapse rate for an actual parcel of air is termed the Environmental Lapse Rate. The standard rates are:-

Dry Adiabatic Lapse Rate - Dry unsaturated air cools at the rate of 3°C for each 1,000 feet increase in height above the surface, this lapse rate remains constant with increasing altitude.

Saturated Adiabatic Lapse Rate - Saturated Air is a parcel of air that has reached a stage when it can no longer hold water in vapour form. This occurs when air rises and is cooled causing condensation to take place. This causes the release of **Latent Heat** which reduces the rate of cooling. The Saturated Adiabatic Lapse Rate is consequently 1.5°C for each 1,000 feet but does not remain constant with height.

This is because temperature, pressure and consequently the amount of condensation decreases with height and as a result the latent heat release will reduce. With height (above 5,000 feet) the Saturated Adiabatic Lapse Rate will approach that of the Dry Adiabatic Lapse Rate.

Superadiabatic Lapse Rate - A general phrase used to describe any lapse rate greater than the Dry Adiabatic Lapse Rate.

For rough calculations the surface temperature may be reduced by 2°C for each 1,000 feet in height as air very rarely falls into exactly the dry or saturated category.

ADVECTION FOG - Land

Advection fog forms over land when a mass of warm air moves over a colder surface causing the air's temperature to drop so increasing its relative humidity. If the air is cooled below its dewpoint temperature and a light wind is present (3 - 8knots) advection fog will form. It may occur during the day or night regardless of the cloud cover as it is purely a result of the temperature differences between the air and the surface.

The likelihood increases if the surface moisture level is high and most commonly occurs between October and March at UK latitudes during a slack pressure gradient. It will disperse with an increase in windspeed, a change in air mass or by surface heating (insolation).

ADVECTION FOG - Sea

Advection fog is formed when tropical maritime (warm moist) air flows towards the UK. As it passes over the colder sea it cools, eventually reaching its dewpoint, where condensation occurs in the form of advection fog. It may occur during the day or night regardless of the cloud cover and may penetrate up to 10 - 15 miles inland, although this will usually clear by surface heating (insolation). Advection fog forms mainly in winter or spring when the sea temperature is at its lowest.

Advection fog over the sea will disperse only by a change of air mass.

ADVISORY ROUTE - ADR

A route along which an Air Traffic Advisory Service is available. It is in the form of a corridor, similar to an airway, having a specified base and with, or without, an upper level. It is not controlled airspace so no control service is available.

An ADR is 10nm wide and provides 1,500 feet terrain clearance within 15nm of the track. On sections where the clearance is not provided the deviation is indicated.

a) The service offered will be a flight information and separation service of known traffic, the service is not based on accurate knowledge.

b) If the advisory service is required the flight must be made under an IFR Flight Plan.

c) Altimeter settings are; Regional QNH below 3,000 feet amsl, 1013 above.

d) The levels at which advisory service is provided is between the published maximum and minimum cruising level, these are shown in the UK Air Pilot.

e) Levels are based on magnetic tracks with quadrantal rules up to FL 245, above this the semi-circular rules applies.

AERODROME - Circuit - Above Surface Definitions

In order that an orderly and safe traffic flow may be regulated into an aerodrome a circuit pattern is created. This enables all aircraft in the circuit to be at the same height, increasing the opportunity for a visual sighting, and to make radio calls clearly defining their positions. The circuit sections are called legs. Circuit directions may be left or right dependent on terrain, or both if used to separate different types of traffic.

CIRCUIT LEG/TURN	PURPOSE	RADIO CALL/ POSITION
Upwind Leg or Dead Side	Not in the active circuit, it is used for descent purposes for aircraft joining the circuit	Descending Dead Side to join RH Crosswind 26*
Turn passing abm the runway into Crosswind Leg	To join the circuit, this should be at circuit height	Joining Crosswind RH 26*
Crosswind Leg	To place the A/C far enough out from the runway so that the Base Leg may be flown straight with enough time to lower flaps and commence a descent.	Crosswind RH 26*
Turn from Crosswind to Downwind Leg	To commence the Downwind Leg	Turning Crosswind RH 26*
Downwind Leg	To visually track parallel to the runway and carry out pre-landing checks	*Call abeam the upwind end of the runway* Downwind RH 26*
Turn from Downwind to Base Leg	To commence the Base Leg	Turning Base RH 26*
Base Leg	Reduce Speed, Lower Flaps, commence descent from circuit height	Base Leg *as soon as the turn has been completed*
Turn onto Final Approach	Line up for a final approach	Turning Finals RH 26*
Final Approach	Trim and adjust power for a steady descent (usually 3°), achieve a track to maintain the runway centreline	Final 26* to Land/Touch & Go *(more than 4nm from threshold call)* Long Final#

Long Final - Aircraft flying a final approach of greater than 4nm are to report **'Long Final'** when beyond 4nm and **'Final'** when 4nm is reached. Aircraft flying a straight in approach should call **'Long Final'** at 8nm and **'Final'** at 4nm and short final, if requested, at 2nm.

* Substitute for circuit direction and relevant runway in use.

Only the Downwind and Finals radio calls are compulsory, the other calls should be made only if requested by ATC or when making blind calls when A/G radio is in-active.

AERODROME FLIGHT INFORMATION SERVICE - AFIS

An AFIS is a service where no approach or aerodrome control service has been established but a licenced Aerodrome Flight Information Service Officer (AFISCO) is available. It is not an air traffic service and pilots must take action to provide their own separation. They will not necessarily be advised of the active runway unless this is requested, and may decide for themselves which runway to use.

The RT suffix is Information. The AFISCO is responsible for:-

a) Alerting safety services.
b) Informing aircraft of the state of the aerodrome and its facilities.
c) Initiating overdue actions.
d) Issuing information (or instructions if to avert a dangerous situation) to aircraft on the manoeuvring area and apron.
e) Issuing information to aircraft flying in the ATZ to assist pilots in preventing collisions.
f) Meteorological Information, supplied in the following order.
  1. Magnetic wind direction and speed
  2. Visibility
  3. Present weather
  4. Cloud base and coverage
  5. QFE, or QNH and aerodrome height
  6. Other relevant meteorological information
g) Relaying messages and clearances from the ATCC to A/C and A/C to ATCC.

AERODROME IDENTIFICATION BEACON

Light Beacons installed at military and civil aerodromes are used to identify the aerodrome by flashing a Morse identification code. The code consists of two letters, flashing every 12 seconds at around 7 words per minute. The lights are red at military aerodromes and green at civil.

At some civil aerodromes where an identification beacon is not installed a white flashing strobe light may be provided for homing purposes. This is referred to as an Aerodrome Beacon.

At civil aerodromes the ground lights are normally used during periods of poor visibility during the day and from sunset to sunrise. At certain aerodromes their use is at the discretion of ATC at night. At Military Master aerodromes they operates continually at night, at other military sites they are used as operationally required.

AERODROME RADIO CONTACT - Approach to Land

To avoid possible interference with other aerodromes on the same frequency contact calls should not be made further out than 10,000 feet and 25nm for approach frequencies and 4,000ft and 25nm for tower frequencies. They should not be made later than 15nm or 5 minutes flying time from the aerodrome traffic zone boundary, whichever is the greater.

The call is similar to a LARS or en-route call and should include the following **after** the initial contact call:-

a) Callsign and aircraft type
b) Departure from .... inbound to ....
c) Estimated position
d) Heading
e) Flight Level or Altitude

f) POB (persons on board) - military aerodromes only

g) Type of arrival required, e.g. VFR - request joining instructions, IFR - request vectors to ILS/request ILS/NDB

ATC will supply:-

a) Runway in use
b) Wind speed and direction (magnetic)
c) Visibility
d) Weather
e) Cloud
f) QFE / QNH
g) Runway Visual Range (if measured)

Note:- A non-public transport aircraft approaching to land on a runway in respect of which there is a notified instrument approach procedure must comply with any relevant aerodrome operating minima in respect to that runway (ANO Am 1990 Article 32A).

AERODROME - Signals and Markings

Where aerodromes are non radio, or have radio but accept non-radio aircraft a signals square is usually provided to indicate information relevant to a safe landing. These are as follows:-

1. Black Ball suspended from a mast - Direction of take off and landing not necessarily the same.
2. Black Numbers - Indicate the runway direction in use.
3. Black Letter C on a yellow background - ATC reporting point, usually the point to be relieved of your landing fee and not necessarily near the tower.
4. Green Flag on a mast - Right hand circuit.
5. Orange and White ground markers not more than 45m apart - If alternating with flags - Unserviceable runway or taxiway area boundary, if without flags marks the aerodrome boundary.
6. Red Balls (2) suspended from a mast - Glider flying in progress.
7. Red L on a dumbbell - Light aircraft may either use the runway or the area marked with the white L.
8. Red Square with single yellow diagonal - Manoeuvring area poor, exercise caution when landing.
9. Red Square with yellow diagonals forming a cross - Landing Prohibited.
10. Red and White striped arrow pointing in a clockwise direction - Right hand circuit.
11. Red and Yellow chequered board with 12 equal squares - The aircraft may move on the manoeuvring area and apron only with ATC permission.
12. White broken line and a continuous white line together - taxiway holding point.
13. White Crosses, two or more, at 45° to the runway centreline, not more than 300m apart of a size visible from the air - Unserviceable runway or taxiway.
14. White Dumbbell - Use hard surfaces only.
15. White Dumbbell with black strips on each ball - Take off and land on the runway, ground movement not confined to hard surfaces.
16. White flat rectangular markers - Boundary of unpaved runway or stopway.
17. White T - Indicating the direction of landing parallel with the shaft of the T and towards the cross arm.

18. White Bar with two white bars at 180° - Glider flying in progress.
19. White disk placed at the top of the cross arm of the white landing T - Direction of take off and landing not necessarily the same.
20. White H - Designated Helicopter area exists.
21. White L - Indicating a part of the manoeuvring area only to be used for take off and landings of light aircraft.
22. Yellow Cross - Glider tow rope dropping area.

The following may also be found on military or disused aerodromes.
1. Green Flag - Right Hand circuit.
2. Orange Triangles - Unserviceable areas.
3. Red L - Light aircraft may land on the area marked with white corner markings.
4. Red Flag - Left Hand circuit.
5. Red square with two yellow bars - landing area serviceable but no safety facilities available.
6. White Cross at 45° to the runway centreline - Do not land, used for storage purposes only.
7. White Cross underlined with a white bar - Surface has been inspected within last 6 months and is fit for emergency use only.
8. White Panel with red diamond superimposed - Carrier training in progress.
Refer also to the section on **Light Signals**.

AERODROME - Surface Definitions
Various words are used to define the surface areas of an airfield.
a) **Aerodrome Elevation**. The elevation shown in the UK Air Pilot. The highest point on the landing area and the aerodrome QFE datum.
b) **Accelerate - Stop distance** - ASDA. The length of the take off run available plus the length of the stopway.
c) **Clearway**. A rectangular area, commencing at the end of the take off run available, selected and prepared as a suitable area over which an aircraft may make a portion of its initial climb to a specified screen height.
d) **Displaced Threshold**. A threshold that is located at a point on the runway other than the designated beginning of the runway.
e) **Emergency Distance** - ED. The length of the declared take off run plus the length of the stopway. The ICAO term is **Accelerate-Stop Distance.**
f) **Instrument Runway**. A runway equipped with electronic navigation aids for which a precision or non-precision approach procedures exists.
g) **Landing Distance Available** - LDA. The length of the runway (or surface when it is unpaved) which is available and suitable for the ground landing run of an aeroplane commencing at visual threshold markings or threshold lights. Where, in the case of an unpaved landing area, no threshold markings are provided, the landing distance is measured from the junction of the surface with a 1:20 approach plane above which no obstructions are permitted.
h) **Manoeuvring Area**. The part of the aerodrome provided for the take off and landing of aircraft and for the movement of aircraft on the surface. It excludes the apron and any part of the aerodrome provided for aircraft maintenance.
i) **Movement Area**. Runways, taxiways and other areas that are used for taxiing, take off and landing of aircraft excluding loading ramps and parking areas.
j) **Non-instrument runway**. Runway intended for the operation of aircraft using visual approach procedures.
k) **Runway**. A rectangular area prepared for the landing and take off run of aircraft

along its length. Runways identified by a two number code relating to the nearest 10° of its magnetic heading.

l) **Stopway**. A rectangular area, commencing at the end of the take off run available, which is suitable for the ground run of an aeroplane decelerating after a discontinued take off.

m) **Take Off Distance Available** - TODA. The length of the declared take off run plus the clearway.

n) **Take Off Run Available** - TORA. The length of runway available and suitable for the ground run of an aeroplane taking off.

o) **Threshold**. The beginning of that portion of the runway used for landing.

AERODROME TRAFFIC ZONE - ATZ
Aerodrome traffic zones have specified standard dimensions of:-

a) **Off-shore Installations** - Mean sea level to 2,000 feet amsl and a 1.5nm radius around the installation.

b) **Non off-shore installations** - Longest runway 1,850 metres or less. Surface to 2,000 feet aal and a radius of 2nm centred on the mid-point of the longest runway. If this would mean that the ATZ would not extend to 1.5nm beyond the end of any runway the radius is increased to 2.5nm.

c) **Non off-shore installations** - Longest runway greater than 1,850 metres. Surface to 2,000 feet aal and a radius of 2.5nm centred on the mid-point of the longest runway.

No flight must enter an ATZ without permission of the ATC, or, if there is no ATC, from the flight information unit or air/ground control. Whilst in an ATZ a pilot must keep a listening watch, and notify the aerodrome on entering or leaving the ATZ, or, if non-radio watch for visual ground signals.

AEROFOIL - Definitions

Angle of Attack	- the angle between the chord line and the relative airflow
Angle of Incidence	- the angle at which the wing is fixed to the airframe relative to the longitudinal axis
Camber	- the distance between the mean camber line and the chord line
Chord Line	- a straight line joining the ends of the curved camber line, the length is the chord
Leading Edge	- front edge of the wing
Mean Camber Line	- a line drawn halfway on the cross section of the upper and lower surfaces
Stalling Angle of Attack	- an angle when passed the streamline flow over the upper surface breaks down (usually at about 16°)
Thickness	- the greatest distance between the upper and lower surfaces
Trailing Edge	- back edge of the wing

AERONAUTICAL INFORMATION CIRCULARS - AICs
AICs are published on a Thursday, every 28 days. They form part of the Integrated Aeronautical Information Package and notify information which is not included in the AIP or issued by supplement. They are colour coded to ease location and filing:-
Green   -   Maps and Charts

Pink	-	Matters which need special emphasis on safety
Mauve	-	(a) UK airspace restrictions imposed in accordance with the temporary restriction of flying regulations (b) Amendments to the Chart of UK airspace restrictions and hazardous areas and to the chart of UK areas of intense aerial activity, aerial tactics areas and military low flying system.
White	-	Administrative matters, examination dates, fees, charges, new or amended publications.
Yellow	-	Operational matters including ATS facilities and requirements

An AIC will lapse on the fifth anniversary of its issue date.

AGONIC LINE
A line drawn on a map joining points of zero magnetic deviation.

AILERONS
The ailerons provide lateral control in the roll of the aircraft. They are located in the trailing edge of the wing and operated from the cockpit by rotation of the control wheel or sideways movement of the control stick.

A movement to the left will raise the left aileron, reducing the wing's lift, whilst lowering the right aileron into the airflow and increasing the right wing's lift.

Coupled Ailerons - on some aircraft the ailerons and rudder are coupled to overcome adverse aileron yaw.

Differential Ailerons - the differential aileron movement increases the drag on the descending wing by increasing the up-going aileron angle of movement in comparison to the down-going aileron on the other wing.

Drooping Ailerons - designed to droop as flaps are lowered, increasing lateral control. Aileron droop is normally limited to 15°.

Frise Ailerons - designed and pivoted to increase the drag of the descending wing. As the aileron is raised the lower part of the aileron projects into the airstream beneath the wing generating extra drag which reduces adverse yaw.

AIRCRAFT CATEGORIES - Nominal Threshold Speeds
Speed Related Categories

The nominal VAT **(Velocity at Threshold)** is calculated as 1.3 x the indicated stalling speed in the approach configuration at maximum landing weight.

Aircraft Category	Nominal VAT (Knots) IAS	Range of Speeds Initial Approach	Range of Speeds Final Approach	Visual Circling
A	0 - 90	90/150 (110*)	70/100	100
B	91 - 120	120/180 (140*)	85/130	135
C	121 - 140	160/240	115/160	180
D	141 - 165	185/250	130/185	205
E	166 - 210	185/250	155/230	240

* Maximum speed for reversal and racetrack procedures.

AIRCRAFT CATEGORIES - Performance
Aircraft whose maximum weight does not exceed 5,700Kg are, for performance purposes, divided into groups C, D and E. Private flights do not legally fall within these categories, but for safety reasons, they should still be used as a basis for any flight operation.

Group C	Aeroplanes with a performance level such that a forced landing should not be necessary if an engine fails after take off and initial climb.
Group D	Aeroplanes with no specific provision for performance after engine failure.
Group E	Aeroplanes not exceeding 2,730Kg for which the extent of performance scheduling is limited.

Group E aircraft will be capable of a performance level similar to that for group C or D, but because of other factors or requirements involving certification the manufacturer may opt for the aircraft to be placed in Group E rather than C or D.

The Certificate of airworthiness or aircraft manual will confirm which performance category an aircraft is placed.

AIRCRAFT CATEGORIES - Pilot Licencing

A pilot's licence contains a page which lists the groups of aircraft the holder is entitled to fly. For private pilots aircraft are divided into three groups:-

Group A	All types of single engined aeroplanes of which the maximum total weight authorised does not exceed 5,700Kg.
Group B	Certain types of aeroplanes having two or more engines of which the maximum total weight authorised does not exceed 5,700Kg.
Group C	Individual types of aeroplanes of which the maximum total weight authorised exceeds 5,700Kg or are considered to be of a complex nature.

AIRCRAFT CATEGORIES - Weight - Aerodrome Operating Minima

Aeroplanes not exceeding 5,700 Kg MTWA. CAP 360 divides this type of aircraft into two types:-

(a) Piston Engine or Turboprop aeroplanes

(b) Turbo Jet aeroplanes

Aeroplanes exceeding 5,700 Kg MTWA. CAP 360 divides this class of aircraft into three types:-

A - Exceeding 5,700 Kg MTWA and less than 25,000 Kg MLWA

B - 25,000 Kg MLWA and up to 68,000 Kg MLWA*

C - Over 160,000 Kg MLWA

* AERAD Group B1, AERAD Group B2 is 'More than 68,000 Kg MLWA and up to 160,000 Kg MLWA'.

AIRCRAFT CATEGORIES - Weight - UK

Microlight - not exceeding 390Kg, wing loading not exceeding 25Kg per sq metre, fuel capacity not exceeding 50 litres, not designed to carry more than 2 persons.

Following classifications relate to **Wake Turbulence Separation:-**

Light Aircraft - 17,000 Kg or less

Small Aircraft - 40,000 Kg or less and more than 17,000 Kg

Medium Aircraft - less than 136,000 Kg and more than 40,000 Kg

Heavy Aircraft - 136,000 Kg or greater

AIRCRAFT DOCUMENTS

An aircraft must have certain current documents to fly legally in the UK, they are:-

158

a) Certificate of Registration
b) Certificate of Airworthiness
c) Certificate of Maintainance Review (N/A to private aircraft*)
d) Certificate of Release to Service
e) Technical Log (N/A to private aircraft*)
f) Aircraft, Engine and Propeller Logs (N/A to fixed pitch props)
g) Aircraft Weight Schedule
h) Radio Licence (if radio fitted)

* Private Aircraft *for the purposes of this list only* relates to aircraft not engaged in public transport or used for any form or aerial work.
Refer to the individual reference sections if specific information is required.

AIRCRAFT WEIGHT SCHEDULE

Under Article 16 of the Air Navigation Order (ANO) 1985 every flying machine or glider with a valid certificate of airworthiness must be weighed and its centre of gravity determined as required by the CAA.

From this, a calculation system is provided so that a pilot may calculate if an aircraft is within safe weight and balance criteria under varying circumstances. The weight and balance calculation must be performed, for safety reasons, by the pilot, before any flight is made.

For details of the CAA requirements refer to the ANO. For a weight and balance calculation refer to the Operators Manual, Pilot's Handbook or Owners Manual for the individual aircraft.

Be aware that one weight and balance schedule may not apply to another aircraft even if it is the same make, model and year.

AIRFIELD ELEVATION

Also known as the **Airport Elevation**. This is defined as the highest point on the landing area and is referred to as the **QFE Datum**. With the aerodrome QFE set the altimeter will read the height above the highest point on the landing area and for landing purposes will give a reading as near to zero on touchdown as possible. Where a precision runway is 7 feet or more below the QFE datum the aerodrome barometric pressure passed to the landing aircraft will equate to the QFE touchdown elevation.

AIR MASSES

An air mass is a large quantity of air which is allowed to remain stationary for several days. It will take on the characteristics of its source region with uniform temperature and humidity. These masses eventually move away from their source regions and as they travel towards the UK and Europe are affected by the land or sea mass over which they travel. They have specific names which describe their source and moisture content. They will tend to exhibit predictable weather on reaching the UK. The official classifications are shown in brackets.

Arctic Maritime (Am)	- Heavy showers or snow over the sea and windward coasts, cloud and showers dying out inland. Cold and clear with good visibility
Polar Continental (Pc)	- Very cold and hazy, dry and clear skies. If the passage was over the North Sea, SC and CU will form giving coastal showers to the East.
Polar Maritime (Pm)	- Rain showers with CU and CB, possible thunderstorms. Visibility generally good. In winter radiation fog may form.

Returning Polar Maritime (rPm)	- Dependent on how far the mass has travelled South. If warm it will give moist, foggy weather overnight. If surface heating is high, CU and CB with showers and thunderstorms. The less far South it travelled the more it will resemble Polar Maritime Air.
Tropical Continental (Tc)	- Very warm and dry with clear skies. Haze and heat wave conditions. If travelled over the Bay of Biscay CU or CB with possible thunderstorms.
Tropical Maritime (Tm)	- Warm, very moist, poor visibility ST and SC. Often clear skies above solid ST layer. Sea and Hill fog. Drizzle. In summer broken SC and CU, joining for ST at night with HZ.

AIR MASS THUNDERSTORMS

These are very active cumulonimbus clouds that occur most commonly in the afternoon when insolation is at its peak especially during a weak depression. Over the sea they may develop from relatively cold air moving over a comparatively warm sea. In either event they may well develop in conditions of overcast cloud, where they are referred to as embedded CBs, under these conditions it is impossible for the pilot to detect them. Refer to the section on Cumulonimbus Clouds.

AIRMET

Airmet is an automated telephone system giving the pilot access to METAR and TAF information for various airfields. Forecasts are renewed four times a day and become available about half an hour before the period of validity. They cover UK Civil and Military airfields and well as a selection of those on the near continent. Telephone charges are at a premium rate.

AIRMISS

In the event that a pilot considers his aircraft was in definite risk of collision with another aircraft in flight he/she should report the incident immediately on the frequency he/she is currently working. If it cannot be made by radio then immediately on landing.

The call should contain:-

a) AIRMISS
b) Callsign
c) Position of airmiss
d) Aircraft heading
e) Flight Level/Altitude
f) Weather Conditions
g) Time GMT
h) Description of other aircraft
i) Description of incident

For any action to be taken the verbal report must be followed up by completion and submission of a form CA 1094 which should be sent to the CAA within 7 days of the incident. If the incident happens abroad the pilot may file the report from an overseas station, in which case he/she will be permitted use of the AFTN to a UK ATCC, they will complete the CA 1094.

The report from the pilot, and from the pilot of the other aircraft if submitted, will be studied by the Joint Airmiss Working Group (JAWG) who will make recommendations and access the incident to be in one of the following categories:-

A - Actual risk of collision. When it can definitely be established that there was a danger of collision.

B - Possible risk of collision. When an actual risk of collision cannot be established but the aircraft concerned came into such proximity that the possibility of a collision occurred.

C - Risk not determined. Where there is either insufficient information or a conflict of evidence that an assessment of collision risk cannot be made.

AIR PILOT

All countries publish a standard format Aerodrome Information Publication, in the UK it is called the Air Pilot. It is updated by means of an update service similar to Aeronautical Information Circulars where the old pages are destroyed and new inserted. Information is broken down into eight sections categorised as follows:-

AGA - Aerodrome classification and limitations, hours of operation, customs, lighting, markings ground signals, service aerodromes and snow clearance plan. The section also includes an aerodrome map.

COM - Radio communication and navigation frequencies of aerodromes, en-route, airways, time signals and long range navigation.

FAL - Arrival, departure and transit procedures, aircraft documentation, customs,import, export.

GEN - General, legislation, registration marks, abbreviations.

MAP - Details maps and charts available.

MET - Meteorological Information with frequencies and Met Offices. Procedures for operating on air routes and meteorological codes.

RAC - Rules, altimeter setting procedures, flight plans, airmiss procedures and danger areas.

SAR - Search and Rescue procedures.

AIRSPEED DEFINITIONS

Airspeed is the speed of the aircraft relative to the air mass through which it is travelling.

Equivalent Airspeed (EAS) The rectified airspeed corrected for compressibility error. Compressibility is a subtracted quantity.

Ground Speed (GS) The speed of the air mass affecting the aircraft added or subtracted from the true air speed.

Indicated Airspeed (IAS) The un-corrected speed as registered on the airspeed indicator. The indication is only accurate in respect of the true airspeed at mean sea level under International Standard Atmosphere.

Mach Number (Mn) The ratio of the true airspeed to the **Local Speed of Sound** (LSS). The Mach number is calculated by TAS/LSS. If TAS = LSS the speed = Mach 1 (the speed of sound).

Rectified Airspeed (RAS) The indicated airspeed corrected for pressure error (due to inherent instrument and position errors). This is known in the United States as **Calibrated Airspeed**.

True Airspeed (TAS) The equivalent airspeed corrected for density error.

AIRSPEED INDICATOR

The air speed indicator displays IAS (indicated airspeed - see definitions above), it only displays the true air speed in International Standard Atmosphere conditions. In any other conditions of density a conversion formula should be applied by using your navigation computer.

Modern instruments are colour coded. These codes remove the need for memorising upper and lower figures for various configurations and are:-

White Arc - Flap range. The lower limit (V_{so}) shows the speed at which the aircraft will stall with flaps and undercarriage extended and no power being applied. The upper limit (V_{FE}) is the maximum speed at which the flaps may be lowered.

Green Arc - Normal Operating Speed range. The lower limit (V_{SL}) is the stalling speed with flaps and undercarriage up and no power being applied. The upper limit (V_{NO}) is the maximum cruise speed for normal operations.

Yellow Arc - Caution Range. This extends from V_{NO} to the Never Exceed Speed (V_{NO}). The aircraft should not intentionally be operated in this range.

Red Line - This denotes the upper limit of the yellow arc and represents the Never Exceed speed (V_{NE}).

Modern multi engined aircraft have two further marks, a red line and a blue line. Both normally are within the white, flap range arc.

Blue Line - Usually referred to as the Blue Line Speed (V_{yse}) it indicates the best single engine rate of climb.

Red Line - The V_{mca} or minimum control speed in the take off configuration.

The air speed indicator uses two sources of pressure. Static pressure from the static vent is fed to the instrument case whilst a combination of static and dynamic pressure (pitot pressure) is fed to a sealed capsule located within the case via the pitot tube. As the pitot pressure increases due to increased forward pressure of the aircraft, the sealed capsule expands. Various mechanical linkages attached to the capsule rotate a needle which indicates the airspeed in knots or miles per hour. Errors that effect the airspeed indicator are:-

System Blockages - if either pressure source become blocked errors will occur. If the pitot tube becomes blocked the pitot pressure will remain fixed. In the event of a descent the static pressure will increase, erroneously compressing the sealed capsule and reducing the reading.

If a climb is commenced the static pressure reduces and the sealed pitot pressure will give a falsely high reading. The electrical pitot heater element should in most cases solve this problem. See the section on the Pitot Tube for further information.

If however the static vent is blocked the pressure inside the instrument case remains constant. If the aircraft descends the pressure fed to the capsule will expand to a falsely high rate due to the low static pressure. The air speed will then read higher than the true rate. In a climb the opposite will occur.

If both systems are blocked there will be no pressure changes in the event of a climb or a descent and the indication will therefore remain the same as that shown when the later source became blocked.

Instrument Error - friction in linkages and minute manufacturing imperfections.

Position Error - due to different configurations of the aircraft it is impossible for the pitot and static head to give invariable results. Refer to the sections on the Pitot Tube and the Static Vent.

Manoeuvring Error - caused by changes in the angle of attack. The aircraft operators manual contains tables which will convert the indicated airspeed (IAS) to rectified airspeed (RAS).

Density Error - the rectified airspeed (RAS) will only be the same as the true airspeed (TAS) in ISA conditions. An increase in altitude will always result in a reduction in pressure and density, this causes a reduction in the air speed indication and under reading of the TAS. Density error indications can be corrected by use of the navigation computer. For private pilots density error corrections will be of little concern, however for commercial pilots, especially those operating in warm climates it can make an appreciable difference.

Compressibility Error - air is subject to compression. At true air speeds below 300 knots the problem may be ignored. Over 300 knots the navigation computer can be used to convert the errant speed to the corrected resultant Equivalent Air Speed (EAS).

AIRWAYS

All airways are controlled and notified as Class A Airspace. The pilot in command in an airway flight must hold an Instrument Rating and a flight plan must be filed and a clearance obtained before entering controlled airspace.

An airway is 10nm wide and its junctions or ends are defined by a radio navigation aid, normally a VOR. They are named by letters of the phonetic alphabet plus the designated number, i.e. Alpha 25. You may come across older pilots referring to them by colours, for instance Amber 25, this is the old method of naming and purely a reflection of the pilots age.

Various reporting points are shown on airways charts, some are compulsory others only on instruction from ATC.

On reaching a reporting point the message is passed; *Callsign, Position, Time (of passing), Flight Level, estimating ....(position) at .. (time).*

Terrain Clearance

Where the lower limit of a section of an airway is defined as a flight level the absolute minimum altitude for the airway base is at least 1,000 feet above any fixed obstacle within 15nm of the centreline.

The lowest usable level is 500 feet above the base, giving a terrain clearance of 1,500 feet. At sections adjacent to CTRs where the lower limit is established at not less than 700 feet agl, ATC will maintain an aircraft at least 500 feet above the base of the airway.

Airways Crossing

Crossing may be achieved by either:-

a) Airways may be crossed at right angles without permission at the base where the lower limit is defined as a flight level.

b) A flight plan form CA48 filed before departure and being granted clearance.

c) Flying a glider. They may cross any airway in VMC by day without compliance with IFR. This excludes Purple Airways.

d) An airborne flight plan filed (see section on Flight Plan) the call should state the following information, and in this order:-

1. Ident	4. FL or Altitude	7. Level of Crossing
2. Aircraft Type	5. Flight Conditions	8. Time of Crossing
3. Position and Heading	6. Place of Crossing	

The request must be made at least 10 minutes before the ETA. On reaching the airway report, *Callsign, Crossing....Airway, position, time, FL.*

e) In an emergency cross at an intermediate 500 feet level.

Airways Joining

Airways joining may be achieved by either:-

a) Filing a flight plan CA48 before departure and being granted clearance.

b) Requesting permission whilst airborne and at least 10 minutes before ETA, the message should state the following, and in this order:-

1. Ident	4. FL or Altitude
2. Aircraft Type	5. Flight Conditions
3. Position and Heading	6. Departure Aerodrome

7. Full Routeing and Point of first intended landing

8. Aircraft's TAS

9. Desired Level on Airway

Flight Levels

The Semi-Circular Rule applies to airways, refer to that section for details.

ALERT PHASE - Emergency

A period where apprehension exists as to the safety of an aircraft and its occupants. This either follows an uncertainty phase or can be the first phase of a declared emergency. It will be raised if:-

a) Following an uncertainty phase;

    i) subsequent attempts fail to establish communication.

    ii) there is no news of the aircraft

b) Received information indicated that the operating efficiency of the aircraft has been impaired.

c) An aircraft that has been cleared to land has not done so within 5 minutes and there is no obvious reason for it.

If no further information is received the emergency will be categorised as being in the Distress Stage.

ALTERNATE AERODROME

This is defined as an aerodrome, selected prior to take-off, to which the flight may proceed when a landing at the original destination is not possible. The standard flight plan form requires at least one alternate aerodrome to be specified, this aerodrome may be the aerodrome of departure.

ALTERNATING CURRENT

In an alternating current circuit an alternator provides an alternating current to flow in a circuit. This means that the direction of current flow is being reversed at regular intervals. A full **cycle** of A.C. is the period from when the current increases from zero to its maximum point and reduces to zero, increases to its maximum point in the opposite direction and again returns to zero.

The **frequency** of a current is the number of **cycles** per second. Each cycle is equal to one **Hertz.** The point reached by the wave front at any time during the formation of a cycle is referred to as the **phase** of the wave and is measured in degrees. The **amplitude** of the current is the peak value of current flow (measured from the mean to the maximum).

ALTIMETER

As pressure reduces with height a simple pressure altimeter can be used to display these changes. Static pressure is fed in to a sealed instrument case. In the case is a stack of two or more aneroid capsules. The capsules are partially evacuated and sealed so that they will expand or contract in direct response to the changing static pressure. Movement of the capsules is amplified by mechanical linkages which operate a needle indicator.

A bi-metallic strip is incorporated in the linkages to compensate for any errors which would occur due to changes in temperature.

A setting device is incorporated which allows variable datum levels to be set so that local changes of pressure can be compensated for. This is referred to as the sub-scale.

Errors that affect the altimeter are:-

Instrument - linkages, friction or design.

Blockages - of the static source by ice or any reason will result in the system being sealed. If this occurs the altimeter will indicate the height at which the blockage occurs, regardless of any changes of height of the actual aircraft. Most aircraft are fitted with an alternate static source within the cabin, if this is selected due to an external vent blockage, the static pressure fed to the altimeter will be lower than the external static pressure causing the instrument to over read.

Position error - due to the positioning of the static vent.

Hysteresis or Lag - due to the time it takes for pressure changes at the static vent to be converted to needle movement. It is especially marked when altitude changes are rapid or prolonged.

Manoeuvring error - similar to position error but varies with the configuration of the aircraft.

Barometric error - the instrument will only indicate the height above the datum set on the sub-scale. If the sub-scale is miss-set or is not adjusted as the aircraft moves from areas of different atmospheric pressure it will display an incorrect reading. This is referred to as barometric error.

Temperature error - although a bi-metallic strip is incorporated into the design it cannot fully compensate for all variations.

The settings used on the sub-scale are referred to as Q codes, see Altimeter Setting Procedures for full explanations.

Encoding Altimeters operate in conjunction with the transponder passing information to ATC whilst the transponder is set to **Mode C.** The system uses a **pneumatic altimeter** with a parallel coded output of 9 to 11 bits representing the aircraft's height above the 1013.25 datum to the nearest 100 feet. Altering the altimeter sub-scale does not affect the ATC read out. Mode C should not be used without ATC permission in controlled airspace if the altimeter and read out differ by more than 300 feet.

Reading an altimeter is relatively straight forward. The longest hand indicates hundreds of feet, or part. The next longest hand indicates thousands of feet or part. A further complication may arise for those pilots who fly pressurised aircraft above 10,000 feet. The third, and smallest, needle indicates each 10,000 or part of 10,000 feet.

As it would be very simple to miss-read the indications, particularly for the inexperienced high flyer, a cut-out revealing a striped segment is provided on the dial face. At the surface the cut-out is filled with the stripes. At 5,000 feet it is half revealed and at 10,000 feet no stripes would be showing. If any part of the stripes can be seen the altimeter is giving a warning - **height less than 10,000 feet**. Altimeters with a digital readout are increasingly being used to avoid this problem.

ALTIMETER SETTING PROCEDURES

The altimeter sub-scale is required to be set to various datums dependent on the flight circumstances. The correct setting ensures adequate terrain clearance and a safe standard of flight separation. The various settings are :-

QFE - this indicates **height** above the surface and is used within an aerodrome circuit and approach to land. If an instrument approach is being made on QNH this must be made clear to the radar controller.

QNH - this indicates **altitude** above mean sea level and is used for the en-route phases of a flight where the aircraft does not climb above 3,000 feet amsl or is flying under VFR. Above 3,000 feet even if VFR it is advisable to comply with the **Quadrantal Rules** and set QNE.

QNE - also known as **Pressure Altitude**, it is a standard subscale of 1013 millibars, or 29.92 inches (US) based on the **International Standard Atmosphere** 1013.25mb. This indicates a **Flight Level**. Above the **Transition Altitude** 1013 should be set and all altimeter readings are then reported as Flight Levels. Indication 5,000 feet with QNE set = Flight Level 50. On initial climb out the aircraft's altitude may be given as a Flight Level providing the aircraft is within 2,000 feet of the Transition Altitude. The transition altitude is generally 3,000 feet in the UK, variations are shown on approach charts.

When cruising on QNE, the second altimeter if fitted, should be set to the **Regional QNH** to provide terrain clearance information in the event of an urgent descent.

Regional QNH - this is the lowest QNH value forecast for each hour. The UK is divided into 15 altimeter setting regions which are allocated the lowest forecast figure for the period H+1 to H+2. They are obtainable from any ATC Unit or by telephone to a ATCC. The longer forecast figure is useful for long flights by non-radio aircraft. The Regional QNH should be requested when entering a new ASR and will be advised by a blanket call to aircraft working a ATCU if it changes on the hour.

If required a chart to convert Altitudes to Flight Levels, or vice versa, is published in the UK AIP RAC Section 2-4.

ANABATIC WINDS

Anabatic winds are caused by solar radiation warming the surface of a slope. As the air close to the surface is warmed it becomes warmer than the air away from that surface at the same height. This then rises and drifts up the slope. Unlike **Katabatic Winds,** anabatic winds are gentle and do not normally affect powered flights.

ANTICYCLONE

An area of **high pressure**, also known as a 'high'. A **Col** is a ridge of high pressure extending out from the centre of the high. Anticyclones are formed when an air mass is subject to divergence and moves away from an area which is then known as the centre of pressure. This results in the upper air within the area of the anticyclone descending towards the surface.

Anticyclones can be warm or cold. In a cold anticyclone air temperatures near the surface are relatively low resulting in a high air density. This will cause the surface winds to be anticyclonic, at altitude the pressure will be low and cyclonic. Wind direction will vary little in strength but may even reverse in direction between the surface and 20,000 feet.

A warm anticyclone will result in high pressure at altitude, wind direction and strength will vary little throughout the system.

There is generally no significant weather associated with an anticyclone. In the UK it is usually signified by a moist stable air mass with low level mist or fog, often with clear skies above.

166

APRON

A defined area on a aerodrome intended to accommodate aircraft for the purposes of loading or unloading passengers or cargo, refuelling, parking or maintenance.

AREA NAVIGATION SYSTEM - RNAV

Also known as a **Radio Navigation System** or **Course Line Computer**. The **RNAV** is an aircraft based computer able to receive VOR, ILS, and DME signals. It is coupled to a Course deviation indicator or Horizontal Situation Indicator. The RNAV differs from conventional radio navigation in that the pilot is able to track to or from a chosen ground location where no station exists. The pilot programmed point is known as a **Waypoint** or **Phantom Station**.

The computer is programmed by setting the frequency of a VOR (or **VORTAC**) station within range, selecting the radial on which the waypoint lies and finally the DME distance on that radial from station to waypoint. The CDI/HSI display then requires setting to the required track to be flown to or from the waypoint.

The RNAV determines the radial and distance to the VOR it is on. It then calculates the angle between that and the programmed radial and distance to the waypoint. With two sides and the angle known the triangle can be completed. It is then able to calculate the distance and bearing to the waypoint. This information is updated every few seconds.

Different models and makes of equipment offer various facilities which include being able to parallel a waypoint or VOR radial, hold and display one DME station whilst using another and a precision approach mode.

Errors and Limitations

The RNAV system works in VOR mode on a VHF frequency and is therefore subjected to the same line of sight limitations a VOR. Some VOR stations do not have a co-located DME system and under these circumstances the computer cannot calculate the position of a waypoint.

Most RNAV systems have an approach mode which makes the CDI more sensitive (usually 0.25nm per dot). To date there are no approved RNAV approach procedures in the UK although they exist in the United States.

According to current UK & Continental interpretations an RNAV is any navigational system capable of maintaining a track to a defined level of accuracy not dependent on over-flying point source aids.

There are two levels of accuracy under this definition:-

a) Basic RNAV - having an accuracy equal to or better than +/- 5nm for 95% of the flight time (with similar accuracy to a VOR or VOR/DME) where VORs are less than 100nm apart, or

b) Precision RNAV - having an accuracy equal to or better than 0.5nm standard deviation (currently achieved with equipment utilising continuous automatic dual DME position fixing and updating.)

ARTIFICIAL HORIZON

The artificial horizon or **Attitude Indicator** is the primary instrument for IMC flight. It is able to mimic a visual representation of the view that would be seen by the pilot if his vision was not obscured by cloud. The displayed information shows the pitch and roll of the aircraft.

The artificial horizon display uses a **Tied** or **Earth Tied** gyro mounted vertically with reference to the Earth. Unlike a turn indicator the aircraft wings represented on the display remain static, it is the horizon that moves in the instrument. In flight the horizon display, linked to the gyro, remains rigid in space, the aircraft moves around it. The instrument is constructed so that the gyro rotates anti-clockwise with a vertically mounted spin axis and inner gimbal. These are mounted at 90° inside the outer gimbal. Any movement of the inner gimbal away from the outer gimbal causes the horizon bar to move up or down on the display. This reflects pitch movements of the aircraft's nose. The rotating movement of the display, reflecting the roll of the aircraft's wings is shown by the artificial horizon casing moving around the display.

The artificial horizon is usually air driven via a suction pump with an electrical turn and slip indicator used as a backup. Electrically driven AHs are available and fitted to some aircraft.

Because of the freedom of movement of the AH a sophisticated system is required to maintain accuracy. To achieve this the air driving the gyro is expelled via four vents in the side of the erection chamber. The chamber is effectively square and the vents are mounted port, starboard, fore and aft of the chamber. A pendulous vane is mounted above each vent so that in a straight and level flight each vane half covers each vent. They are pivoted off centre so that they will respond to movement of the casing by blocking or totally unblocking the vents.

Any toppling of the gyro is corrected by the vanes. If for instance the gyro attempts to topple backwards towards the rear of the aircraft the starboard vent will pivot backwards exposing more of the vent and releasing a jet of air. Its opposite partner pivots so that its vent is covered. The force from the air jet precesses at 90° forcing the gyro to re-erect. If the gyro attempts to pivot towards the nose the vanes will act in an opposite effect.

During this process the fore and aft vanes remain unaffected. These are used to prevent toppling about the latitudinal axis.

Errors affecting the Artificial Horizon

Acceleration Errors - This error is only noticeable when an aircraft is starting its take off roll. The artificial Horizon will show a nose high, right wing low indication.

The pitch indication error is caused by the port and starboard vanes. As the aircraft accelerates the vanes tend to lag behind pivoting over the vents. As a result the port vent becomes covered and the starboard vent fully exposed. The precession of the air jet force results in the nose high indication.

The roll error has a much simpler cause. The acceleration causes the mass of the erection chamber to tilt back towards the tail of the aircraft, temporarily displacing the centre of gravity. The longitudinal force is precessed into a lateral movement which shows an apparent roll to the right. The combination of level acceleration and the port and starboard vanes quickly correct the error.

Design Errors and Limitations - No roll limits, +/- 85° in pitch, if this is exceeded the giro is liable to topple. If this occurs allow up to 10 minutes for re-erection. Old instruments may be limited to +/- 60° in pitch and +/- 110° in roll.

AUTOMATIC DIRECTION FINDING - ADF

Refer to the reference section on Non Directional Beacons for information on the transmitter used in ADF systems.

Automatic direction finding facilities use a ground sited Non Directional Beacon transmitting in the LF and MF frequency range. To receive these transmissions the aircraft is equipped with an ADF receiver. The receiver operates a loop aerial and via a bearing display indicates the aircraft's bearing to the beacon.

The ADF Receiver

The receiver is used to identify the bearing of the signal received from an NDB. The

NDB transmits a vertically polarised signal. A loop aerial in the aircraft rotates about a vertical axis. When the plane of the loop is parallel to the polarised signal a current is induced in to the loop. This is because one vertical element of the signal is closer to the transmitter than the other. The difference between these signals is known as the **Phase Difference**.

The current induced in the loop is used to activate a motor which rotates the loop aerial, as the aerial reaches a point where there is no phase difference the motor will stop. This is referred to as the Null Point. The switching to the motor is phase sensitive and will therefore always take the shortest route to the Null Point. There are now two Null Points, one 180° removed from the other. To eliminate the erroneous indication the system removes the opposite Null Point leaving only the correct sense indication. The motor is also connected to the ADF Bearing Indicator which displays the Null Point in the form of a direct indication of the ground location of the transmitter.

Frequency Selection and Identification Equipment - ADF
The frequency selection is simply displayed by an adjustable digital display which can be changed by turning three knobs. The frequencies of beacons are shown in the COM section of the AIP and on aeronautical maps. The usable ranges are limited and discussed fully in the following section. Aside from the volume knob, used to adjust the Morse ident to the required level, the receiver has one other switch, usually labelled OFF- ADF - ANT (Antenna) - BFO (Beat Frequency Oscillator), variants are shown below.

ADF (or COMP - Compass) with this selection the bearing indicator will display the relative bearing to the beacon.

ANT (or REC - Receive) this selection makes the beacon bearing unusable because it removes the loop aerial from the circuit. A sensing aerial is used to receive the Morse ident. This selection is used for A2A Beacons.

BFO - this selects the Beat Frequency Oscillator. Again with this selection the bearing information is unusable as the loop aerial is removed from the circuit. This setting is used to identify NONA1A beacons.

Before any beacon is taken as being usable the following selections should be made.
Select ANT - confirm the Ident is as expected and that there is no A2A station ident interference.
Select BFO - check for a steady DF tone and that there is no A1A station interference, also that the noise level is normal.
Select ADF - check that the bearing indicator points in the expected direction.
Select ANT - check the needle turns away from the bearing.
Select ADF - confirm the needle returns to the original bearing.
Due considerations should then be given to the following errors affecting the range and accuracy of LF & MF Beacons:-

Coastal Refraction - Radio waves travel faster over water than land and a signal crossing a coastline at any angle other than 90° will be refracted (bent). The ADF indicator will tend to indicate to the point of refraction rather than the beacon itself. The effect may be minimised by using these beacons at 90° or a close as possible and by the aircraft being as high as practicable.

Mountain Effect - A range of mountains or hills may reflect a surface wave. The reflected wave will then be received by the aircraft from the direction of the reflection and from the original transmission. The loop aerial will take a mean value of the two and ADF needle will indicate to the mean point.

Night Effect - Due to the change of the ionosphere at night LF and MF signals may become returned to the aircraft as sky waves (see the reference section under Radio Waves). The combined sky wave and surface wave signals received at the ADF receiver are very likely to be out of phase and will give a fluctuating and unreliable needle indication.

Quadrantal Error - This is caused by the effect of radio waves upon a metallic airframe. Signals received from the aircraft's relative axis of 360°, 270°, 180° or 90° are not affected but those off of those angles, at worst by 45° are subject to refraction within by the airframe.

Thunderstorms - Thunderstorm (cumulonimbus) clouds produce large amounts of electrostatic charge. This mostly affects LF and MF frequencies. In the vicinity of a thunderstorm the ADF needle is more likely to point towards the centre of the storm than at the NDB and use of the beacon should be avoided until clear of the interference. The only useful indication the ADF needle will give under these circumstances is that it will indicate the direction of the most active storm cell.

Failure Warning Systems - very few ADF systems incorporate a system warning flag or indicator. The needle may continue to point in the direction of an NDB even if the transmitter or receiver has failed. This would cause serious safety implications after a beacon has been passed, particularly on instrument approach procedures. Serious consideration should be given to remaining above the sector safety altitude where no independent cross reference is available.

ADF & NDB Usable Ranges

An NDB must not be used outside its **Promulgated Range**. This range is

published in the COM Section of the UK Air Pilot. The published range is based on a daytime protection ratio of wanted and unwanted signals of not less than three to one. This limits bearing errors to +/- 5° or less. Errors above this limit will be found at distances outside of the published range or at night.

It is possible for an NDB to have a range of 300 miles over land or 1,000 miles over the sea, the use of such ranges is now rare as they are now primarily used for aerodrome approach aids.

AUTOMATIC TERMINAL INFORMATION SERVICE - ATIS

The type of ATIS varies, it is basically a recorded message updated by ATC to reduce the repetition of information to pilots. They may provide arrival, departure or a combined information service. They will contain:-

Arrival ATIS

a) Weather reports for the aerodrome

b) Runway in use, QNH, QFE and details of approach aids in use

c) Un-serviceability of navigation aids or runways

d) Any other relevant information

Departure ATIS

a) Aerodrome QNH

b) Magnetic surface wind direction and speed

c) Temperature and dewpoint

d) Departure runway

e) Details of un-serviceability of runways or navigation aids

f) Any other relevant information

AVGAS

Aviation Gasoline is supplied in various grades to cater for different specifications of piston engines. The grades are colour coded to avoid the incorrect type being loaded. AVGAS is coloured blue and the aircraft refuelling points are painted red. Also the fittings do not allow for an **AVTUR (Aviation Turbine Fuel)** refuelling nozzle to be used.

Normal fuel for a light aircraft is **100LL (Low Lead)**. The 100 refers to the level of compression that the fuel will take, in comparison to other grades, before it will self detonate. Higher octane/numbered fuels have lead added to improve their anti-detonation properties.

It is essential to use the correct grade of fuel. Using a higher grade will not improve performance for long. Spark plugs, exhaust valves and seatings will become fouled or eroded. Using a lower grade, or date expired correct grade will result in pre-detonation, especially at high power settings. This may result in severe engine damage. Some aircraft may be cleared for the use of **MOGAS**. This fuel is not, contrary to popular misconception, 4 star motor fuel. It is a special fuel produced to a particular specification and quality. It cannot be bought from motor filling stations.

AVGAS refuelling installations may be identified by a grade label, 15cm x 10cm on the tank. It has white writing - AVGAS 100LL - on a red background with a 2.5cm vertical blue stripe up the side. The pipelines carry a similarly worded sticker, 50cm long with a 10cm vertical blue stripe and a 10cm vertical pipeline coloured stripe.

All aircraft owners are recommended to overpaint or remove the word TURBO from piston engined aircraft to avoid being supplied with AVTUR Fuel.

BALANCE TABS

There are two types of balance tabs, fixed and pivoted. The **Fixed Balance Tab** is a small metal tab of a type that may be easily bent by hand but will retain its rigidity in flight. It is used to correct a flying fault, such as one wing low, or a slight left yawing turn, and is fitted to the trailing edge of the appropriate control surface.

The **Balance Tab** is incorporated into the elevator and designed to reduce the control pressure required from the pilot. This is achieved by a pivot that operates the balance tab in the opposite direction to the elevator. It produces a small aerodynamic force which tends to hold the elevator in place.

BANNER CLOUDS

These clouds form from mountain peaks where the air finds it easier to go around the peak than to go over the top. Some of the air is lifted upwards in back eddies and may form 'windsock' like clouds dispersing gradually as it flows downwind. They are also referred to a **Cloud Banners**.

BEARING

This is the angle measured in a clockwise direction between a theoretical line through the longitudinal axis of the aircraft and a line drawn from an object to the centre of the aircraft. A bearing may be magnetic, true or relative.

BEAT FREQUENCY OSCILLATOR - BFO

This is an electronic device used in **Automatic Direction Finding** (ADF) equipment which when used converts un-modulated A^1 emissions to become audible. On some older equipment the BFO switch may be labelled CW/Voice. CW should be selected to ident A^1 beacons and BFO off/Voice position selected for A^2 NDBs. Refer to the sections on Automatic Direction Finding and Non-Directional Beacons in the reference section for more information.

BEAUFORT WIND SCALE

Part of the Beaufort Wind Scale is produced below. With apologies to Admiral Sir Francis Beaufort who devised the scale in 1805 we have omitted the sea specifications and devised an airfield and aircraft specification based around the actions of a 7 foot (small airfields) and 14 foot (major and international airfields) windsock. The average windspeed has been used for each Beaufort scale in relation to the windsock angle.

Force	Description	Land Specification	Windsock & Aircraft	Knots	MPH
0	Calm	Smoke rises vertically.	Windsock limp.	-	-
1	Light air	Direction of wind shown by smoke drift, but not by wind vanes.	Windsock 12°(7'), 9°(14').	1-3	1-3
2	Light Breeze	Wind felt on face;leaves rustle, wind vane moved by wind.	Windsock 30°(7'), 22.5°(14')	4-6	4-7
3	Gentle Breeze	Leaves and small twigs in in constant motion; wind extends light flag.	Crosswind limit of small light singles. Windsock 51°(7'),38°(14').	7-10	8-12
4	Moderate	Raises dust and loose paper, small branches are moved.	Crosswind limit of some light singles. Windsock 78°(7'), 58°(14').	11-15	13-18
5	Fresh	Small tress in leaf begin to sway; crest wavelets form on inland waters.	Crosswind limit of light twins. Windsock 90°(7'), 83°(14').	16-21	19-24
6	Strong	Large branches in motion; whistling heard in overhead wires; umbrellas usable with difficulty	Light a/c difficult to taxi. All windsocks at 90°.	22-27	25-31
7	Near Gale	Whole trees in motion; inconvenience felt when walking against wind.	Wing walkers needed to move light aircraft. Tie downs strongly recommended.	28-33	32-38
8	Gale	Breaks twigs ; off trees generally impedes progress.	Hangarage recommended Tie downs essential.	34-40	39-46
9	Severe Gale	Slight structural damage occurs (chimney pots and slates are removed)	Tie downs on light aircraft can be dragged.	41-47	47-54
10	Storm	Seldom experienced inland; trees uprooted; considerable structural damage occurs.	Light aircraft overturned or damaged by debris.	48-55	55-63
11	Violent Storm	Widespread Damage	-	56-63	64-73
12	Hurricane	Widespread Damage	-	64+	74+

BERGERON PROCESS

Also referred to as the **Ice Particle Theory** which dictates that before precipitation can commence there must be ice particles present in the upper part of the cloud. As the cloud develops above freezing level some of the water droplets will remain in a supercooled state and the others will freeze. The proportion of the frozen droplets increases with height and the reduction in temperature. The size of the droplets increase by sublimation or by collision with the supercooled droplets until they are unable to be supported by the updrafts and start to fall. They increase in size by collision with other droplets during the descent. They will reach the ground either as a solid or a liquid dependent on the temperature.

The theory fails to offer an explanation as to how precipitation is formed in clouds where the temperature is above freezing. Refer to the reference section describing the **Coalescence Theory** for an alternative.

BERNOULLI'S PRINCIPLE

At any point in a tube through which a fluid is flowing, static pressure and dynamic pressure equal a constant. (Under this principle air is referred to as a fluid). It simply explains that if there is an increase in velocity there must be a decrease in static pressure.

The airflow over an aerofoil will produce low pressure above resulting in lift. Lift also produces a by product of drag.

BIRD SANCTUARIES

Classed as a prohibited or restricted area. These areas are marked on navigational maps, normally with a reference to the upper height limits and the months of activity. Pilots are requested to avoid such areas, especially during the breeding season, and are warned of the high risk of bird strikes in these areas.

It is not possible to plot bird migration corridors as there are no heavily used, closely defined routes in the UK. Most migrating birds fly below 5,000 feet and the greatest density is in the South East of England.

BIRD STRIKES

The likelihood of bird strikes can be minimised by avoiding areas of bird concentrations such as bird sanctuaries. Off-shore islands, cliffs and estuaries attract flocks of birds at various times of the year for feeding and breeding. Large flocks may be found at up to 1,500 feet and 20nm of such locations. Low level flight over the sea near cliffs may result in flocks being frightened up into the path of an aircraft.

All bird strikes whether they cause any structural damage or not must be reported to the CAA. This applies to all aircraft including helicopters. A form CA 1282 should be used.

BLOCK TO BLOCK TIME

The period between the time an aircraft first commences to move under its own power with the intention of flight, to the time it comes to a stop after the flight.

BUYS BALLOT'S LAW

Buys Ballot's Law states that - if an observer in the Northern Hemisphere stands with his back to the wind then the low pressure will be on his left. This refers to the wind at 2,000 feet above the surface, being free from the drag of surface friction. It demonstrates that as, in the Northern Hemisphere, the wind blows parallel to the isobars, it must circulate anti-clockwise around a low and clockwise round a high.

Although the Earth is obviously rotating in the same direction, the opposite applies in the Southern Hemisphere. **Thermal Winds** also behave in accordance with this law with the modification that the area of low temperature will lie to the left.

CAP CLOUD

A cap cloud will form over the summit of a mountain on a dry day when the air fails to reach its dew point at a lower level. The cloud takes the shape of a giant cap perched just off the top of the summit and appears to be stationary, even with a fresh wind blowing. This is due to the cloud formation becoming less saturated and dispersing as the air sinks and warms on the leeward side. The original cloud formation is then replaced by fresh saturated air from the windward side.

CAVOK - Meteorological

This is an expression added to a Meteorological Aerodrome Report (METAR) as a TREND.

CAVOK means:- Visibility 10Km or more.

> No cloud below 5,000ft or below the highest minimum sector altitude, whichever is the greater, and no Cumulonimbus.
>
> No precipitation, sandstorm, duststorm, thunderstorm, shallow fog or low drifting snow, dust or sand.

Conditions could deteriorate within two hours from this to a visibility of 6km and/or a ceiling of 1,600ft without the TREND being considered incorrect. The criteria for significant changes for TREND type forecasts are given in Table K of the MET Section of the UK AIP.

CENTRE-LINE THRUST AIRCRAFT

These are twin engined aircraft which have their engines mounted along the fuselage centreline. In the event of one engine failing they are not subject to the same directional control problems caused by asymmetric thrust or drag as conventional twins.

One problem is taking the correct action after the recognition that one unit has failed. Although the engines are placed front and rear the controls are always laterally aligned which can cause problems or at least a delay when feathering is required.

Although a multi-engine rating is added to a licence on completion of training, pilots whose experience has not included the required hours on conventional twins will have the licence endorsed to restrict the rating to use on centre-line thrust aircraft only.

CERTIFICATE OF AIRWORTHINESS

A valid certificate of airworthiness, issued for a three year period, is required for any aircraft to make a legal flight. It is issued by a CAA licenced maintenance organisation. The exceptions for certification are kites, gliders (not being used for public transport or aerial work) or an aircraft with a Permit to Fly. Other criteria apply, refer to Article 7, Air Navigation Order (ANO) 1985. Article 8 specifies the categories.

CERTIFICATE OF MAINTENANCE REVIEW

This certificate only applies to aircraft engaged in public transport or aerial work.

Various provisions cover its validity and are detailed under Article 9 of the Air Navigation Order 1985.

CERTIFICATE OF REGISTRATION

Issued by the CAA, (for UK registered aircraft) it is a legal requirement for such a certificate to be issued before an aircraft may be flown. The CAA must be advised of any changes or part changes of ownership within 28 days, or if the aircraft is destroyed or permanently withdrawn from use. Other criteria apply and part ownership is clarified. Refer to Article 3, ANO 1985.

CHART SCALES

The scale or other unknowns of a chart can be calculated by the following. Ensure that the units used for CL and ED are the same (i.e.Inches). CL = Chart Length, ED = Earth Distance, F = Scale.

$$F = \frac{CL}{ED} \qquad\qquad CL = \frac{ED}{F} \qquad\qquad ED = CL \times F$$

CHART TYPES

1) **Equivalence Charts** - the representation of an area in correct proportion to that on the earth.
2) **Lambert Projection** - the basis of many aeronautical charts and is known as conformal. The lines approximately follow great circles and distances may be taken from the charts with great accuracy.
3) **Mercator Projection** - more commonly used for nautical charts and by the Armed Forces for long range navigation. For this conformal projection, rhumb lines are represented by straight lines and great circles are represented by curved lines.
4) **Orthomorphic Projection** - a European term for the conformal class of projections.

CIRCUIT BREAKER

An electrical device, the modern equivalent of a fuse, which 'pops out' if tripped or overloaded. It can be reset by pushing it back in. No circuit breaker should be reset more than twice as it is indicating a fault. A landing should be carried out at the earliest opportunity and the fault investigated.

CIRRUS CLOUDS

Cirrus is the name given to the highest level of cloud type, usually with a base of 20,000 feet upwards. The cloud at this height is composed entirely of ice crystals. The concentration of cirrus may vary. A distant wispy fibrous cloud, often indicating the approach of a warm front, may give way to a patchy or rippled effect as in Cirro-cumulus. If the sky becomes thinly overcast or veiled by Cirrus it is referred to as Cirro-stratus. A pattern of cirrus clouds is often referred to as **Mares' Tails**.
Cirrus clouds do not cause precipitation, exist in turbulent areas, or present an icing risk.

CLEAR AIR TURBULENCE - CAT

Turbulence encountered in clear air, when no meteorological phenomenon indicates its presence. It is usually encountered near the **Jet Stream** it is classified as follows:-
Light - Causing slight, rapid, rhythmic bumpiness without changes in altitude, attitude or indicated air speed.
Moderate - As light turbulence but more pronounced with changes in altitude, attitude and indicated air speed. IAS fluctuations of up to 25 knots. Aircraft controllable.

Severe - Extensive, abrupt changes in altitude and attitude resulting in the aircraft being out of control temporarily. Air speed indications fluctuating in excess of 25 knots.

CLOSURE OF AERODROMES

Pilots will not be refused permission to land or take off at CAA and public licence aerodromes solely because of bad weather conditions. Pilots should be aware of the minimum descent heights and of the requirements not to attempt an approach below certain published minimas.

The only circumstances when a public civil aerodrome may be closed to normal air traffic are:-

a) At times and conditions specified in NOTAMS and the Air Pilot.

b) When the landing area is unfit (e.g. soft surface, temporary obstruction, snow build, black ice).

c) If essential runway facilities are unserviceable (whether a facility is essential is at the discretion of ATC)

A pilot in an emergency will be allowed to land regardless of the above.

CLOUD

Cloud is a mass of air in which condensation has occurred. The condensation takes the form of very small water droplets (0.2mm or less in diameter), or ice crystals. If the base of the cloud is at the surface and visibility is reduced to less than 1,000 metres it is referred to as **Fog**, if visibility is 1,000 metres or more it is known as **Mist**.

For cloud to form the following is required:-

i) A supply of moist air, usually from maritime regions.

ii) Some form of cooling process, usually by being forced to lift.

The lifting process may be caused by:-

a) Turbulence, usually resulting in layer or stratiform cloud. This will give only slight showers or drizzle. Flight above the cloud will be smooth. In the cloud there will be light to moderate turbulence with poor visibility. Below the cloud visibility will be poor.

b) Orographic Lifting - the type of cloud formed will be dependent on whether the lifted air is stable or unstable. Stable air will form **Stratiform Clouds** with similar characteristics to turbulence clouds.

Unstable air will form **Cumuliform Clouds**, with their development being bound by the extent of the instability.

c) Convective Lifting - the formation of this type of cloud starts at daybreak where, after a clear night, re-radiation has been strong enough to form an inversion close to the ground. By early morning the inversion has disappeared and the warm surface air mixes with the higher levels. Approaching midday the rising air cools until it reaches saturation level forming the cloud. This will continue until the afternoon when the process will slowly reverse.

For a description of particular cloud types refer to the Glossary Section

CLOUD - Classifications

Clouds are classified according to their appearance and height above the ground. The classifications relate to temperate latitudes.

Low Cloud	Base below 7,000 feet	Nimbo, Strato or Cumulo
Medium Cloud	Base between 7,000 and 20,000 feet	Alto
High Cloud	Base above 20,000 feet	Cirro
Heap Cloud	Forming at any height	

176

CLOUD - Descriptions for TAF & METARS

For forecasts (TAFs) and actual reports (METARS) the following expressions are used. They are based on eighths (1/8ths) of cloud cover. These eighths are referred to as **Oktas.**

SKC   -   Sky Clear
NSC   -   No Significant Cloud
CAVOK   -   Refer to the section on CAVOK
SCT   -   Scattered, indicating 1 to 4 Oktas
BKN   -   Broken, indicating 5 to 7 Oktas
OVC   -   Overcast, indicating 8 Oktas

Heights that are given to accompany the cloud covering indicate the base and are in hundreds of feet above aerodrome level.

CLOUDY ICE

Cloudy ice can quickly coat any aircraft, it is formed on an aircraft flying through a cloud containing large super-cooled water droplets. On impact part of each droplet instantly freezes into **rime crystals**, the temperature of the remainder is raised by the latent heat release and runs back in the airflow to freeze more slowly as clear ice.

For further details refer to the section on Icing - Airframe.

COALESCENCE THEORY

This theorises that water droplets become big enough to fall to the surface by collision. As altitude increases so does the concentration of droplets, as they increase in size the speed at which they are uplifted decreases, increasing the probability of collision with smaller droplets. When the droplets reach a size that can no longer be supported by the updrafts they fall as precipitation.

As with all precipitation theories this one has a flaw in that it fails to explain how collision occurs in clouds with uniform updrafts. Refer to the section on the Bergeron Process for an alternative theory.

COL

An area surrounded by two diagonally opposed depressions and two diagonally opposed anticyclones.

CO-LOCATED NAVIGATION or APPROACH EQUIPMENT

For practical purposes various navigation equipment may be co-located. This may be:- NDB/VOR, VOR/DME, DME/TACAN, or DME/ILS.

For co-located VOR/DME equipment, the most common combination, the equipment is frequency paired to that only the VOR frequency need be selected. This will automatically select the correct DME channel.

It may happen that equipment is used in a similar geographical area but not located on the same site. It is then termed **associated**.

Associated means:-

a) They are co-located or are situated so close that no difference is apparent when used for navigational purposes. When used for en-route navigation they must be within 2,000 feet of each other. When used for approach they must be within 100 feet of each other.

b) They are frequency paired.

c) They transmit identical three letter Morse idents, the VOR transmits every 10 seconds with the DME transmitting every 30 seconds suppressing each third VOR tone. The idents are transmitted at different tones.

Not Associated but serving the same location means:-
a) They may be used for en-route navigation providing they are not more than 6nm apart.
b) They are frequency paired.
c) The first two letters of the Morse ident are the same, the last letter of the DME is changed to Z. The transmission periods are as associated stations shown above.

COMPASS - MAGNETIC

The magnetic compass is a finely engineered instrument, for its apparent simplicity a standard (popular name - E2B) compass may contain more than 80 parts. Physical problems with a compass are unusual. Its basic condition may be checked by:-
a) Visual inspection of the casing for excessive air indicating a faulty seal and resultant leakage.
b) Visual inspection of the fluid for cloudiness indicating internal corrosion.
c) A slow performance or movement of the display indicating contamination of the fluid and/or increased friction at the pivot point.

A lightning strike on an aircraft can cause the corrector and main magnets to drain. A **Compass Swing** is a mandatory requirement after a lightning strike.

Turning Errors - The compass display lags when turning through the near pole and leads when turning through the far pole.

Acceleration/Deceleration Errors - In the northern hemisphere, acceleration shows a turn to the North, deceleration shows a turn to the South.
The following Mnemonic may help

ANDS - Anticipate North Delay South
ANDS - Accelerate turns to North Decelerate turns to South

Summary of Compass Errors - Northern Hemisphere

Action	Direction of Magnet	Compass Error
Accelerate East	Clockwise	Apparent turn North
Decelerate East	Anti-clockwise	Apparent turn South
Accelerate West	Anti-clockwise	Apparent turn North
Decelerate West	Clockwise	Apparent turn South
Turn NW - N - NE	Clockwise	Under reads & Lags
Turn NE - N - NW	Anti-clockwise	Over reads & Lags
Turn SW - S - SE	Clockwise	Under reads & Leads
Turn SE - S - SW	Anti-clockwise	Over reads & Leads

See also Deviation - Compass in the reference section.

CONDENSATION

The term given to the process of change when water vapour changes to liquid. This is normally caused by air passing over an object cooler than itself. As it cools it is unable to support as much water vapour as warmer air and condensation results.

CONTOUR CHARTS

Contour charts are constructed to plot upper winds. A pressure contour line is a line joining points of equal atmospheric pressure. The **Contour Gradient** is the difference in height over the horizontal spacing between two contour lines.
Contour charts are produced for various pressures.
They are:-

Height	10,000	18,000	30,000	53,000
Millibars	700	500	200	100

CONVECTION - Heating

Heat from the Sun warms areas of the Earth's surface at different rates. If the difference covers a large area convective heating will result. For instance, in the case of a large city surrounded by an area of vegetation the concrete and tarmac will heat faster than the vegetation. The air over the city will therefore become warmer causing it to become less dense and consequently rise.

CONVERGENCE - Meteorological

When two opposing streams of air meet they will flow to the area of lowest pressure causing an upward flow. This is known as convergence.

CONVERGENCY - Geographical

Geographical convergency refers to the angular difference between two meridians measured at a given latitude. Convergency is maximum at the poles reducing to nil at the Equator.

CO-PILOT

A licenced pilot acting in any piloting capacity other than as P1 (Pilot in Command).

CORIOLIS EFFECT

In the Northern Hemisphere the **Coriolis Force** deflects all air movement to the right. The opposite applies in the Southern Hemisphere. This also causes the effect where water escaping down the plughole spirals clockwise in the Northern Hemisphere, anti-clockwise in the South, and down without spiralling on the equator.

The effect has less influence on air movements and there is no geostrophic wind within 15° of the Equator and all movement is with the pressure gradient. Refer to the reference section on Geostrophic Wind for further information.

CORIOLIS ILLUSION

An abrupt head movement during a prolonged turn may create the illusion of turning or accelerating in a completely different direction. The pilot's automatic response to this incorrect indication may seriously endanger the safety of the flight. It is thought to be a cause of **Spatial Disorientation**.

COURSE LINE

The boundary of points nearest to the runway centre line in any horizontal plane at which there is no difference in depth of modulation.

CRITICAL ALTITUDE

The maximum altitude at which, under ISA, it is possible to maintain, at a specified propeller RPM, a specific power or a specific manifold pressure. Unless otherwise defined, the Critical Altitude is:-
a) The maximum continuous power, in the case of engines for which this power rating is the same at sea level as at the rated altitude.
b) The maximum continuous rated manifold pressure, in the case of engines, the maximum continuous power of which is governed by a constant manifold pressure.

CRITICAL ENGINE

In respect of multi-engined aircraft, the critical engine is the one whose failure would most adversely affect the performance or handling qualities of the aircraft. The Second or Third Critical Engine are named on the basis that the critical engine has not failed.

Twin Engine Aircraft

When the propeller rotation direction is the same for a twin engined aircraft the slipstream and asymmetric effects will cause one engine to have a higher minimum control speed than the other. In engines which rotate clockwise, when viewed from behind, a failure in the left engine will result in a higher Vmc.

Where the aircraft is equipped with propellers which rotate in opposite directions the minimum control speeds will normally be the same. There will be no critical engine.

CUMULIFORM - Clouds

Cumuliform or **Cumulus** clouds have domed shaped upper surfaces and a greater vertical extent in contrast to horizontally extended stratiform types. When the lower atmosphere is well mixed and fairly dry the cloud base may be 4,000 to 6,000 above the surface with a very level starting point. With Strato-cumulus formations it may be as low as 1,500 feet.

Strong developments such as **Cumulonimbus Clouds** can be very violent in nature. Cumuliform clouds may form individually with clear sky between them or in a continuous line such as in a line squall along a cold front. Precipitation may be heavy but short lived. Airframe Icing and turbulence will depend upon the vertical development. **Cumulus Fractus** appear as irregular shreds, as if torn from the main body of a cumulus cloud.

CUMULONIMBUS - Clouds

Moderate cumulonimbus clouds are dark, dense and usually produce **Virga** and precipitation. **Cumulonimbus Mamma** is a cumulonimbus cloud which has hanging extensions, likened to pouches or udders, indicative of severe turbulence.

Well developed cumulonimbus clouds are more commonly known as **Thunderstorms**. The requirements for a thunderstorm are instability, high moisture and trigger action. The unstable layer must be at least 10,000 feet in depth and the trigger action may be any form of lifting. This may be convective, frontal, or a combination. It is the source of the lift that categorises the type of thunderstorm into either **Air Mass Thunderstorms** or **Frontal Thunderstorms**.

There are three stages of development.

(a) The Development Stage - This is where several small cumulus clouds will combine to form one larger cloud. The base may be in excess of 5 miles across. Updrafts are created sucking in air from the base and side of the cloud. This stage lasts approximately 30 minutes.

(b) The Mature Stage - A developed cumulonimbus cloud will be dark in appearance with massive towers that may well extend well into the Stratosphere. Beneath the base there may be heavy rain or hail (regardless of the localised temperature) together with violent up and downdrafts. It is possible for a **Tornado** or **Waterspout** to be formed. The most violent stage in an individual cloud is unlikely to last more than 30 minutes.

(c) Dissipating Stage - At this stage the downdrafts become most prevalent throughout the whole cloud and the updrafts abate. Any anvil formation will show at its most pronounced as the upper water droplets, by now usually ice crystals, drift downwind in the direction of the prevailing 10,000 feet (700mb) wind. This stage will usually last less than one hour unless it is 'topped up' with further active cumulonimbus clouds.

Cumulonimbus Cloud - Hazards to Aircraft

Severe up and downdrafts of comparable intensity often in close proximity to each other exist within thunderstorms and may reach speeds in excess of 3,000 feet per minute. The top of a developing cell has been observed to rise at more than 5,000 feet per minute. The vertical extent varies but may reach 40,000 feet in temperate latitudes and 60,000 feet in sub-tropical and tropical regions.

Do not attempt to climb to fly over a building or mature thunderstorm. Avoid flying over the top of small convective cells whenever possible, they may grow very quickly. Severe turbulence may be encountered several thousand feet above the tops of active thunderstorm clouds. Also do not fly under active cumulonimbus clouds. There may be turbulence, rain, hail, snow or lightning. Lightning can occur between two clouds or between a cloud and the ground. Most lightning strikes occur where the temperature is between +/-10° degrees centigrade.

There may also be a low cloud base, poor visibility and possible low level windshear. Winds caused by the outflow of cold air at the base of a storm cell have been recorded as changing by as much as 80 knots and 90 degrees within a few hundred feet.

If lightning does strike an aircraft the magnetic compass should not be relied upon. Whilst flying in thunderstorm areas altimeters and vertical speed indicators may display errors of up to +/- 1,000 feet. It is essential that ground clearance levels take this into account.

High Level Thunderstorms - these are often brought to the southern UK by south easterly winds from the French mainland. They have a short life but each storm tends to generate a new one as it dissipates. If the upper winds are light the storms appear to circle an area.

CUSTOMS - Clearance & Procedures

Following the relaxation of customs regulations between EC member states the following procedures were applied from the 1st January 1993. Licenced aerodromes holding a prior notice Customs concession are listed in the Air Pilot.

UK to another EC Country

The flight departure may be from any airfield or strip. No notification to Customs or Immigration is required.

UK to a Non-EC Country

The local Customs and Immigration must be notified in advance for departure from a concession aerodrome. If the departure airfield has a permanent customs presence prior notification is not required.

EC Country to the UK

The flight arrival may be to any airfield or strip. The Customs & Excise office nearest to the landing place must be notified in advance. Their telephone number is shown in the local telephone directory. Prior notice periods vary.

The information to be passed should include:-

a) Flight Plan details.

b) Names and nationalities of passengers (if non-EC nationals are carried the Immigration Service must be contacted to arrange clearance).

c) A declaration of any birds, animals, prohibited or restricted goods on board. Notification may be made on behalf of the aircraft commander but it is his/her responsibility to ensure that it is done.

Non-EC Country to the UK

Landing may be made at a Customs & Excise airport without notice or, UK & EC passports holders may use a Customs concession aerodrome providing no duty free allowances are exceeded. Prior notice periods for these aerodromes vary.

Arrangements for immigration clearance must be made before departure to the UK. This should be made through a Customs office who will liaise with Immigration. The following information will be required:-

a) Flight Plan details.

b) Full names, nationalities and dates of birth of passengers.

c) A declaration of any birds, animals, prohibited or restricted goods, duty free stores and goods in excess of the duty free allowances.

Channel Islands

They are not in the EC but are in the Common Travel Area. This means that departures may be made from the Islands into any Customs and Excise Airport or Customs concession aerodrome even if the flight includes non-EC passport holders.

CYCLONE

The word cyclone is normally used to denote a low pressure weather system or depression. Refer to the reference section on Depressions for more information. The word is also mis-used to denote a Tornado, or, in latitudes around the tropical oceans to describe a **Tropical Cyclone, Hurricane** or **Typhoon**. The official classification of tropical cyclones are:-

Winds up to 34 Knots	Tropical Depression
Winds of 35 to 64 Knots	Tropical Storm
Winds of 65 Knots or more	Hurricane or Typhoon

A cyclone which forms and moves along a front, deforming the line of the front with a wave like cloud formations is known as a **Wave Cyclone**.

CYCLOSTROPHIC FORCE

Wind is caused by the movement of air from high pressure to low. This is affected by the rotation of the Earth (**Coriolis Effect**) which results in the wind flowing parallel to the isobars. This movement is referred to as the **Geostrophic Wind**.

This wind only exists when isobars are straight and parallel. In reality isobars are curved and for the wind to follow the curves an additional force is required. This is referred to as the **Cyclostrophic Force (CF).**

The cyclostrophic force is a **centrifugal force** when acting from the centre of the curved isobars as in the case of a high pressure system and a **centripetal force** when acting towards the centre. The applies for the Northern Hemisphere and has the reverse effect in the Southern.

The following formulas can be used to calculate the various forces where PGF = Pressure Gradient Force and GF = Gradient Force.

Low Pressure System PGF + CF = GF	PGF = GF - CF
High Pressure System PGF - CF = GF	PGF = GF + CF

DANGER AREAS

These areas consist of weapon test and practice ranges and captive balloon flying areas. Some danger areas listed in the RAC Section of the Air Pilot have upper limits of 500ft agl/amsl or less. These are used for small arms and rifle practice. Care should be taken to avoid such sites if flying low level.

DANGER AREA ACTIVITY INFORMATION SERVICE (UK) - DAAIS

The purpose of the service is to provide civil pilots, via a Nominated Air Traffic Service Unit, an airborne update of the activity status of a participating danger area. This information is stated as being *'to assist the pilot in deciding whether it would be prudent, on flight safety grounds to penetrate the area'.*

It does not absolve the pilot from the responsibility of checking NOTAMS and securing as much information as possible of the proposed route. Requests for danger area status are made to the appropriate frequency at least five minutes before the ETA at the boundary. If no reply is received from the DAAIS the area should be assumed to be active. **A DAAIS does not constitute a clearance to cross a Danger Area.** Further details may be found in the UK AIP RAC 5-1-2.

DEAD RECKONING
The phrase used to describe navigation by determining the distance and direction between two points. A heading and time for the flight can be calculated taking into account the windspeed, wind direction and the ground speed.

DEAD STICK LANDING
An expression used to describe a landing where the engine or all engines are inoperative.

DECISION HEIGHT - DH
Decision height and **Minimum Descent Height** (MDH) are closely related.

The decision height is the height in a precision approach at which a pilot must decide whether it is safe to continue an approach by visual reference. The minimum descent height is the height in a non-precision approach below which the pilot should never descend unless it is safe to do so by visual reference.

Before making an instrument approach the DH or MDH must be calculated, dependent on whether it is a precision or non-precision approach.

Calculations are made from:-

a) The system minimum for the type of approach to be flown

b) The Obstacle Clearance Height for the Category of aircraft flown

c) An addition of 50 feet for altimeter errors (if no other known)

d) If no instrument rating is held add 200 feet with an absolute minima of 500 feet for a precision approach and 600 feet for a non-precision approach

e) An allowance for lack of recency and or experience

If Obstacle Clearance Height (OCH) is shown on the approach plate for the selected procedure. The MDH is shown on the aerodrome Minimas listing for each aerodrome which will also include a minimum Runway Visual Range (RVR).

If the RVR passed to the pilot is below that minima an approach must not be attempted. The system minimas are as follows:-

Approach Aid	Minimum Height
Instrument Landing System	200 feet
Precision Approach Radar	200 feet
Instrument Landing System without Glidepath	250 Feet
Precision Approach Radar without Glidepath	250 feet
Surveillance Radar Approach terminating at 0.5nm	250 feet
VHF Omni-directional Range (with or without DME)	300 feet
Non Directional Beacon or Localiser	300 feet
Surveillance Radar Approach terminating at 1nm	300 feet
VHF Direction Finding (QDM or QGH)	300 feet
Surveillance Radar Approach terminating at 2nm	350 feet

Precision Operation Categories (UK)

		Operational down to	RVR
Category 1	-	Not less than 200 feet	Not less than 800 metres
Category 2	-	Not less than 100 feet	Not less than 400 metres
Category 3a	-	Less than 100 feet	Not less than 200 metres
Category 3b	-	Runway Surface	Not less than 50 metres
Category 3c	-	Runway Surface	Zero Visibility

DE-ICE SYSTEMS

Some modern light aircraft and all large commercial aircraft have de-icing equipment. This is to enable them to fly into areas of known icing and to be able to remove ice accretion in flight.

Electric - heating wires or coils are used to warm certain parts of the airframe to prevent or reduce the possibility of ice forming. Heating elements are always used for the pitot tube.

Fluids - alcohol based fluids are pumped through strips attached to the leading edges. Nozzles provide de-ice spray to the propeller and windscreen. Two settings are normally available; anti-ice, which provides a continuous preventative discharge, and de-ice, which provides twice the rate to remove ice already formed.

Pneumatic - rubber boots are attached to the aircraft's leading edges.

The boots can be expanded by air being pumped into them which causes the ice to crack and break away. The disadvantages of this system are that:-

a) Ice must be allowed to build up before they can be used

b) If left inflated ice may build up over them rendering them useless

c) Large lumps breaking off the leading edges of the wings have been known to cause tailplane damage.

Pneumatic systems will normally have electric propeller heating and an electric heating element in a small section of the windscreen.

With all these systems the use of pitot heat, carburettor heat, alternate air and windscreen heat must all be considered.

DENSITY ALTITUDE

The altitude in the standard atmosphere corresponding to a particular value of air density.

DENSITY OF AIR

If an aircraft flies from an area of warm air into an area of cold air the density will increase causing the rectified airspeed to increase.

Pilot's should ensure that altimeters are reset when flying through different altimeter setting regions to ensure adequate terrain clearance and be aware that the instrument will over read if flying from high to low pressure areas.

$$\text{Density} = \frac{\text{Pressure}}{\text{Temperature x Gas Constant}}$$

The International Standard Atmosphere states that the air at mean sea level is 1225 grammes per cubic metre. This reduces with height dependent on the local temperature. For an exact calculation use the formula.

$$\text{Density Height Change per millibar} = 96 \times \frac{\text{Mean Temperature}}{\text{Pressure}} \, (^\circ \text{ Absolute})$$

Air expands when warm and will expand upwards as well as outwards. The height of a mass of warm air will be higher than that of the cold and the datum from which it begins to put pressure on that below it is higher. It is then the case that at any vertical point downwards from this datum will record a higher pressure than that of cold air.

DEPRESSIONS

An Area of **Low pressure**, also known as a **Low** or **Trough**. Most depressions affecting the UK develop from disrupted waves in the **Polar Front**. Others may form as follows:-

Lee Depressions - also known as **Orographic Depressions** occur on the leeward side of mountain ranges. Moving air finds it difficult to pass over mountains and even passing fronts may be held up temporarily. The result is that a low pressure area will form in the leeward valley and the geostrophic force will cause it to become cyclonic. These low pressure areas are usually temporary and localised but occasionally grow to develop fronts.

Polar Depressions - occur in winter when very cold polar air blows into latitudes where the sea is much warmer. They are not as strong as the thermal land lows but as the upper air tends to be so comparatively cold the bad weather produced tends to be severe and last for several days.

Secondary Depressions - usually form at the point of an occlusion and on the trailing edge of a weakening front. They are small areas of low pressure adjacent to a larger depression and within its circulation. They will usually form as the primary depression is filling or become inactive and effectively prolong the bad weather. They bring a low cloudbase and continuous precipitation. In summer thunderstorms are a common accompaniment together with gale force winds changing rapidly in strength and direction.

Thermal Depressions - these form as a land mass becomes heated, causing the air above it to rise, the reduction in pressure at the surface pulls in cooler air, usually from the sea. The pressure at high altitude of the warm area will be higher than that around it causing it to flow away to surrounding areas. Geostrophic Force will cause the resulting wind to become cyclonic and a thermal depression will be created at the surface. This may trigger clouds and rain when areas around it are clear.

In the Northern Hemisphere the wind always blows anti-clockwise around a low pressure system due to the geostrophic force.

DEVIATION - COMPASS

The magnetic compass fitted in an aircraft is always placed as far away from magnetic fields and metallic objects as possible. Despite this precaution electrical fields and the metal in the aircraft will still deflect the compass from pointing at Magnetic North. This deflection is referred to as Deviation. The compass indication is referred to as Compass North and differs from Magnetic North by the amount of deviation.

Deviation West is referred to as -, deviation East as +.

Deviation is kept as low as possible by regular compass swinging (an engineering procedure carried out during routine maintenance). A correction card is kept near the compass and advises the pilot of how to correct compass headings to accurate magnetic headings.

DEWPOINT

The dewpoint is the temperature to which air can cool, with no change of pressure, without condensation occurring. At this temperature the air is saturated and any cooling below this temperature will cause condensation. **Relative Humidity** and dewpoint can be evaluated by use of a **Wet and Dry Bulb Thermometer**.

DIRECT CURRENT

If the polarity of a source of electricity remains constant the current in the circuit will flow in one direction. This is referred to as a Direct Current Circuit.

DIRECTIONAL INDICATOR or Directional Gyro Indicator

This instrument provides the pilot with magnetic heading information. It is required because the magnetic compass suffers from acceleration and turning errors and is very difficult to read in turbulent conditions.

It can not be relied upon in isolation as if mis-set it will continue to give erroneous information until it is correctly set. The magnetic compass is used to set the DI and it should be checked and re-set if required every 10 - 15 minutes in flight.

Re-setting is achieved by pushing in a caging knob which locks the inner gimbal at right angles to the outer gimbal and engages a gear with another gear attached to the outer gimbal. This allows the gyro to be rotated and synchronised with the compass display.

The device also allows instant re-erection of the instrument if the gyro had toppled and prevents toppling and damage that would otherwise be caused by manoeuvres which exceed pitch and roll limits.

The reading from the magnetic compass should only be taken when the aircraft is in straight & level flight and giving a steady indication. Some more sophisticated aircraft will be equipped with a gyro slaving system. If the DI becomes out of synchronization with the magnetic compass an electrical system will automatically adjust the gyro to the correct heading.

The Directional Gyro Compass uses a tied gyro with freedom of movement in three planes and maintains rigidity with the yawing plane of the aircraft. The gyro axis is mounted on an inner gimbal and its spin axis is calibrated to compass North. This is mounted on an outer gimbal which rotates through 360° of the aircraft's normal axis.

A scale is connected to the outer gimbal. As the aircraft turns, it turns the DI instrument case around the scale, which remains in a fixed position due to its rigidity.

If aircraft manoeuvers cause the inner gimbal to rotate up to a pre-set limit (usually 55° to 85°) it will be forced against fixed stops. This will cause precession of the outer gimbal and the instrument will topple, the gyro spin axis having been forced out of the yawing plane.

Various systems are used to maintain gyro erection, the most commonly used are the twin air jet and the wedge plate.

The twin air jet system has a similar construction to a hollow tuning fork, the air jet forced from the ends of the fork impacts against small buckets cut in to the gyro wheel. When the gyro is erect the force from each jet is equal. If the rotor topples it causes the jet's impact upon the rotor to become unequal.

One jet continues to impact with the buckets whilst the other hits the rim of the gyro which produces a precessing force at the point of impact, reacting at 90° around the gyro re-erecting it.

The wedge plate system is very similar. The rotor is contained within a shell. Air is forced in and again impacts with buckets cut in to the rotor causing it to rotate. The air is forced to exit via a tube whose air jet is equally divided by a V shaped plate. If the gyro topples the two streams become unequal. The pressure affects the outer gimbal which in turn affects the inner gimbal. The force is precessed at 90° around the gyro and re- erects it.

Errors affecting the Directional Indicator.

The basic errors of wander, real, transport and apparent are covered in the section under gyroscopes. More detailed information affecting the DI is as follows:-

Apparent wander is related to latitude and the rate of wander can be calculated by using the following formula. *Apparent Drift = 15° x sine of the latitude (degrees/hour).* This must be applied to the direction of drift. The Earth rotates anti-clockwise. In the Northern Hemisphere the DI will therefore progressively under read, this is referred to as negative wander.

In the Southern Hemisphere the DI progressively over reads and therefore the wander is referred to as positive wander.

Apparent drift can be automatically corrected for, by the use of a latitude nut. The nut is mounted on one side of the inner gimbal opposite a counter balance weight. Adjustment of the nut up or down a threaded bold causes a calculable precession in the gyro. This causes the spin axis to move in the yawing plane at the same rate as the apparent drift but in the opposite direction.

The latitude nut requires re-adjustment if the aircraft is to be operated at a different latitude or significant and compounded errors could result.

DIRECTION FINDING - DF

Direction Finding is the term used when bearing information is advised to an aircraft by a ground station. It is used for cloudbreak procedures and homing. It should not be used, unless other navigation equipment has failed, for en route navigation.

A ground based receiver uses a 'H' shaped aerial which is rotated so that the received signal can be converted into a compass bearing indication which is then displayed to the ground operator.

DF uses normal ATC speech (RT) frequencies in the 118.00Mhz to 135.975Mhz range spaced at 25Khz. DF is also referred to a VDF, Very High Frequency Direction Finding. Military Units use UHF and VHF equipment.

Bearing Information will be given to the pilot in the form of Q codes and are as follows. All bearings if used as headings assume zero wind conditions and due allowance must be made for the wind if a track is to be made good to or from a station:-

QDM - is the magnetic bearing of the station from the aircraft.

QDR - the magnetic bearing of the aircraft from the station.

QTE - the true bearing of the aircraft from the station.

QUJ - the true bearing of the station from the aircraft.

A QDM procedure is most likely to be encountered. The following should be used in respect of headings to make good.

| To the station | QDM more steer more | QDM less steer less |
| From the station | QDM more steer less | QDM less steer more |

DF bearings are classified according to the accuracy and the classification will be passed to the pilot with the first bearing. If it is not passed the pilot must assume Class B.

> Class A - Accurate to within +/-2°
> Class B - Accurate to within +/-5°
> Class C - Accurate to within +/-10°
> Class D - Accuracy less than Class C

VHF line of sight range will normally apply to DF. The theoretical range of a VHF transmission is calculated by the formula; Range = 1.25 x (H1 + H2) where H1 = Square root of the height of the VOR Station, H2 = Square root of the height of the receiver (aircraft).

DISTANCE MEASURING EQUIPMENT - DME

DME is a secondary radar system that provides a pilot with accurate range information to a fixed ground station.

The system is initiated by the aircraft based transmitter. It transmits an omni-directional pulse train consisting of a continuous series of pulse pairs. The time between the two pulses of a pair is 12 microseconds but the time between each pair is varied at random. The random timing ensures that any one pulse train is unique to its interrogator.

DME range is restricted to the normal line of sight range. Provided the aircraft is in line of sight of the station to which it is tuned and there are no more than 100 aircraft working the station it will reply. The pulse train is amplified and transmitted back to the aircraft omni-directionally on a frequency 63Mhz lower or higher than that used by the aircraft. The aircraft receiver searches through all the pulse trains being received, including those from other aircraft, and recognises its own unique pulse repetition frequency.

It also calculates that the received pulses are arriving back at a constant time interval after they were sent.

The equipment uses this time interval to calculate the distance to the ground station by a simple formula using the speed of propagation.

Whilst initially attempting to contact a DME ground station the aircraft transmitter will send out pulses at 150 per second. When a 'lock' is made the pulse rate is reduced to 24 per second.

Frequency Range

The DME system uses frequencies in the UHF band between 960 and 1213Mhz at 1Mhz spacing. Each channel consists of two carrier wave frequencies 63Mhz apart. The frequency received at the ground station must be changed and re-transmitted otherwise the aircraft receiver would receive transmissions from itself and from a ground return from the surface.

DME channels are allocated a X or Y. X means that the interrogation carrier wave is 63Mhz higher than the response carrier wave (for channels 1 - 63) and Y means that the response is 63Mhz lower (for channels 64 - 126). A full listing of the DME channel pairings can be found in Pooley's and British Airways Aerad Supplement.

Operational Accuracy and Errors

The DME is limited to line of sight or theoretically to the formula; Range = $1.25 \times (H1 + H2)$ where H1 = square route of the height of the aircraft and H2 is the height of the transmitter.

When locked on the information is accurate to +/- 1nm. The information displayed will be a slant range to the aircraft's position in space and not the distance from the ground station to the ground point the aircraft is passing over. Given total system accuracy an aircraft flying overhead a DME station at 6,000 feet would display a 1nm distance to run.

Identification

As with all radio navigation equipment it is essential that the station is identified before it is used. This involves checking the actual ident transmitted and comparing it with the desired station; not just checking that a Morse ident is heard. The DME ident is usually a three letter Morse group and is transmitted every 30 seconds.

Additional Receiver Facilities

Providing an aircraft is tracking directly to a DME station the receiver is also able to provide a ground speed and time to station indication.

DME Checks & Inspections

DME installations are routinely inspected by the CAA Flight Calibration Service once every five years. In the event of any unusual DME indications it is a pilot's responsibility to advise their current ATC unit of the problem.

Co-located DME Equipment

For practical reasons DME equipment is often combined with other navigation equipment, this may be with an ILS, VOR or TACAN. Refer to these reference sections for more information on the individual equipment or to **Co-Located Navigation Equipment** for frequency pairings and qualifications for the title of co-located.

DISTRESS PHASE - Emergency

A situation where there is reasonable certainty that an aircraft or its occupants are in imminent danger or require immediate assistance.

It will usually follow a Uncertainty or Alert Phase but in the case of d) may be the only phase.

a) Further attempts to establish contact have failed.

b) Fuel is considered to be exhausted.

c) Information indicated that the aircraft may be forced to land.

d) Information is received that the aircraft has made a forced landing.

DIURNAL

A daily cycle, occurring and repeating every 24 hours.

DOPPLER EFFECT

An effect used in radar to determine the velocity of moving targets. It utilises the way in which a frequency appears to increase as the wave source approaches a fixed point and decreases as it departs. This frequency difference is known as the **Doppler Shift**. **Doppler Radar**, designed to exploit the effect, is a primary system which measures two or more attributes of a target enabling it to calculate the unknowns.

DRAG - Definitions

Drag is the aeronautical term used to describe the resistance of the air as an aircraft moved through it.

Induced Drag - as a result of lift, it results in vortices at the trailing edge and wingtips.

Parasite Drag - is a result of the airflow passing over parts of the aircraft, the greater the eddies and turbulence created, the greater the parasite drag.

Form Drag - when the airflow becomes so turbulent it lifts away from the aircraft surface causing further air disturbances which causes further drag.

DROOP LEADING EDGES

Based on the same idea as wing slats which automatically extend at low airspeeds increasing the wing and lift area, droop leading edges are hinged and rotate down at low airspeed.

DUST DEVILS

Dust devils are intense spiralling vortices of air which form over very hot surfaces and usually under clear skies.

They may rise to several hundred feet and be visible due to the sand and dust sucked up by the low pressure area in the centre of the system. The base is generally black with debris and is often referred to as a **Black Blizzard** or **Whirlwind**.

DYNAMIC PRESSURE

Dynamic pressure is static pressure plus pressure due to relative movement. The faster an aircraft (or object) moves through air the more molecules of air will impact with it, increasing the pressure. Alternatively an object may be static and air is blown into it will produce a similar pressure.

It can be shown that dynamic pressure when expressed as *1/2 Rho V-squared* reduces with height.

Where Rho is air density, V is the speed of the body relative to the air (or speed of the air relative to the body).

EARTH

Refer to the section on Troposphere for details of the atmosphere around the Earth. For keen students the Earth is an oblate spheroid with an equatorial diameter of 6,884nm and circumference of 21,626nm. The polar diameter is 6,860nm and circumference 21,550nm.

ELEVATOR

The elevator is a horizontal control surface hinged to the rear of the tailplane. It provides for longitudinal control in pitch. It is operated by forward or backward movement of the control column of stick.

On aircraft where the whole of the tailplane pivots the surface is referred to as a **Stabilator**.

EMERGENCY CEILING

The highest altitude at which a multi-engined aircraft can maintain a rate of climb of 50 feet per minute with one engine inoperative.

EMERGENCY LOCATOR TRANSMITTER

This is a radio transmitter fitted within an aircraft but powered by its own batteries. It may transmit on 121.5Mhz, 243Mhz or both. It is designed to be activated at an 'injurous' impact force automatically and will transmit an audio tone two or four times a second.

EMERGENCY PHASE

Used in connection with a distress or Mayday call, it may be used to describe, in roll of gravity; Uncertainty Phase, Alert Phase or Distress Phase.

EMERGENCY TRIANGLE

Military Flight Information Publications publish a procedure designed to attract help where, in Visual Meteorological Conditions, radio and navigational failure is compounded by being lost. This procedure should not be seen as replacing transponder codes 7600/7700 and should only be flown in real conditions as any attempt to practice the manoeuvre may result in the unnecessary scrambling or diversion of aircraft.

The procedure should be flown as follows, taking into account the estimated winds. The aim is to provide a radar controller with a fixed pattern on his screen that is clearly an emergency triangle.

a) Switch Transponder to Emergency Code.

b) Continue to attempt to make radio contact and listen out on the appropriate emergency frequency.

c) If the receiver only is operating, fly a triangular pattern to the right, holding each heading for two minutes for aircraft flying below 300 Kts TAS and one minute for aircraft flying above 300 Knots TAS.

  The aircraft should fly at best endurance speed and all the 120° turns should be made as tight as possible. At least two such patterns should be flown before resuming the original heading, the pattern should then be repeated at intervals.

d) If both receiver and transmitter are inoperative a similar pattern should be flown as above but to the left.

The ground radar observing will attempt to contact the aircraft offering heading instructions. If the aircraft fails to comply it will notify the appropriate agency so that a shepherd aircraft may be scrambled or diverted. It will also contact the appropriate ATC Authorities so that other aircraft in the area can be diverted to avoid collision.

The intercepting aircraft will escort the distressed aircraft until visual contact is established with an aerodrome.

Another method of alerting radar controllers to an emergency and radio failure situation is by dropping **Chaff.** These are packets containing strips of aluminium foil which are dropped into the slipstream of the aircraft in distress. They paint a distinct following trail from an aircraft on the controllers screen.

ENVIRONMENTAL LAPSE RATE - ELR

This is the actual rate at which the ambient air temperature changes with height. The International Standard Atmosphere environmental lapse rate is stated at 1.98°C reduction per 1,000 feet but this is rarely the case in actual circumstances. The ELR can vary greatly from the ISA to the extent that the temperature may not change with height and is known as being **isothermal,** if it actually increases with height a **temperature inversion** is said to exist.

ESTIMATED ELAPSED TIME

The estimated time required to proceed from one significant point or Flight Information Region to another. This information is required on the flight plan form CA48.

ESTIMATED OFF BLOCK TIME

The estimated time at which an aircraft will commence movement associated with departure.

ESTIMATED TIME OF ARRIVAL

A term applied to Instrument Flight Rules flights. It is the estimated time that an aircraft will arrive at a pre-designated point from where an instrument approach will be commenced or is expected to commence. Where no instrument approach exists for the aerodrome it is the time at which the aircraft expects to be overhead the aerodrome. In respect of Visual Flight Rules flights it is the time the aircraft expects to arrive overhead the aerodrome.

EVAPORATION

The term given to the process where liquid water changes into a gaseous state and is absorbed into the air as water vapour. The process requires the **latent heat of vapourisation** or **evaporation.** It is also possible for ice crystals to be vapourised without going through the water vapour stage. This is known as **sublimation**.

EXHAUST GAS TEMPERATURE GAUGE - EGT

An instrument which, via a probe fitted to the exhaust system of an engine, indicates the temperature of the escaping gasses.

The mixture control may be adjusted to set the optimum efficiency setting of the air/fuel ratio as indicated by the gauge.

EXPECTED APPROACH CLEARANCE TIME

The time at which it is expected that an aircraft will be cleared to commence an approach to land.

EXPECTED APPROACH TIME - EAT

The time at which air traffic control expects that a holding aircraft, following a delay, will leave the hold to commence its approach to land.

EXTENDED CENTRELINE

An imaginary line extending out from the actual centreline of a runway. The phrase is used for position reporting and area avoidance.

EXTENDED OVER WATER OPERATIONS

With respect to aircraft other than helicopters :-
An operation over water at a horizontal distance of more than 50 nautical miles from the nearest shoreline.
In respect of helicopters:-
An operation over water at a horizontal distance or more than 50 nautical miles from the nearest shoreline and more than 50 nautical miles from an offshore heliport structure.

EXTREMELY HIGH FREQUENCIES

Radio frequencies in the range 30,000 to 300,000 Mhz with a wavelength of 1mm to 1cm. They are used for experimental and **Airfield Surface Radar.**

FACILITATION - FAL

The word used to describe the provision of facilities relating to the departure and arrival of passengers and aircraft at airports.

FALSE HORIZON

A potentially dangerous meteorological situation where an obscured horizon, a dark surface and stars are further complicated with geometric ground light patterns. This can provide confusing visual information and if it disorientates (spatial disorientation) the pilot it is unlikely the correct horizon will be regained.

FIN

The fixed vertical surface which affects the directional stability of an aircraft.

FINAL APPROACH FIX - FAF

The last navigational fix, designated on the published approach plate, which an aircraft will make in a standard instrument approach procedure, before the final instrument approach is commenced.

FINAL APPROACH POINT - FAP

The point designated on the published approach plate where final approach descent may be commenced providing the aircraft is within pre-defined limits. The FAP is applicable to non-precision approaches where a FAF has not been established.

FLAPS

The primary purpose of flaps is to give the required lift at a reduced airspeed. This is achieved by changing the aerofoil shape and/or increasing the wing area, this also has the side effect of increasing the drag. They are fitted to the trailing edge of the wings and operated from the cockpit by a manual or electrical connection.

Fowler Flap - this type moves backwards and down increasing the wing area and aerofoil shape.

Simple Flap - lowers a section of the wing down increasing the aerofoil shape for the inner section of the wing.

Slotted Flap - as the flap moves down it exposes a slot through which air from beneath the wing will flow out and over the flap.

Split Flap - a design which lowers a flap from the lower trailing edge of the wing without any change to the upper surface area.

Other devices used to lower the stall speed are **Leading Edge Slats** which can be manually or automatically extended to expose a slot which forces high energy air from below the wing up through the slot and across the upper surface. This reduces the tendency for the airflow to break away and allows the wing to be effective at slower speeds.

If flap is used, especially full flap, due consideration must be given to the crosswind. The owner's manual or operators handbook will give the recommended limits.

Retractable Undercarriage Aircraft - If flaps are raised immediately after touchdown to improve braking, tyre adhesion, or elevator effectiveness, great care must be taken to avoid selecting the gear up lever. The electric flap and gear levers are on some aircraft, almost identical.

FLIGHT INFORMATION SERVICES - FIS

See also the reference section relating to Radar Services - Air Traffic Control.

An **Air Traffic Control Centre** will provide a **Flight Information Region** (FIR) Service for aircraft in its area and outside of controlled airspace. The controller does not issue clearances, give collision avoidance advise or exercise positive control over the aircraft. He will pass on information including the positions of other known traffic likely to affect the flight. As the service covers un-controlled airspace there may be traffic operating that is not in contact with the FIS.

To contact a FIR a standard contact message should be made suffixed with, *"Request Flight Information Service"*.

The FIS will provide information on:-

a) Airfield facilities

b) Airfield serviceability

c) Accept Airborne flight plans

d) Meteorological warnings, METARs and TAFs for the route, destination and alternate

e) Obtain airways joining or crossing clearances

f) Pass on ETAs

g) Pass on safety information, primarily details of known traffic

h) Advise on the serviceability of navigation or approach aids

As a flight leaves the ATC area the controller will suggest that you freecall the next FIR or a specific ATCU. The pilot will always be passed the contact frequency which should be read back.

Under no circumstances should a flight change frequencies without informing the current controller. This can cause a great deal of work as a controller attempts to trace a missing aircraft and could result in search and rescue being scrambled.

FLIGHT LEVELS

For all flights in Instrument Meteorological Conditions outside controlled airspace, it is compulsory to comply with the quadrantal rule. It is also a strong recommendation that VFR flights above 3,000 feet amsl comply with it.

The rules applies for all flights below 24,500 amsl after which the **Semi-Circular Rules** apply.

The rule states that for a given **magnetic track** an aircraft should be:-

Magnetic Track	Rule	Available Flight Levels
000° - 089°	Odd Levels	30, 50, 70, 90, 110 etc
090° - 179°	Odd + 500	35, 55, 75, 95, 115 etc
180° - 269°	Even Levels	40, 60, 80, 100, 120 etc
270° - 359°	Even + 500	45, 65, 85, 105, 125 etc

For flights in airways at any height and for all flights above 24,500 feet amsl outside controlled airspace in IFR the semi-circular rule must be followed.

Below 24,500 feet amsl in airways (unless authorised by ATC).

Magnetic Track 000° to 179° - Odd Flight Levels, 30, 50, 70, 90 etc
180° to 359° - Even Flight Levels, 40, 60, 80, 100 etc

Outside Controlled Airspace

Magnetic Track 000° to 179° - Flight Levels 250, 270, 290, 330 and
every 4,000 feet thereafter.
180° to 359° - Flight Levels 260, 280, 310, 350 and
every 4,000 feet thereafter.

A similar rule applies in the USA, from 3,000 feet to FL 290 and is known as the **Hemispheric Rule**.

FLIGHT PLAN

A flight plan is filed by completing a **Form CA48** (in triplicate, the pilot retaining the bottom copy) and handing it into ATC at the departure aerodrome at least 30 minutes before clearance or start up is to be requested. If the departure aerodrome is not connected to the AFTN the flight plan must be telephoned through to a suitable aerodrome ATC Unit.

A flight plan may also be filed whilst airborne, usually this will occur only when entering controlled airspace that was not originally planned for. The airborne plan must be filed at least 10 minutes before entry is required and is instigated by calling the ATCU that the aircraft is working and stating; *Callsign - I wish to file an airborne flight plan.* Followed by details of the intended flight.

A flight plan **may** be filed for any flight, IFR, VFR, IMC, VMC, in controlled airspace or out!

A flight plan is **advisedly** filed:-

a) For a flight that is likely to go beyond 10nm of the UK coast.
b) When a flight is to be carried out over sparsely populated or mountainous area and radio equipment will not be carried or the flight will be out of radio contact for any period.

A flight plan **must** be filed:-

a) When the flight will be in controlled airspace in IMC or at night.
b) When a pilot elects to conduct a flight in IFR in controlled airspace when he/she could have flown VFR.
c) When a flight is conducted in class A controlled airspace.
d) If a flight on an Advisory Route requires an advisory service.
e) When a flight on Special VFR requires the destination aerodrome to be informed of his movements.
f) For flights in certain Special rules Zones and Areas regardless of the weather conditions.

g) For any flight from a UK aerodrome to a destination not more than 40km away when the MTWA exceeds 5,700Kg.

h) For all flights within the Scottish and London Upper FIRs.

i) For any flight to or from the UK which crosses the UK FIR Boundary.

If the flight lands elsewhere than the flight planned destination the pilot must inform the ATCC and the original destination aerodrome within 30 minutes of the ETA to avoid a search and rescue operation being mounted.

A flight plan may be cancelled at any time whilst airborne by advising the ATCU currently being worked, *"Callsign - Cancel Flight Plan"*. ATC cannot approve or disapprove the request.

They will merely reply, *"Callsign - Flight Plan cancelled at ...(Time)"*. If it was an IFR flight plan they may advise if the flight is likely to encounter IMC later in the flight but this is not a requirement.

Booking In or Out with air traffic control is required for any flight, however where a flight plan has been filed there is no need to book out. On reaching the destination the flight must still book in.

FLY BY WIRE

A flight control system using electronic controls which operate electrical circuits, which in turn mechanically operate aircraft control surfaces. The technology associated with this type of aircraft normally uses three cross checking computers to monitor logical responses as well as triplicated wiring to all flight control and safety systems. There are no mechanical linkage systems to back up the electrical systems.

FOEHN WINDS

Any wind blowing across the surface of the Earth will attempt to find the easiest route. If the route is blocked by a range of mountains or hills it will attempt to find a valley or ravine that will offer an easier passage rather that go over the top. This causes a **Valley Wind**. If however there is no way round, such as with the French Alps (from where the Foehn Winds found their name), the air is forced to rise over it. The wind that blows on the leeward side of the mountains is known as a Foehn Wind.

The climb and descent has an effect on the moisture content of the air. As the air rises it cools adiabatically at the **Dry Adiabatic Lapse Rate.** If the mountains are sufficiently high and the air holds enough moisture it will eventually reach its **dewpoint temperature.** As the air rises further, condensation will form and further cooling results at the **Saturated Adiabatic Lapse Rate** with extensive cloud and rain covering the windward side.

On reaching the peak the air will start to descend. The air will now be much less moist and as it descends it will warm at the Saturated Adiabatic Lapse Rate. It will reach its condensation level at a much greater height than on the windward side. As it descends further it will warm at the Dry Adiabatic Lapse Rate. The resultant air now flowing down the leewards side will be warm and dry.

FREE FALL PARACHUTE SITES - FFPS

These areas are marked on navigational maps and listed as hazardous areas. They normally have an upper height limit of FL 120. Parachuting only takes place in visibility of at least 3nm, clear of cloud and in sight of the surface. Sites are listed in the RAC Section of the Air Pilot.

FREEZING RAIN

During conditions where a cold winter spell is about to be overtaken by an advancing warm front, rain, falling from the front, passes through the sub-zero air below and becomes supercooled. If it comes into contact with an aircraft it will freeze in the form of **Clear Ice**. Upon reaching the ground it will freeze instantly forming a coating of ice on most surfaces, including vegetation, taxiways and runways. At the surface it is referred to as **Glazed Frost**.

FREQUENCIES

Various units of frequency are used to describe multiples of Hertz.

$$1 \text{ Hz} = 1 \text{ Cycle per second}$$
$$1,000 \text{ Hz} = 1 \text{ Kilohertz} - 10^3 \text{ (Khz)}$$
$$1,000,000 \text{ Hz} = 1 \text{ Megahertz} - 10^6 \text{ (Mhz)}$$
$$1,000,000,000 \text{ Hz} = 1 \text{ Gigahertz} - 10^9 \text{ (Ghz)}$$

A radio wave travels at approximately the speed of light (300,000,000 metres per second or 300×10^6), this is also referred to as the speed of propagation and is a constant.

Frequencies and wavelengths can be calculated using the following formulas where W = wavelength, F = frequency and C = (by convention) speed of propagation.

$$W = \frac{C}{F} \qquad F = \frac{C}{W}$$

Individual frequency ranges are detailed in their alphabetical sections, a couple of the less common are:-

Infrasonic Waves - a frequency of less than 20Hz, below range of the human ear.

Microwaves   - any frequency over 1,000Mhz.

FRESH - Winds - Meteorological

According to the Beaufort Wind Scale winds are fresh when they reach force 5. If the wind reaches 16 - 21 knots (19 - 24 mph) it is said to be fresh.

FRONTAL FOG

Frontal fog is the name given to cloud which descends to the surface over high ground or which forms close to a weather front along the surface. The area covered by the fog may be as large as the rain belt and as much as 200 miles ahead of the fronts surface position. The fog will clear with the passage of the front.

FRONTAL LIFTING

The sloping face of a weather front will have the effect of forcing warm air upwards. Refer to the reference section on **Fronts** for more information.

FRONTAL THUNDERSTORMS

The advance of a front will cause warm air to be forced upwards causing the formation of thunderstorms. Refer to reference section under Cumulonimbus Clouds for further details of the formation and resultant hazards. Frontal thunderstorms are usually associated with the line squall of a cold front due to their formation in a line along the front. They can also occur with the passing of a warm front. The line squall may be up to 100 miles long and are most prevalent in winter.

FRONTS

Front is the term used to describe the line where one classification of air mass ends and another starts. The types are as follows:-

Cold Front - this is the surface boundary between cold air and the warm air ahead of it which it is undercutting. The warm air is forced to rise so rapidly that it produces a line of cumulonimbus clouds (line squall). This will produce heavy but short lived rain showers and possibly hail and thunder. *The frontal passage is unlikely to last more than an hour.* It is shown on a weather map as a black line with small triangles in the direction of its path.

A warm front's speed is between 1/3rd and 1/2 of that of a cold front, and so a cold front will often be shown as catching up with the warm front ahead. At the point that the fronts meet an **Occlusion** is said to exist. A cold front will give predictable changes in advance, in passing and after passing a fixed ground point or observer. The changes are tabulated below:-

Characteristic	In Advance	In Passing	After Passing
Barometric Pressure	Sudden Drop	Sudden Rise	Steady/Rising
Cloud Amount	Unaffected	Increase	Decrease
Cloud Base	Low	Very Low	Rapid Rise
Cloud Type	Stratus	Cumulonimbus	Cumulonimbus
	Fractostratus	Fractocumulus	Cumulus
	Stratocumulus	Nimbostatus	Altostratus
			Altocumulus
Surface Wind	Backs Increases	Sudden Veer	Steady/Veers
Visibility	Misty/Foggy	Poor in rain	Very Good
Weather	Rain	Rain Thunder	Hail /Showers

Intertropical Front - converging winds either side of the Equator meet to form an intertropical front. The temperature difference between the two zones is not great but is enough to develop some convection clouds.

Polar Front - this is where most frontal activity affecting the UK starts. It is the dividing line between the northern polar air and the warmer sub-tropical air. The front generally lies between Newfoundland and the North of Scotland in winter and between Florida and the South West of England during the summer.

Any movement of the polar front will cause a wave to develop. These waves sometimes run along the front without developing but can often grow into an independent pressure system with the sector of warm air being undercut by cold air. In temperate latitudes this results in a **Depression**.

Warm Front - this is the ground level boundary between warm air and cooler air ahead of it. The **Warm Sector** is being pushed along by a further mass of cold air behind it. As the warm air rises over the cold air, it will form a shallow uphill slope. It is up this slope that the cloud and weather forms.

Several hundred miles downwind the first wisps of ice crystal cloud will become visible to the observer. They are termed **Cirrus** clouds and will be several miles high. As the front approaches these will be replaced by **Cirrostratus** which will eventually block out any sunshine.

The cloud base will steadily lower with a band of **Altostratus** which will give rain or snow. This will be light or heavy dependent on the intensity of the front. This will last for several hours during which time the lowest cloud, **Nimbostratus** will pass giving hill fog.

Weather charts show a warm front as a black line with equally spaced black semi-circles in the direction of movement of the front. A warm front will give predictable changes in advance, in passing and after passing a fixed ground point or observer. The changes are tabulated below:-

Characteristic	In Advance	In Passing	After Passing
Barometric Pressure	Steady Fall	Steady	Steady
Cloud Amount	Increasing	Total - Max	Decreasing
Cloud Base	Lowering	Hill Fog	Low
Cloud Type	Cirrus		Stratus
	Cirrostratus	Nimbostratus	Altostratus
	Fractostratus	Fractostratus	Stratocumulus
Dew Point	Rising	High - Max	Steady - Max
Surface Wind	Backs - Rising	Veers - Falls	Steady
Visibility	Good	Poor, Mist/Fog	Poor
Weather	Rain/Snow	Rain/None	Drizzle/None

FUEL INJECTION SYSTEMS

The Fuel Injection System is an alternative to the carburettor as a method of fuel metering for combustion engines. The system is made up of three parts:-

a) Fuel Injector or Fuel Control Unit - this monitors the volume of air entering the system and meters the fuel flow.

b) Flow Divider, Fuel Distributor or Fuel Manifold Unit - keeps the fuel under pressure and injects it to the cylinders at the required rate. It also closes individual nozzle lines when the idle cut off is used to shut down the engine.

c) Fuel Discharge Nozzle - injects the fuel into each individual cylinder head, or into the inlet port prior to the inlet valve.

The advantage of fuel injection is that Induction (venturi) icing is almost eliminated as fuel vapourisation occurs near the cylinder, and that metering and the delivery of the fuel is much more finely controlled offering better performance and economy.

GALE - Winds - Meteorological

According to the Beaufort Wind Scale a gale is a force 8 wind. If the wind reaches 34 - 40 knots (39 - 46 mph) it is said to be gale force.

GEOSTROPHIC WIND

The geostrophic wind is the flow of air at around 2,000 feet above the surface. The normal tendency of air is to flow from high to low in accordance with the **Pressure Gradient Force.** This flow is affected by the rotation of the Earth which causes the wind to blow parallel to the **isobars.** This force is known as the **Coriolis Effect.** This effect when related to wind is known as the **Geostrophic Force.**

In the Northern Hemisphere the **Coriolis Force** deflects all air movement to the right. This also causes the effect where water escaping down the plughole to spirals clockwise in the Northern Hemisphere, anti-clockwise in the South, and down without spiralling on the equator. The effect has less influence on air movements and there is no geostrophic wind within 15° of the Equator all movement are with the pressure gradient.

The geostrophic wind only exists when isobars are straight and parallel which is very rare. The geostrophic wind in reality is further modified to become the **Gradient Wind.** Refer to this section for further information. It follows that for increase in latitude there must be an increase in geostrophic force.

This may be calculated with the formula.

$$GF = 2 \ w \ p \ v \ Sin0$$

198

The transposed formula can be used to calculate the speed of the wind.

$$V = \frac{GF}{2 \, w \, p \, Sin0}$$

w = Earth's rotational velocity, p = air density, V = windspeed, 0 = latitude.

GLIDER LAUNCHING SITES

Known sites are listed in the AGA Section of the Air Pilot and are shown on instrument approach and landing charts. Launching normally takes place within 4nm of an aerodrome reference point and the launch cables and gliders may be taken up to 1,500 feet before being released.

GLOBAL POSITIONING SYSTEM - GPS

or **Satellite Navigation System** is the most modern innovation in navigation equipment. It is based on a constellation of 24 satellites orbiting the Earth at around 11,000 miles. Each satellite orbits the Earth every 12 hours.

The system works by the aircraft based receiver tracking the nearest three or four satellites. By a process of measuring signal time it measures the distance to the satellites and by downloading their position in space is able to calculate its own position above the Earth. In a similar way to an RNAV unit, it is then possible to input a **Waypoint.** An inbuilt course deviation indicator LED display advises the pilot of a turn left/right indication to maintain the desired track after the waypoint.

Other facilities in the receiver include a time estimate to the waypoint, ground speed, distance to run, and altitude. GPS's accuracy is due to advanced electronics and time measurement., Each satellite has four cross referencing atomic clocks on board accurate to 0.000000001 of a second. The system synchronizes the satellites with the receiver with a **pseudo-random code** so ensuring that the time calculation of the transmission time to the receiver time is as exact as possible. The GPS signal transmission is basically a timing mark.

System Error and Inaccuracies

Ionospheric - the ionosphere, 80 to 120 miles above the Earth is a blanket of charged particles that affect the speed of light and so affect the speed of the GPS radio signals. Water vapour can also affect the signals. Some allowance can be made for these errors but a discrepancy of up to 20 feet may occur.

Receiver Error - it is possible for a receiver to round off a mathematical calculation or be affected by electrical interference. If the error is large it will be obvious. If it is small it may affect the measurement by a few feet.

Selective Availability - the satellite system is operated and funded by the United States Department of Defence. Selective availability or S/A is the phrase used to describe the deliberate degradation of the systems accuracy. This is designed to deny hostile forces the tactical advantage of GPS and was implemented during the Gulf War.

Summary - Typical Error Sources

Satellite Clock Error	2 feet
Ephemeris Error	2 feet
Receiver Errors	4 feet
Atmospheric / Ionospheric Errors	12 feet
Selective Availability (if implemented)	25 feet
Total (root-square sum) dependent on S/A	15 - 30 feet

The actual error is calculated by multiplying the above error by the **Geometric Dilution of Precision**. GDOP under good conditions range from 4 to 6, the total accuracy expected would be:-

Typical - Good receiver   60 - 100 feet
Worst case   200 feet
If Selectively Availability implemented   350 feet

GPS Code and Frequencies

GPS uses carrier frequencies from 1,227.6Mhz to 1,575.42Mhz in the L-Band.

The USA Department of Defence controls access to the system. There are two separate forms of pseudo-random code, the **C/A Code** (**Clear/Acquisition**) and the P code. The **P Code** is encrypted so only military users can use it. It is superimposed on a carrier that is ten times the frequency of the C/A carrier. The civilian code transmits a sequence of 1023 pseudo-random, binary, biphase modulations on the GPS carrier at a chip rate of 1.023Mhz.

The original intention was that the C/A code would be less accurate than the P code. Modern design innovations have resulted in there being no practical difference.

GRADIENT WIND

Wind is caused by the movement of air from high pressure to low. This is affected by the rotation of the Earth (**Coriolis Effect**) which results in the wind flowing parallel to the isobars. This movement is referred to as the **Geostrophic Wind**.

This wind only exists when isobars are straight and parallel. In reality isobars are curved and for the wind to follow the curves an additional force is required. This is referred to as the **Cyclostrophic Force.**

The cyclostrophic force is a **centrifugal force** when acting from the centre of the curved isobars as in the case of a high pressure system and a **centripetal force** when acting towards the centre. This applies for the Northern Hemisphere and has the reverse effect in the Southern.

The following formulas can be used to calculate the various forces where PGF = Pressure Gradient Force, CF = Cyclostrophic Force and GF = Gradient Force.

Low Pressure System   PGF + CF = GF   PGF = GF - CF
High Pressure System   PGF - CF = GF   PGF = GF + CF

GREAT CIRCLE

A great circle is an imaginary line drawn on the surface of the Earth, with a radius the same as that of the Earth, and with a plane that passes through the centre of the Earth.

GREENWICH

The location of the British Observatory, near London. It is the location of the zero reference for the **Prime Meridian**. All positions of longitude are based on being East or West of the prime meridian. It is also the base for **Greenwich Mean Time** (GMT).

GROUND EFFECT

If an aircraft flies close to the ground the vertical component of the airflow around the wing is restricted by the Earth's surface. The ground effect is the interference upon the upwash, downwash and wingtip vortices. This interference is of a positive nature as a reduction in the induced flow causes a reduction in induced drag, but no direct effect on parasite drag.

GROUND LOOP

A description normally used in accident reports. An occurrence, most common in tailwheel aircraft and in the take off or landing roll of a flight, where the aircraft pivots about the axis of one of the wingtips.

GROUND SPEED

The speed of an aircraft in relation to the surface of the Earth over which it is travelling. Ground speed is calculated by taking the true airspeed and adding or deducting the windspeed with due allowance for its direction and effect.

GUSTS - Meteorological

Gusts are defined as a temporary increase in windspeed. They are usually reported to the pilot when the difference between Gusts and **Lulls** are at least 10 Knots. Increases of windspeed in excess of 15 knots to a peak of 20 knots or more and lasting more than one minute are known as **Squalls**.

GYROSCOPES

Gyroscopes are used in the Directional Indicator, Artificial Horizon and the Turn & Slip Indicator. A gyroscope is a rotating wheel or rotor spinning about a moveable axis. When such a mass spins it exhibits two properties, Rigidity in space and Precession.

Rigidity in space - a spinning gyro will continue to point in the same direction as it was originally set unless an external force is applied. This rigidity is proportional to its speed of rotation and the radius at which the mass is concentrated. The rigidity can be increased if the speed is increased or if the mass of the rotor is concentrated near the rim. If an external force is applied the spin axis will move in proportion to the force applied.

Precession - if a force is applied to the spin axis of a gyro the reaction will be as if the force had been applied at a point 90° onwards in the direction of rotation.

Various effects bear upon a spinning gyro, they are:-

Gyro Wander - Any movement of a gyro axis away from its current direction is termed wander, there are two types of wander, Real and Apparent. Apparent Wander has a complementary error termed Transport Wander.

Real Wander - this is any movement of the spin axis caused by a force, usually unwanted and is commonly caused by instrument imperfections. These may be imperfections in the balance of the gyro wheel itself or unequal friction at the spin axis or gimbal bearings.

Apparent Wander - due to the property of rigidity, the gyro will remain aligned to a fixed point in space. The Earth however rotates, apparently making the gyro appear to point to a variable point in space. Imagine that an aircraft is overhead an airfield at around 70° North, with a spinning gyro compass pointing due West. It is in fact pointing at a point in space which relates to due West.

After one hour the earth will have rotated by 15°. The gyro compass will still indicate due West (270°) whereas if the gyro is again compared to a ground reference it would actually be pointing at 284°, (the Earth spins anti-clockwise). Apparent Wander is a function of latitude and there is no apparent wander at the equator. Refer to the reference section under **Directional Indicator** for full details.

APPARENT DRIFT = 15DEG x SINE OF THE LAT (DEG/HR)

Whilst in the air the wander is further complicated by Transport Wander, this is where the aircraft is either flying with or against the direction of the Earth's rotation and therefore either reducing or complementing the Apparent Wander.

Gyro Topple or Drift - if the axis of a horizontally mounted gyro wanders it is said to drift. If it wanders in the vertical plane it is said to topple. The axis of a vertically mounted gyro can only topple.

Types of Gyro are:

Space Gyro - a spinning wheel mounted inside two gimbals. The inner gimbal which contains the wheel's axis is itself mounted inside an outer gimbal pivoted at 90° from the wheel's axis. The outer gimbal is pivoted at 90° by a fixed bracket. The construction allows the gyro freedom of movement in all planes. In this form it is of very little use in aircraft instruments which in order to perform their function must be restricted in some way.

Tied Gyro - this is a gyro that has freedom of movement in three planes. This is used in the Directional Indicator which maintains rigidity in line with the yaw axis of the aircraft.

Earth Gyro - this retains its rigidity in relation to the Earth's vertical and is used in the Artificial Horizon.

Rate Gyro - this uses only one gimbal and therefore only has movement about two axis. This is used for the Rate of Turn Indicator.

Gyro Power Systems

Gyros are electrically or air pressure driven. Air driven systems use either a pressure pump which blows air over gyro cups (similar to a water wheel) or a suction pump which sucks air out. Suction pumps are favoured as the air that is blown through by a pressure pump may contain oil or dirt from the pump itself which may contaminate the gyro.

The disadvantages or air driven instruments are:-

i) That they require air lines and filters to function.

ii) That air reduces in density with height and as air pumps have a fixed quantity supply capacity they will supply less air with height which results in a reduction in gyro speed.

iii) By virtue of their design air must pass through the instrument, even with filters this will contain dust and moisture and will contaminate the pivots and bearings.

Most aircraft use a combination of air and electrically driven instruments, in particular the Artificial Horizon and the Turn and Slip indicators. If one system should fail the aircraft can be flown with the remaining system even in instrument meteorological conditions.

HAIL

Hail is formed when snow or water droplets are continually tossed up and down by the updrafts inside a cumulonimbus cloud. They alternately melt and re-freeze until they become balls of ice that are heavy enough to overcome the up current. In the UK hail is most frequent in the summer when cumulonimbus clouds are at their largest.

In Equatorial regions, especially mountainous areas the hailstones can reach the size of a grapefruit. At UK latitudes they are usually pea sized but have been recorded up to the size of golf balls. Hail damage to aircraft has been recorded as high as 45,000 feet.

HEADSETS

The use of headset microphones is a legal requirement for all public transport flights under FL150.

Headsets are manufactured in various shapes, sizes and prices. The speaker elements are of similar construction. The microphones are classified into three groups:-

Carbon - The original and most common type of microphone. It works on the basis of variable resistance between carbon granules. They are subject to internal interference by moisture and packing.

Dynamic - Designed to replace carbon microphones and to provide automatic noise cancellation.

Electret - Most modern innovation with noise can lation, greater frequency response and dynamic range. It is unaffected by electro-magneti_ _ iterference.

The latest trend in manufacturing is headsets with **Automatic Noise Cancellation**. Other generics are **Active Noise Equalisation** and **Active Noise Reduction**. The purpose of these type of headsets is to sense noise in the cockpit environment, amplify it, and after inverting the frequencies to 180° out of phase, feed it into the headset. This it does very effectively, especially at filtering out engine noise.

Pilots should, if using these headsets, be very aware of the inherent dangers.

a) It is possible that there may be an additional delay in noticing an engine failure, particularly in a single engine aircraft. This can be crucial on the take off run and climb out phase of the flight.

b) It may be difficult to detect minor rough running, often a good indicator of pending problems.

c) On a twin or multi-engine aircraft it makes synchronising the engine tones by ear virtually impossible. Twin engine aircraft particularly tend to generate a pulsing effect. With ANR headsets the effect may reach the stage that is physically felt by vibration before it is heard.

d) Stall warning or other audible warning sounds may not be heard.

HIGH FREQUENCY - HF

Radio frequencies in the range 3Mhz to 30Mhz and wavelength 10 - 100 metres. They are used for high frequency radio telegraphy, usually by the military and for civilian airlines on long range flights.

HIGH INTENSITY RADIO TRANSMISSION AREAS - HIRTAs

Classed as a prohibited or restricted area. These areas are marked on navigational maps, normally with a reference to the base and upper height limits. Dependent on the type of operations, power and frequencies of a HIRTA the effect, listed in severity, may be:-

a) Interference with navigation and communication equipment

b) Damage to navigation and communication equipment

c) Triggering of electrically operated explosive devices carried or fitted to aircraft

d) Possible damage to the health of pilot or passengers if remaining in the area for more than one minute

HIGH SPEED TAXIWAY

A taxiway system provided at some major airfields to minimise main runway occupancy time. A series of high speed run offs which can accept fast moving aircraft, usually up to 60 knots, feed away from the main runway allowing braking time before linking into a conventional taxiway system.

HILL FOG

Hill fog is often caused by low stratus clouds drifting over high ground. It may also be caused by orographic lifting such as a valley fog rising up a hillside. It can occur at any time of the year and will disperse as the cloud formation passes on or by surface insolation.

HOLDING PROCEDURES

All holds are the shape of a an oval racetrack, hence a hold is often referred to as a **racetrack procedure.** A standard hold takes 4 minutes to complete, 1 minute for each leg and 1 minute for each turn. All turns must be made at rate one. **En-route holds**, used to maintain position, usually whilst awaiting clearance to enter controlled airspace, or for separation purposes, are right hand.

Holding patterns are published for most instrument approaches and are designed to be used for stacking aircraft in the event of several aircraft reaching the area at the same time, or, to hold aircraft because of a landing problem. This may be a meteorological state expected to clear shortly or a physical runway obstruction.

HORIZONTAL SITUATION INDICATOR

This is a Radio Magnetic Indicator which can also display ILS and VOR information. It is otherwise very similar to the Omni-bearing Indicator except that for approach information to be accurate the localiser indicator must be set to the final approach heading.

HURRICANE - Winds - Meteorological

According to the Beaufort Wind Scale a hurricane is a force 12 wind. If the wind exceeds 64 knots (74mph) it is said to be hurricane force. In the western hemisphere hurricane is used to describe a **tropical cyclone**.

HYDROMETEOR

Expression used to describe water, whether in liquid or solid form, introduced into the atmosphere by the wind. For example sea spray or blowing snow.

HYPOXIA

The symptoms and effects of hypoxia (lack of adequate oxygen) will affect people at different levels but it is generally agreed that for any flights at or above 10,000 feet amsl oxygen should be used.

Symptoms - At levels up to 10,000 feet normal healthy individuals are hardly affected. Between 10,000 and 15,000 feet a seated pilot or passenger will show few symptoms but the ability to navigate and control the aircraft will be impaired. If the exposures continues for 10 to 20 minutes severe headaches will often be experienced.

Between 15,000 and 20,000 feet symptoms occur even in individuals at rest. Thinking slows, judgement is impaired. Individuals may become emotional, belligerent or even physically violent. They are also unlikely to recognise their condition. Other effects are tingling of the limbs and lips and even unconsciousness.

At heights above 20,000 feet unconsciousness will occur without warning. At 25,000 feet unconsciousness will occur within 2.5 - 6 minutes and within 1.5 - 3 minutes at 30,000 feet.

Prevention- Supplemental oxygen must be used for all flights exceeding 10,000 feet. At the earth's surface and up to 10,000 feet the oxygen content of the air is approximately 21%. The amount of pure oxygen must be increased with height. To totally prevent hypoxia at 18,000 feet 42% oxygen is required. At 34,000 feet 100% oxygen is required. Obviously this cannot be increased. At 40,000 feet 100% oxygen is equivalent to an un-pressurised altitude of 8,000 to 10,000 feet. Above 40,000 feet positive pressure breathing of a pressure suit is required.

Note - total cessation of oxygen results in unconsciousness in 6 - 8 seconds and irreversible brain damage after 4 minutes.

HYSTERESIS

An expression commonly used to describe a problem with pressure controlled aircraft instruments. It describes the **Lag** between an action and re-action. For instance, in the case of an altimeter, the time difference between a pressure change at the static vent to the display needle.

ICING - AIRFRAME - In Flight

Airframe icing will only occur when the ambient and airframe temperatures are both below 0°C. For ice crystals to form water droplets require **Ice Nuclei**. These are not present in the atmosphere in such great quantities as condensation nuclei and so it is often the case that there are not enough ice nuclei to match the amount of water droplets. As a result the water droplets continue to be cooled below 0°C and remaining a liquid. This temperature drop can be to as low as -40°C and is then referred to as **Supercooled Water Droplets** (SCWD). These droplets exist most often between 0°C to -10°C.

If an aircraft, with its skin below 0°C, comes in to contact with the SCWDs it will act as the ice nuclei and the droplet will turn to ice attaching itself to the airframe.

The extent of ice accretion is controlled by the temperature of the SCWD and its weight. For a liquid to change to a solid the latent heat stored in the droplet must be released.

One gram of water needs approximately 80 calories of latent heat to change from ice to liquid, for the reverse to occur 80 calories of latent heat must be released.

One calorie of heat energy is required to raise the temperature of 1 gram of water by 1°C.

It follows that for each degree centigrade that a SCWD is below 0°C, 1 eightieth part of it will freeze on impact. For example if a SCWD is -20°C on impacting the airframe one quarter will freeze instantly, the rest will freeze as it flows back over the airframe.

In flight Icing

All in flight icing can produce a threat to flight safety. It is important for a pilot to recognise the conditions which will produce icing and avoid them. Some aircraft are cleared for flight in icing conditions, they use de-ice systems. Refer to the reference section on **De-icing Systems**. There are various classifications of icing that are liable to occur in flight, they are :-

Clear Ice - also known as **Glaze Ice**. This will form on aircraft which are flying through sub-zero temperatures in rain. Common conditions for this are when an aircraft is flying in the cold sector towards a warm front. The rain falling from the warm front will pass through the sub-zero air of the cold front, becoming supercooled. As it contacts the airframe it will form clear ice.

Clear ice is difficult to detect (up to two inches of clear ice has remained un-detected by crews). It is most prevalent when temperatures are just below freezing and accretes rapidly to the aircraft. Melting ice can also cause problems by melting off the leading edges and re-freezing in some equally problematical area.

Rime Ice - rime is the term used to describe a milky and opaque granular deposit of ice formed by the rapid freezing of supercooled water droplets as they strike an airframe. It occurs only in cloud and is most likely to occur between 0°C and -10°C. At heights below the 0°C isotherm obviously no icing risk exists. At heights above -10°C and -40°C a risk of rime ice still exists but reducing with height.

In most cloud types, at above -20°C its composition will be mostly ice crystals, but with more active updrafts in clouds such as cumulonimbus, supercooled water droplets may be carried up to great heights and in such quantities that they are unable to find sufficient icing nuclei. They will fall, still as supercooled droplets, and freeze on impact with an airframe.

Hoar Frost - this may form in flight or on the ground. In flight it occurs when an aircraft has been cruising at a height above the freezing level. If the aircraft then descends into an area of warm moist air the moisture in the air will attach to the sub-zero airframe by sublimation. This type of icing is the least dangerous as it will disappear as the temperature of the airframe is raised by the warmer air. Temporary effects will be cockpit visibility and VHF radio interference.

ICING - AIRFRAME - On Ground

Hoar Frost - this may occur in the air or on the ground. On the ground it occurs on nights when the temperature has fallen below zero and the aircraft has been left outside. If the air is dry it may cool to 0°C without reaching its dewpoint, sublimation will occur when it comes in contact with the skin of the aircraft.

Hoar frost is most likely to occur during anticyclonic conditions with light winds and clear skies. As with all types of frost all trace must be removed before flight is attempted.

Glazed Frost - in the air this is known as clear ice. It occurs when rain falls through a temperature inversion typically ahead of a warm front. Rain falls from the front into the sub-zero air below causing it to become supercooled, usually the surface and any aircraft on it will also be below freezing. On contact the supercooled droplets will form a thick, heavy sheet of ice on aircraft, taxiways and runways.

Rime Frost - this will form when fog drifts over frozen or snow covered surfaces during the winter. The air in contact with the surface cools initially to dewpoint temperature forming freezing fog. Further cooling results in it becoming supercooled and on impact with any solid object it forms rime ice. The deposit is of an uneven, white, opaque appearance composed of droplets containing small air pockets.

ICING - CARBURETTOR

The commonly used expression 'Carburettor Icing' is more correctly described as **Piston Engine Induction System Icing**. It may occur in temperatures as high as 30°C increasing in probability proportionately with increasing humidity. It can become so severe that the engine may stop.

There are three types of induction system icing:-

Carburettor Icing - this is caused by the sudden drop in temperature due to fuel vapourisation and the reduction in pressure at the carburettor venturi (venturi effect) and results in moisture in the induction air forming ice. As the build up increases it restricts the venturi and alters the fuel/air ratio progressively causing a reduction in engine power. Float type carburettors are more prone to this type of icing than pressure jet types. Engines with fuel injection systems are not affected.

Reduced power settings, normally in the descent, increase the risk of carburettor icing as the temperature drop at the venturi will be more marked. Also the position of the butterfly will be closer to the casing increasing the likelihood of an icing restriction.

Fuel Icing - water held in suspension in the fuel can freeze and become a solid. In sufficient quantities it will block induction piping and fuel jets. Because of its greater volatility and possible water content fuel icing is more likely to occur in Mogas than with Avgas.

Impact Ice - this is the term used for any precipitation which is frozen (sleet or snow) or freezes on impact with the aircraft blocking air intakes or filters. It will occur at any time if the temperature of the aircraft is below 0°C but will build up most rapidly at a temperature of -4°C in which conditions there will be a visible ice build up on other parts of the aircraft.

Icing Indications

Carburettor and fuel icing may occur in clear air although the likelihood increases whilst in cloud. Carburettor icing may occur at temperatures as high as 30°C and the relative humidity as low as 30%.

Induction system icing is an insidious problem. With a fixed pitch propeller the only indication will be a slight drop in RPM, usually with no other indications or rough running. The pilot's natural tendency to increase the throttle setting will normally mask the problem. Where a constant speed propeller is fitted the drop in engine power would have to be large before the RPM reduced and already at a serious point.

The only instruments that will indicate a problem are the exhaust gas temperature gauge (EGT) which will show a slight drop, and the manifold pressure gauge which will show a clear drop.

Prevention and Cure

Prevention is far better that attempting a cure once the problem is fully established.

Dependent on temperature and humidity the carburettor heat should be applied at regular intervals. The regularity increased if regular slight reductions in power are noticed.

In the event of the engine running roughly on the application of carburettor heat under no circumstances must the lever be returned to cold. The rough running will be caused by the ice being ingested into the engine and melted. This is proof that the heat is working. The heat must be kept fully on (on very few aircraft do the operating manual specify partial heat to be applied) for 15 - 20 seconds.

Typical requirements of a heat exchanger are that it will provide a temperature rise of 50°C at 75% power, it follows that the heat exchanger will take some time to re-heat after application.

Particular use of carburettor heat should be made in the circuit and approach to land. (Refer to Pilot's Operating Handbook or Manual) Bearing in mind that icing risk increases with reduced power such as on final approach and that if a go around is required full power is essential. On most engine types it is recommended that the heat be selected to cold for the last few hundred feet to ensure full power is available.

In the event of a full engine stoppage the heat should be selected as it is possible for enough residual heat in the exchanger to enable power to be restored. If impact ice is encountered select alternate air 'on' in case the selector valve becomes immovable due to packed ice.

ICING - ENGINE - Jet and Turbines

Air intakes are affected by impact icing by supercooled water droplets freezing on to the intake rim, braces and the first stage of the compressor. Further inside the engine itself temperatures immediately melt any potential ice formation. Ice guards protect the intake from large pieces of break away ice.

Adiabatic cooling at high RPM speeds may result in a drop of up to 5°C and if the humidity is sufficient engine icing may occur. Prevention and removal methods include circulating a heated fluid around the intake and induction areas, alcohol based fluids introduced into the fuel to prevent fuel icing and hot air from the air intakes blown across the compressor blades.

IDENTIFICATION - Manoeuvre

Under conditions where no secondary radar contact is possible, and primary radar is in use, the Air Traffic Controller may request a turn on to a specific heading to provide positive identification of an aircraft. This is usually followed by verbal confirmation that the aircraft has been identified and it may now resume its own navigation.

IDENTIFICATION - Navigation Aid Identification

For information on the ATC instruction 'squawk ident' refer to the section on Transponders.

Before using any navigation aid it is essential that it is positively identified. This is achieved by the aid emitting a Morse code identification two, three or four letter group. The group usually related to the geographical position of the aid. It is essential that the ident is heard and checked against that expected. If a Morse signal is heard and not positively checked it could be:-

a) A Morse ident 'TST' - in which case the aid should not be used.

b) A breakthrough ident from another station on the same frequency. This becomes more likely with altitude. It is not possible for another station on the same frequency to have the same ident.

c) A change of ident, temporary or permanently. Contact the ATCU you are working to confirm the situation before using the aid.

Idents are on similar audio frequencies (except Marker Beacons - refer to the reference section for further details) but transmitted over different periods.

DME - Two or three letter ident every 30 seconds. Various differences will apply to co-located equipment.

ILS - Two (military), three or four letter ident every 7 seconds. Most ILS systems have an 'I' ident prefix. Outside the UK a voice identification may be carried on the frequency.

NDB - Two or three letter every 10 seconds.

VOR - Three letter ident every 10 seconds. Some may carry a voice identification, others a recorded weather message including the station identification.

IN FLIGHT REFUELLING AREAS

Classed as a prohibited or restricted area. These areas are marked on navigational maps, normally with a reference to the base and upper height limits. In flight refuelling takes place under radar control but will not necessarily conform to the semi-circular of quadrantal flight rules. Pilots should note that aircraft involved in refuelling cannot take quick collision avoidance action.

INITIAL APPROACH

The stage of an instrument approach where the aircraft arrives at the first navigational facility associated with the procedure.

INITIAL APPROACH AREA

An area defined as lying between the preceding navigational fix or dead reckoning area and either the facility to be used for making an instrument approach or a point associated with the facility that signifies the termination of an initial approach.

INSOLATION - Solar Radiation

The Earth is heated by the sun. The atmosphere is heated by the Earth, or objects upon it, reflecting this heat back into the atmosphere. This is known as **conduction**.

Approximately 70% of the Sun's heat that reaches the Earth's atmosphere reaches the surface. Approximately 50% of this heat is reflected back, the remainder increases the surface temperature.

The temperature of the atmosphere decreases with height as it becomes further away from the heat source. The atmospheric heat escapes at night when the sun falls below the horizon. The rise and fall of the temperature over a 24 hour period is referred to as the **Diurnal Variation of Temperature**.

The amount of insolation varies with latitude concentrating most strongly on the equator. The maximum daytime temperature is reached at approximately 1400 hours local time. Various factors affect the retained local temperature. They are:-

Cloud - Clouds absorb solar radiation as well as reflecting it back before it can reach the surface. They also prevent heat from being re-radiated back into the atmosphere. In areas where there is a large amount of cloud cover the diurnal variation will be minimal.

Humidity - Due to evaporation the relative humidity of an air mass will have a large effect on its temperature. Heat is taken from the atmosphere when water is converted to water vapour.

Surface - Dissimilar substances absorb heat at different rates. The ratio of the amount of electromagnetic radiation reflected by a body to the amount incident upon it is known as **Albedo**. The amount of albedo is expressed by percentage.

Large areas of water, particularly the sea, change very little over a 24 hour period, usually no more than 1 degree. The surface also tends to reflect much of the heat as do areas of snow or ice which have albedoes as high as 85%. Areas of vegetation, being mainly water, also tend to vary little. Built up areas will however experience significant temperature changes.

INSTRUMENT LANDING SYSTEM - ILS

Refer to the reference section on the Omni-Bearing Indicator and Horizontal Situation Indicator for further information on the use of this navigation aid.

The Instrument Landing System is a pilot interpreted approach aid providing heading and descent information. It enables an aircraft to make an approach to land without external visual reference. The extent to which a pilot may descend is limited either by the privileges of his/her licence, the published **Minimum Descent Height** (MDH) or the ground based equipment. Refer to the reference section on Decision Heights for information which may increase the pilot's decision height above that of the operational performance of the ILS.

Marker Beacons are used in conjunction with the ILS system. Refer to the reference section for further details.

ILS Frequencies - The glideslope and localiser use UHF & VHF respectively and are always frequency paired. This enables receiver equipment to be standardised. Selecting a VHF frequency will automatically select the paired UHF frequency.

The Glidepath uses 40 UHF frequencies ranging from 329.15Mhz and increasing by 150Khz up to 335Mhz.

Localisers use 40 VHF frequencies from 108.10Mhz increasing by 50Khz up to 111.95Mhz.

The ground equipment comprises of:-

Localiser Transmitter - This is usually located some 300 metres beyond the upwind end of the instrument runway. They comprise of aerials 4 metres high and extending up to 25 metres wide. If it is not possible to place the aerials equidistant of the runway centre line they may be erected to the side of the runway. This is known as an offset localiser approach.

The ILS localiser transmitter uses VHF frequencies in the range 108.10Mhz to 111.95Mhz using the odd tenths and odd tenths + 50Khz. It transmits two lobes of a signal on the same frequency with the lobe to the left (known as the yellow sector) of the approaching aircraft amplitude modulated at 90Hz. The lobe to the right (blue sector) is amplitude modulated at 150Hz.

The receiver in the aircraft is able to identify the modulation differences and calculate the area in which there is no difference. This area is known as the **Equisignal** Area. If the aircraft approaches in this area a cockpit display will centre a needle indicating the runway centre line.

The localiser beam is usable up to an altitude of 6,250 feet and a distance of 25 nautical miles from the front course line and are protected from interference within this range. It is checked for accuracy to a range of 10nm. Coverage extends up to 35° for the first 17nm either side of the centre line, from 17 to 25nm this reduces to 10°·

Localisers paired with a glide path provide coverage of 35° for the first 10nm either side of the centre line and from 10 to 18nm this reduces to 10°. A Localiser should not be used outside of these limits.

Localisers can be used for position fixing as the aircraft flies through the localiser centre line. Back beam approaches, commonly found in the USA, are not approved in the UK.

Glideslope Transmitter

The glideslope transmitter consists of two aerials mounted on 10 metre masts erected 300 metres from the threshold. For practical reasons they are mounted to the side of the runway. As with the localiser the transmitter emits two lobes of signal on a designated UHF frequency.

In this instance an upper and lower lobe is emitted. The upper lobe is amplitude modulated at 90Hz and the lower lobe at 150Hz. The equisignal area is sloped upwards usually between 2.5° to 3.5°, although installations exist in the UK giving a slope as steep as 7.5°.

In order that the system may give guidance to a very low level the lower lobe is beamed along the surface. A side effect of this is for the radio waves to be reflected up into the upper lobe. This then has the effect of producing false areas of equisignal.

These will occur at a predictable angle, at about twice the glideslope angle. For instance on a 3° glideslope the false slope will be at 6°. It is possible for an approach to be commenced descending on a false, steeper glideslope. This should easily be recognised due to the high rate of descent required to maintain the slope and by reference to runway approach plates which specify the aircraft's height at various approach points.

If the aircraft is on a false glideslope the heights will be at least twice that shown on the plates. For this reason a glideslope is always captured from below by flying level until the first (correct) glideslope is intercepted.

The glideslope extends in azimuth 8° either side of the centre line to a range of 10nm. The vertical limits are calculated by multiplying the glideslope angle by 0.45 for the lower limit and 1.75 for the upper limit. This equates to coverage from 1.35° to 5.25° above and below a 3° glide slope.

The Runway - Precision Operation Categories (UK)

		Operational down to	RVR
Category 1	-	Not less than 200 feet	Not less than 800 metres
Category 2	-	Not less than 100 feet	Not less than 400 metres
Category 3a	-	Less than 100 feet	Not less than 200 metres
Category 3b	-	Runway Surface	Not less than 50 metres
Category 3c	-	Runway Surface	Zero Visibility

ILS Checks & Inspections

Before an ILS approach may be commenced a definite identification of the aid must be made. This is achieved by an audio Morse code ident which is modulated on the localiser carrier wave. In the UK this is the letter 'I' followed by two or three letter Morse group. In the aircraft this is carried out by switching the nav box to 'ident'. As the glideslope is always frequency paired separate identification is not required.

As with all radio navigation aids it is crucial that the ident is correctly identified and not just a Morse signal heard. At Exeter, for instance, the ILS operates on the same frequency as the Cherbourg ILS which is about 100nm away. The Cherbourg ident 'MP' can be heard whilst attempting to ident the Exeter system.

When an ILS is undergoing maintenance, or is radiating for test purposes only, the ident signal will be removed completely or replaced by a continuous tone. Under these circumstances no attempt should be made to use the equipment.

ILS installations are routinely inspected by the CAA Flight Calibration Service every four or six months, dependent on the ground equipment and its demonstrated history. In the event of any unusual VOR indications it is a pilot's responsibility to advise their current ATC unit of the problem.

Formulas - ILS

To calculate unknowns the following formulas apply:-

H = Height, GA = Glideslope Angle, ROD = Rate of Descent.

$$\text{Distance to threshold} = \frac{H \times 60}{GA} \qquad GA = \frac{\text{Height (ft)} \times 60}{\text{Distance to Go (ft)}}$$

$$\text{Height} = \frac{GA \times \text{Distance to Go (ft)}}{60} \qquad ROD = \frac{GA \times 100 \times GS}{60}$$

INSTRUMENT METEOROLOGICAL CONDITIONS - IMC

Meteorological conditions under which it is not possible to comply with **Visual Flight Rules** (VFR). In IMC flight must be carried out under **Instrument Flight Rules** (IFR). It is possible to fly under IFR in **Visual Meteorological Conditions** (VMC).

The UK (at time of publication, and under review) operates a system where a Private Pilot or BCPL holder may obtain an **IMC Rating** which entitles them to fly in IMC, under IFR subject to certain criteria stated in the UKAIP. It also alters the criteria imposed on them to comply with VFR. (Refer to the reference section on Visual Meteorological Conditions for full details).

It does not permit instrument flight in Airways or airspace notified for the purposes of Air Navigation Order Schedule 8 in conditions less than the specified minimum weather provisions.

This rating is not valid in any other country in the world and the privileges must only be exercised in UK Airspace.

INTERCEPTION OF CIVIL AIRCRAFT

An aircraft which is intercepted by another aircraft shall immediately follow the instructions given by the intercepting aircraft, interpreting and responding to the visual signs in accordance with the following table.

Pilots are warned that should they become involved in an interception they should as soon as posssible:-

a) Notify the appropriate ATSU and/or

b) Attempt to establish radio communication with the intercepting aircraft by making a general call on 121.5Mhz and 243Mhz (if so equipped) using the call signs **Interceptor** and **Intercepted Aircraft** as appropriate. The identity and the nature of the flight should be transmitted

c) Select Mode A Code 7700, if equipped, or as instructed by ATC

SIGNALS FOR USE IN THE EVENT OF INTERCEPTION

Signals initiated by intercepting aircraft and responses by intercepted aircraft
Series 1
Actions of Intercepting Aircraft by:-

DAY
Rocking Wings from a position in front and, normally, to the left of the intercepted aircraft and, after acknowledgement, a slow level turn, normally to the left, onto the desired heading.

NIGHT
Same and, in addition, flashing navigational lights at irregular intervals.

Note 1 - Meteorological conditions or terrain may require the intercepting aircraft to take up a position in front and to the right of the intercepted aircraft and to make a subsequent turn to the right.

Note 2 - If the intercepted aircraft is not able to keep pace with the intercepting aircraft, the latter is expected to fly a series of race track patterns and to rock its wings each time it passes the intercepted aircraft.

Meaning - You have been intercepted - follow me

Actions of Intercepted Aircraft to mean - Understood I will comply

FIXED WING - DAY
Rocking wings and following

FIXED WING - NIGHT
Same as day plus flashing navigational lights at irregular intervals

HELICOPTERS - DAY OR NIGHT
Rocking aircraft, flashing navigational lights at irregular intervals and following

Series 2
Actions of Intercepting Aircraft by
DAY OR NIGHT
An abrupt break-away manoeuvre from the intercepted aircraft consisting
of a climbing turn of 90° or more without crossing the line of flight of the intercepted aircraft

Meaning - You may proceed

Actions of Intercepted Aircraft to mean - Understood I will comply

FIXED WING - DAY OR NIGHT
Rocking wings

HELICOPTERS - DAY OR NIGHT
Rocking aircraft, flashing navigational lights at irregular intervals and following

Series 3
Actions of Intercepting Aircraft by

DAY

Circling aerodrome, lowering landing gear and overflying runway in the direction of landing or, if the intercepted aircraft is a helicopter, overflying the helicopter landing area

NIGHT

Same as day and, in addition, showing steady landing lights
Meaning - Land at this aerodrome
Actions of Intercepted Aircraft to mean - Understood I will comply

FIXED WING - DAY

Lowering landing gear, following the intercepting aircraft and, if after over-flying the runway landing is considered safe, proceeding to land

FIXED WING - NIGHT

Same as day and, in addition, showing steady landing lights (if carried)

HELICOPTERS - DAY OR NIGHT

Following the intercepting aircraft and proceeding to land, showing a steady landing light (if carried)
Signals initiated by intercepted aircraft and responses by intercepting aircraft

Series 4

Actions of Intercepted Aircraft by.

DAY

Raising landing gear while passing over the landing runway at a height not exceeding 1,000 feet, but not exceeding 2,000 feet, above aerodrome level, and continuing to circle the aerodrome.

NIGHT

Flashing landing lights while passing over the landing runway at a height exceeding 1,000 feet, but not exceeding 2,000 feet, above aerodrome level, and continuing to circle the aerodrome. if unable to flash landing lights, flash any other lights available
Meaning - The aerodrome you have designated is inadequate.
Actions of Intercepting Aircraft to mean - Understood follow me

DAY OR NIGHT

If it is desired that the intercepted aircraft follow the intercepting aircraft to an alternate aerodrome, the intercepting aircraft raises it's landing gear and uses the Series 1 signals prescribed for intercepting aircraft, or **Actions of Intercepting Aircraft to mean - Understood you may proceed.**

DAY OR NIGHT

If it is decided to release the intercepted aircraft, the intercepting aircraft uses the Series 2 signals prescribed for intercepting aircraft.

Series 5

Actions of Intercepted Aircraft by

DAY OR NIGHT

Regular switching on and off of all available lights but in such a manner as to be distinct.

Meaning - I cannot comply
Actions of Intercepting Aircraft to mean - Understood

DAY OR NIGHT
Use Series 2 signals prescribed for intercepting aircraft

Series 6
Actions for Intercepted Aircraft by

HELICOPTERS AND FIXED WING - DAY OR NIGHT
Irregular flashing of all available lights
Meaning - I am in distress
Actions of Intercepting Aircraft to mean - Understood

DAY OR NIGHT
Use Series 2 signals prescribed for intercepting aircraft

INTERNATIONAL STANDARD ATMOSPHERE

The ISA is a set of figures used to calibrate aircraft instruments or in the specification of aircraft. The main items are:-

Pressure at mean sea level	1013.25 millibars
Temperature at mean sea level	+15° Centigrade
Density at mean sea level	1225 gm/cubic metre
Temperature lapse rate of	1.98°C/1000 feet between sea level and the tropopause (averaged at 36,090 feet)
A constant temperature of	-56.5°C above the tropopause

Using these figures manufacturers can test instruments and publish correction formulas for altitudes and environments which depart from the standard conditions.

Several other constants are assumed and used with regard to aircraft prototypes and certification. The details are beyond the scope of this book.

INTERTROPICAL CONVERGENCE ZONE

The zone enclosing the Intertropical Front. Typical associated weather may be showery rain and cumulonimbus clouds.

INTERTROPICAL FRONT

The division line between the wind systems of the Northern and Southern Hemispheres, commonly known as the **Doldrums.**

INVERSION - Temperature

A temperature inversion is said to exist if the temperature increases with height as opposed to the normal situation when it reduces. If the temperature remains constant throughout several thousand feet the layer is known as isothermal.

At certain aerodromes a warning of a marked temperature inversion is issued when a difference of 10°C or more exists between the surface and any point up to 1,000 feet above the aerodrome. This information will be passed to the pilot by ATC or by VOLMET if equipped.

IONOSPHERE

The ionosphere is the layer of atmosphere surrounding the stratosphere.

In this layer ultra-violet rays from the sun cause electrons to separate leaving a positive charge referred to as ions, hence ionisation. The ionosphere starts at around 50km and extends to as high as 500km.

It is made up of several named layers, D, E or Heaviside Layer and the F1 and F2 layers known as the Appleton Layers. The structure and position of these layers in relation to the Earth's surface varies according to latitude, the season and sunspot activity.

ISALLOBARIC WIND

The isallobaric wind component is the term used to describe the inertial effect caused by a pressure gradient of such strength that it delays the effect of the geostrophic force.

The effect in an area of low pressure will be that air will converge towards the centre and because of the aggregation some of the air will be forced upwards resulting in adiabatic cooling and condensation.

The effect on an area of high pressure will be that air will move away from the centre causing adiabatic heating and evaporation dispersing any cloud.

JET A-1 FUEL - AVTUR or Kerosene

AVTUR, or **Kerosene** is used in gas turbine engines, (jets). It is straw coloured and has a very distinctive smell. Aircraft filler points are colour coded black (AVGAS are red) to prevent the loading of the incorrect fuel.

JET A-1 refuelling installations may be identified by a grade label, 15cm x 10cm on the tank. It has white writing - JET A-1 - on a black background with two 0.5cm vertical white stripes up the side. The pipelines carry a similarly worded sticker, 40cm long with an alternating vertical black/white stripe and a vertical pipeline coloured stripe.

JET STANDARD ATMOSPHERE

This is an internationally agreed set of standards that are used for instrument design and calibrations.

Mean Sea Level Temperature	-	+15° C
Mean Sea Level Pressure	-	1013.25
Mean Sea Level Density	-	1225 grams per cubic metre
Temperature Lapse Rate	-	2° per 1000ft with no tropopause

JET STREAMS

Jet streams are created when the **thermal gradient** is large. They are tubes of fast moving thermal wind which occur just under the **tropopause** and can reach speeds in excess of 200 knots. It is meteorologically described as a jet stream when it reaches a speed in excess of 80 knots. They are caused by the steep thermal gradient which is found at the Polar Front. This results from the difference in height of the tropopause. At the point when these cross sections meet there is a substantial a difference in temperature over a very small distance.

The jet itself is caused by the air's attempt to equalise the differential. The centre of a jet stream will always be formed in the warm side of the polar front and may be several hundred miles long, up to 200 miles across and two miles deep.

Jet stream activity and the resultant **Clear Air Turbulence** will only affect the heights used by pressurised aircraft. The Jet stream can cause fuel and flight time estimate problems if it is unexpectedly encountered. The clear air turbulence can be uncomfortable and hazardous as it is impossible to detect in advance, either visually or on radar. The only advance indications will be sudden changes in wind direction and temperature.

KATABATIC WINDS

Katabatic Winds are caused by the cooling of a slope where the surface warmth is re-radiated back into the atmosphere. The air closest to the surface cools faster than the air away from it and being more dense flows down the slope.

This action can result in winds of significant strength even up to gale force. This can present a considerable danger to pilot's of light aircraft flying towards a mountain area that is experiencing a katabatic wind as the downdraft may well exceed the climb performance of the aircraft.

LAND BREEZES

A land breeze may form after sunset when the Earth's surface becomes cooler than that of the sea. It causes a drift of air from land to sea and is the opposite of the cycle of events that cause a **Sea Breeze**. Refer to that reference section heading for a more detailed explanation.

LATENT HEAT

The term used to describe the heat required to convert liquid into vapour without a change of temperature. From an aeronautical point the types of latent heat that affect the pilot are:-

Latent Heat of Evaporation (or vapourisation) - If an air mass absorbs water vapour from a moist source, some form of energy is required to convert the water to water vapour. This is known as the latent heat of evaporation and is stored in the vapour until a further change takes place.

Latent Heat of Condensation - This is the opposite process but with an apparent side effect. When saturated air is cooled to a temperature below its dewpoint condensation will occur. As this happens the latent heat stored in the vapour is released and slows the rate of cooling.

Latent Heat of Fusion - The heat released during the change from water to ice or the amount absorbed in the change from ice to water.

Latent Heat of Sublimation - The heat released during the change from water vapour to ice or released in the change from ice to water vapour. Note in sublimation there is no liquid stage.

In practice this process affects the formation of clouds through variations in **Adiabatic Lapse Rates**.

LATITUDE

A line of latitude is an imaginary line drawn to the North or South of the Equator. They are measured in degrees and minutes, 1 minute of latitude is equal to 1 nautical mile. When expressing co-ordinates the latitude is always expressed first.

L-BAND

Frequency range from 390Mhz to 1,550Mhz. Now more often mentioned as the band contained most of the frequencies used by Global Positioning Systems.

LENTICULAR CLOUDS

These often form in **Mountain Waves** but can also be found on the leeward side of a large range of hills. The clouds may show as a dotted line decreasing in size downwind or a pile of lens shaped clouds piled upwards showing various saturated levels with clear air in between.

LICENCE - Pilot's

Regardless of age or flight experience every private pilot must, every 13 months, submit his licence and personal flying log book to an authorised examiner for a check of his flying experience over that period.

To retain the right to fly the aircraft listed in the licence the holder is required to obtain a certain amount of flying experience during the 13 month period, or to pass a flight test at the end of the period.

The minimum flying experience required to maintain a group A is:-

5 hours experience as pilot in command (a maximum of 2 hours dual flying instruction can count towards this total) of an aircraft in the same class as that which the pilot wishes to fly.

The minimum flying experience required to maintain a group B is:-

As Group A except that at least one flight in command and unsupervised, i.e. not pilot in command under supervision, shall have been made in a multi engined aircraft.

LIGHTNING

Lightning occurs between two clouds or between a cloud and the ground. It is caused by glaciation in the cloud triggering the separation of ions. The positive ions collecting at the top of the cloud, the negative near the base, typically near the -10°C isotherm. This builds until there is a discharge of lightning together with **Thunder** which is due to the violent expansion of the gases along the line of the lightning.

Most strikes on aircraft occur at levels where the temperature is between +10°C and -10°C. The lightning flash can temporarily blind a pilot but there is unlikely to be much damage apart from burn marks at the point of entry and exit, although radio aerials are often destroyed. A **Compass Swing** is a mandatory requirement after a lightning strike.

LIGHT SIGNALS

Light signals are still used as a reserve in the event of radio failure or when aircraft are non-radio. Pyrotechnics, a type of flare, is used to warn aircraft of possible dangers. The meanings of the various lights are:-

Light Signal	Meaning to aircraft on the ground	Meaning to aircraft in the air
Flashing Green	Authorises movement on the manoeuvring area and apron	Return to the circuit or remain in the circuit and await for permission to land
Steady Green	Authorises take-off	Authorises landing
Flashing Red	Move clear of landing area immediately	Aerodrome is unfit for landing, go away, land elsewhere
Steady Red	Movement prohibited	Give way to other aircraft and continue circling
Flashing White	Return to your starting point	Land after receiving a green light and then after receiving green flashes proceed to the apron
Red Pyro or Flare		Landing prohibited for the time being, previous landing permission withdrawn
Red or Green Lights or Stars		You are in an active danger area, do not alter your height and get out by the shortest route OR you are about to enter a danger, prohibited or restricted area.

Light signals may also be directed to ATC from an aircraft, their meanings are:-

Signal	Meaning
Red Pyro or Flare	Immediate assistance is requested (it doesn't explain how ATC are meant to get up there to help you!)
Continuous Green Flashes or Pyro	By Night: May I land? By Day: May I land in a different direction to that Green indicated by the landing T ?
White Flashes, Pyros or switching on and off of aircraft lights	I am compelled to land

LOG BOOKS

Under Article 15 of the Air Navigation 1985 it is a requirement for UK registered aircraft to keep:-

i) An **Aircraft Log Book.**

ii) An **Engine Log Book** for each engine fitted to the aircraft.

iii) A **Propeller Log Book** for each variable pitch propeller fitted to the aircraft.

Various criteria and conditions apply to these documents, refer to the ANO 1985 for full conditions.

LONGITUDE

A line of longitude is an imaginary line drawn from the True North Pole to the True South Pole, they are also known as meridians. Longitude is measured in degrees and minutes and one minute is equal to one nautical mile only at the equator.

The prime meridian is also known as the **Greenwich Meridian**. It passes through Greenwich, London and has a value of zero degrees. It is used as the datum for positions East and West of this line.

LORAN

A radio navigation system originally introduced in the 1940's as Loran A operating in the 1.9Mhz band. Loran C, operating on 100Khz, is the modern equivalent and as with the original system utilises a pulse hyperbolic system. Position is determined by the relative travel time of pulse signals from two or more radio stations, one must be a master station the other(s), synchronised slave station(s).

The long term continuation of the system is debatable, particularly in view of the dramatic reduction in price of GPS. Many airborne units are still in use and it is a prime system for marine navigation.

LOW FLYING RULES

There are many rules and exceptions, the following is listed only as an aide-memoire, refer to the Air Pilot for clarification.

a) Catch All - No closer than 500ft to any person, vessel, vehicle or structure. The UK does not include the Earth's surface, the sea or a large body of water in this rule although ICAO rules do.

b) Towns, Cities and Settlements - the highest of:-

i) Being able to glide clear without damage to persons or property.

ii) 1,500ft above the highest fixed object within 2,000ft.

c) Assembly of persons - No closer that 3,000ft of any assembly of more than 1,000 persons, (unless you were unaware of the gathering).

LOW FREQUENCY BAND

Frequencies in the range 30 and 300Khz with a wavelength of 1 -10Km. They are used for Decca, Loran, Non Directional Beacons and broadcasting in the long and medium waves.

LOW LEVEL CIVIL AIRCRAFT NOTIFICATION PROCEDURE - CANP

Refer to AIC 79/1992 Yellow 70 for full details of procedures.

CANP is a system where all civil traffic involved in aerial work at or below 1,000 feet agl should notify the Tactical Booking Cell of the London Air Traffic Control Centre (Military) - LATCC (Mil) before commencing such work. A freephone number is provided to encourage use.

LULL - Meteorological

Lull is the term used to describe a temporary decrease in windspeed, the opposite is known as a Gust. These are usually reported to the pilot when the difference between a gust and a lull is at least 10 Knots.

MACH NUMBER

A Mach number is calculated from the true airspeed of the aircraft divided by the local speed of sound. It may be directly displayed in an aircraft by a **Machmeter**. This is an air speed indicator with calibration linked to the ambient temperature. **Hypersonic** is the name given to speeds converting to Mach 5 or above.

MAGNETIC EQUATOR

The aclinal line of zero magnetic dip. It lies south of the equator in America and the eastern Pacific, and to the north of the equator across the Indian Ocean and Africa.

MAGNETIC POLES

The Magnetic North and South Poles do not lie in the same position as the true or Geographic North and South Poles. The magnetic meridians (great circles passing through both poles) do not lie in the same position as the true meridians. The angle of difference between the meridians is known as variation.

Physically a magnetic compass is unusable beyond 70° North or South. This is no longer a problem for polar pilots since the GPS system became so available. But in case it interests the reader, the magnetic poles do not exist as points, but rather as areas several hundred square miles in extent. The Magnetic North area lies around 15° from the geographic pole, around 101° west. The South Area is around 23° from the geographic south pole, at around 143° east.

MANOEUVRING AREA

The part of the aerodrome provided for the take off and landing of aircraft and for the movement of aircraft on the surface. It excludes the apron and any part of the aerodrome provided for aircraft maintenance.

MARITIME RADIO BEACON COVERAGE

In 1992 the maritime MF NDB network was re-organised, all frequencies were changed and a number of beacons withdrawn. All beacons transmit only a carrier signal with no modulation. The carrier signal is keyed to provide a Morse ident but the ADF equipment must have a BFO facility to make an audio identification.

These can be used by aircraft and details of the frequencies and positions are published in AIC 28/1992 (Yellow 53). Pilots are warned that the beacons are not subject to NOTAM and that other beacons with ranges of around 10nm are not listed, these may be on similar frequencies but with differing idents.

MARKER BEACONS

Refer to the reference section on the Marker Receiver for information on the reception of marker beacon signals, various types of marker beacons are as follows:

Marker beacons or **Fan Markers** emit a narrow vertical elliptical coned shape beam which can only be received by an aircraft flying within the area of the beam. Due to this restricted transmission area all marker beacons transmit on the same frequency of 75Mhz.

The beacons are provided for:-

a) **Airways Reporting Points** - and are located on the airway centre line. They are high power beacons and can be received by transitting aircraft up to a height of 50,000 feet.

b) **Middle Markers** - for precision range information for Instrument Landing System Approaches. They are not provided at a fixed distance from the runway threshold but vary with the approach. Each airfield's published approach chart shows the markers location from threshold in metres but is normally between 1,000 and 2,000 metres. They usually have a vertical range of 5,000 feet.

c) **Inner Markers** - are rarely used in the UK, if provided are located very close to the threshold.

d) **Outer Markers** - are located between 3 and 6 nautical miles from the threshold with a vertical range of 5,000 feet. They are sometimes co-located with a low powered NDB and referred to as Locator Outer Markers and are used as a starting point for an approach procedure.

Marker Receiver

Marker receivers are automatically activated when VOR or ILS equipment is switched on. The only switch on the receiver is a HI-LO-TEST selector. The HI (high) and LO (low) settings alter the strength of the audio and visual strength of the over beacon indicators. The TEST selection will illuminate the three beacon indicator lights and should be checked before commencing an instrument approach.

The passing of a marker beacon is signalled to the pilot by:-

Outer Marker

Audio - 400Hz low pitch dashes of the Morse letter 'M' (_ _) at two characters per second.

Visual - Blue flashing light marked 'O'.

Middle Marker

Used to define a point along the glide slope of an ILS and is normally located near the point of decision height in respect of a category I ILS.

Audio - 1,300Hz medium pitch alternating dash dot dash of the Morse letter 'K' (_ . _) at three characters per second.

Visual - Amber flashing light marked 'M'

Inner or Airways Marker

Used on a category II & III ILS and located between the middle marker and the end of the ILS runway.

Audio - 3,000Hz high pitch dots of the Morse letter 'E' (.) at six characters per second.

Visual - White flashing light marked 'A'.

MAYDAY - DISTRESS MESSAGE - EMERGENCY

An emergency may be declared by a source other than the pilot, under various conditions various phases are allocated, **Uncertainty, Alert,** or **Distress.** Refer to those sections for more details.

A mayday call is to be transmitted in the event of the threat of serious and/or imminent danger to the occupants of the aircraft to the frequency that the aircraft is currently working, in the event of no reply the transmission should be made on the appropriate reserved frequency.

It should contain as much as possible of the following information;

Mnemonic - **R**est **I**n **P**eace **H**orace **H**edgehog

    MAYDAY MAYDAY MAYDAY
    NAME OF STATION YOU ARE CALLING
    AIRCRAFT CALL SIGN & TYPE

R - REASON FOR DISTRESS MESSAGE
I - INTENTION OF THE PILOT
P - POSITION
H - HEIGHT (FLIGHT LEVEL OR ALTITUDE)
H - HEADING

! - Any other useful information. Your qualification*, number of people on board, anything that will help the controller to help you.

* Knowing that you do/don't have an instrument or IMC rating will ensure that the controller does not give you headings into conditions beyond your experience. Inexperienced civil pilots should use the call sign prefix TYRO to indicate their lack of experience.

Frequencies Internationally Allocated

121.5 Mhz, 243.0 Mhz (Aeronautical Frequencies)

500 Khz, 2182 Khz (International Distress) - Dinghy Radios

8364 Khz (Survival Craft)

Transponder should be selected to 7700, Mode as directed.

All stations or aircraft hearing a distress call should stop transmitting and maintain a listening watch. An aircraft which hears a distress call which is not immediately acknowledged should endeavour to notify an appropriate ground station. The message should be relayed and suffixed *'This is'* and the relaying aircraft's call sign three times. If necessary an aircraft intercepting a message may be required to relay from the distressed aircraft to a ground station. As soon as a ground station acknowledges a Mayday he will transmit the message *'ALL STATIONS - STOP TRANSMITTING - MAYDAY'*.

All non distress stations should then maintain a silent listening watch until the cancellation message is heard.

If the RT is weak, distorted or unintelligible pilots should transmit carrier wave only codes (**The Speechless Code**). These are sent by depressing the aircraft transmit button for less than a second for a short code and two seconds for a long code. Both without speaking and emulating the spacing used in normal speed Morse.

Transmission	Morse	Morse Letter	Meaning
1. One short	.	E	Yes
2. Two short	..	I	No
3. Three short	...	S	Say Again
4. Four short	....	H	Request homing
5. One long	_	T	Last instruction completed
6. One long, two short and one long	_.._	X	My aircraft has developed another emergency

Cancellation - if the distress situation no longer exists a cancellation message should be transmitted, either to the station controlling the distress traffic or to *'all stations'*, if appropriate. All stations used during the distress should also be notified.

MEAN SEA LEVEL
The average height of the surface of the sea for all stages of tide. Used as a reference for QNH altimeter settings.

MEDIUM FREQUENCY
Frequencies in the range 300Khz to 3Mhz and a wavelength of 100 metres to 1 Km. They are used for Non-directional beacons, Loran and medium wave broadcasting stations.

MERIDIANS
A meridian is a great semi-circle joining the True North and True South poles. They are used to define positions of Longitude.

METEOROLOGICAL AERODROME REPORT - METAR
A METAR is referred to as an '**Actual**' and is used to advise pilots of the actual weather at an aerodrome. It must be borne in mind that there are physical limitations to how up to date this report is. They are compiled at half-hourly or hourly intervals and a further period of time is taken before these become promulgated. Full details of a METAR decode are given in AIC (Yellow) but will always take the following form.

Location Identifier - The ICAO four letter code for an aerodrome.

Time - The time of observation in hours and minutes followed by the letter Z (Zulu Time).

Wind - The direction in degrees **true from** which the wind is flowing followed by the measuring unit (usually KTS Knots but could be KMH or MPS).

Horizontal Visibility - The visibility given in metres, 9999 means visibility in excess of 10Km. If it varies significantly in different directions this will be indicated.

Runway Visual Range - R denotes runway followed by the runway number, if it is followed by R C or L it denotes right, centre or left runway. This will usually be followed by /P1500 which means that the RVR is in excess or 1,500 metres.

If the information given is other that /P1500 it is unlikely that a Non-IMC or Instrument rated pilot will using the airfield. Pilots should refer to the MET Section of the AIP for decodes.

Weather - Indications will follow some logic for example SHRA - Showers of Rain, +BLSN - Heavy Blowing Snow. The abbreviations in the glossary section give the decode, and meteorological, < /// + type codes are on page 272.

Cloud - This will be given as SCT - Scattered, BRK -Broken or OVC - Overcast followed by the height of the base of the cloud in hundreds of feet above aerodrome level. If significant cloud types are around it will be given after this. Example:- CB-Cumulonimbus.

Temperature/Dewpoint - Given in degrees centigrade, M indicates Minus.

QNH - Rounded down to the nearest whole millibar and reported as a four figure group, if the value is under 1,000 the first digit is shown as a 0.

Recent Weather - The type of operationally significant recent weather will be given if it has passed since the previous observation. It is prefixed RE.

Windshear - Prefixed WS, followed by TKOF (Take-off) or LDG (Landing) it will be given if it is reported along the take off or approach paths in the lowest 1,600ft with reference to the runway.

TREND - This will indicate significant changes (or lack of them) during the two hours after the observation time.

Runway State - This is only added to the end of the METAR if the runway is affected by snow or other contamination. A decode of this will be found in the MET Section of the AIP.

Information that is missing from a METAR will be shown by diagonals or slashes (///).

METEOROLOGICAL FORECAST - Personalised

Self briefings are available from most larger aerodromes, and by telephone or Fax. A personalised met forecast (not briefing) is available if the appropriate notice is given. 4 hours for flights of 500nm or more, 2 hours otherwise. Application must be made to a **Main** or **Subsidiary Meteorology Office**. If the pilot cannot appear personally at the office arrangements may be made for the information to be passed by telephone, or with a particularly co-operative office, by Fax. The forecast does not alleviate the pilot to self brief for the route as normal.

The following information, when appropriate, will be provided for a given period of time:-

	European Route	North Atlantic Route
Significant Weather Chart	Yes	Yes
Isotach Charts for Appropriate Levels	No	Yes
Upper Spot Winds and Temperatures	Yes	No
Tropopause Charts	No	Yes
Maximum Wind Charts	No	Yes
0° Isotherm Levels on 1,000s feet	Yes	No
Aerodrome Forecasts including Alternates	Yes	Yes

METFAX

A facility provided by the Meteorological Office, Bracknell. It allows access to all the charts and forecasts, including TAFs and METARS that are available in self briefing Met Offices at the larger airfields. A Fax machine is required and the telephone charges are at premium rates. The index page may be obtained on 0336 400 501.

METFORM 215

This is the name given to the low level area and route forecast issued by the Meteorological office at Bracknell.

It covers the same area as the Metform 214 and so are normally used together. The sheet shows both pictorially and in text the expected flight conditions from the surface to 15,000 feet. The period of validity is shown on the top left, the time and date of issue, bottom right. A full decode and explanation of symbols is given on Metform 216.

The charts are issued at fixed times and cover standard periods:-

Charts Available At	Fixed Time Validity	Suitable for Initial Departures and Flights Between
0500	0800	0600 - 1100
0900	1200	1000 - 1500
1300	1600	1400 - 1900
1700	2100	1800 - 2400
2300	0300	0000 - 0600

MILITARY AIR TRAFFIC ZONE - MATZ

At most military aerodromes an additional zone is established around the ATZ to provide increased protection to aircraft flying within that airspace. The MATZ comprises of the airspace in a radius of 5nm from the aerodrome reference point, from the surface to 3,000 feet aal. On some MATZs projecting from this circle is one or more stubs, aligned with the main runway centreline. It is 5nm long and 4nm wide extending from 1,000 feet aal to 3,000 feet aal.

It is not a civil requirement to request permission before penetrating MATZ airspace but it is required in order to comply with the current Rules of the Air Regulations. It should be borne in mind that the MATZ will also contain an **Air Traffic Zone** of a certain radius and height (see under that section for details) based around the centre of its longest runway. Permission **is** required before this may be entered.

If a MATZ penetration is required a call should be made at the greater of 15nm or 5 minutes before the zone boundary. The call should contain:-

a) Callsign and Aircraft type
b) Position
c) Height and Heading
d) Destination, or, if not direct track, next turning point
e) The phrase *'Request MATZ Penetration'*

Permission may be granted and if so maintain a listening watch and advise the controller when clear of the MATZ. The controller will provide radar separation or, if not available, a vertical separation of 500 feet. The altimeter setting passed to you will be based on Aerodrome QNH and he will expect the aircraft to maintain a specified height and track. Call when clear of the MATZ.

If the aircraft is making an approach or landing he/she should set QNH unless QFE has been requested and agreed as the datum with ATC, however, if the approach is into Yeovilton, Portland, Culdrose, Lee On Solent, Merryfield or Predannack he/she should set QFE unless QNH has been requested and agreed with ATC as the datum.

If for operational reasons MATZ penetration cannot be granted the pilot will usually be offered radar headings to steer the aircraft around the airspace. As soon as it has been cleared the pilot will be instructed to *'resume your own navigation'*, so ensure you keep a track of where the controller is routing you.

Outside normal hours of operation special operations or night flying may be taking place so do not assume the MATZ is inactive.

Two consecutive radio calls should be made before entering the zone and a good look-out kept. Further details may be found in the UK AIP RAC 3-2-12 & AIC 25/1989 (Yellow 137). QNH/QFE details are in AIC 105/1991 (Pink 35).

Some are designated as **Military Emergency Diversion Aerodromes** (MEDA) which offer any distressed aircraft radar vectoring (if required) and landing facilities on a 24 hour basis.

MILITARY TRAINING AREA

Classed as a prohibited or restricted area. These areas are marked on navigational maps, normally with a reference to the base and upper height limits. These are areas where intense military flying training takes place and flights will not comply with quadrantal rules. Unless a flight is to cross the area during hours published as being inactive the areas should be avoided.

MILLIBAR - Mb

A unit of atmospheric pressure, equal to the **Hectopascal**. Used in aircraft altimeters to set a datum point. American altimeters have a sub-scale calibrated in inches of pressure.

MINIMUM SAFE ALTITUDE

Various minimas are advised by pilots on charts to provide adequate terrain clearance:-

En-Route AERAD Radio Navigation Charts

Each degree of latitude and longitude box has a **Safe Clearance Altitude** shown. The height shown (e.g. **5**5 = 5,500 ft amsl) provides for terrain and obstacle clearance in accordance with the list below.

Obstacle up to and including 5,000ft	Clearance 1,000ft
Above 5,000ft and up to 10,000ft	2,000ft
Above 10,000ft	2,000ft

Where this method of SCA is not used airways show a height in brackets (e.g. 5,500ft amsl) which indicates safe clearance within a 30nm range along the track plus a semi-circular 30nm radius before and beyond each end of the track. The figure gives clearance in accordance with the above chart.

ICAO - 1:500,000 Visual Charts

These show a **Maximum Elevation Figures** (MEF) in each half a degree of latitude and longitude box.

The height shown (e.g. **5**5 = 5,500 ft amsl) shows the highest known feature within that box and must be pilot interpreted for calculating a safety height. It provides no element of clearance.

Instrument Approach Charts

Sector Safety Altitudes (SSA) - these are depicted on approach charts and provide obstacle clearance of at least 1,000 feet in a radius of 25nm from the aerodrome reference point.

In computing these figures an additional 5nm around each sector is taken into account. These are for emergency purposes only and do not guarantee continued reception of navigational equipment. The clearance given is in accordance with that shown above for en-route charts.

Standard Instrument Arrival (STAR) and Departure Charts (SID)

These show a pecked line showing an approximate 25nm radius from the aerodrome together with a black quartered circle indicating the SSA for the quadrants. Beneath that is a **Minimum Sector Altitude** (MSA) figure based on 10nm either side of the SID track.

MISSED APPROACH POINT - MAPt and PROCEDURES

The missed approach point is the point in an instrument approach procedure at or before which the **Missed Approach Procedure** (MAP) must be initiated. This will be either; when the aircraft has descended to the decision height and has not established visual contact, or when directed by ATC to go around.

The MAP is either published on the approach plate or will be passed to the pilot during the approach. If an un-published procedure is instructed radar vectors will be passed to the pilot.

MIXTURE CONTROL

All aircraft carburettors are designed to mean sea level conditions in the International Standard Atmosphere. As aircraft rarely operate at this height the mixture control is provided to allow adjustment of the fuel/air mixture reaching the cylinders. This is known as leaning the mixture.

Leaning is required because at higher temperatures and/or altitudes the density of the air decreases. With a decrease in density the same volume of air passing through the carburettor will contain less molecules and therefore, weight. This will result in too much fuel in comparison with the amount of air. This results in excessive fuel consumption and if prolonged, possible rough running.

The mixture control is connected to a needle in the carburettor which restricts the main jet fuel flow, redressing the height/temperature variation.

In flight the mixture is leaned by reference to the **Exhaust Gas Temperature Gauge** (EGT) which will indicate a middle range temperature when the mixture is correct.

For aircraft not equipped with an EGT the setting is obtained by experimentation and will never be 'in the same place at this height'.

The mixture control is slowly pulled out until the engine revs flutter or decrease and there is slight rough running. The control is then pushed back in slightly to gain the best 'RPM for throttle' setting. Smooth running should now be felt. The control is then pushed in again slightly to ensure that the engine is receiving a mixture on the rich side of the chemical equation.

The **Idle cut-off** facility on the mixture control allows the engine to be shut down without any fuel being left in the induction passages or cylinders.

MOGAS

Some aircraft may be cleared for the use of **MOGAS**, this fuel is not, contrary to popular misconception, 4 star motor fuel. It is a special fuel produced to a particular specification and quality.

It cannot be bought from motor filling stations.

MOGAS refuelling installations may be identified by a grade label, 15cm x 10cm on the tank. It has white writing - MOGAS - on a red background with a 2.5cm vertical yellow stripe up the side. The pipelines carry a similarly worded sticker, 50cm long with a 10cm vertical yellow stripe and a 10cm vertical pipeline coloured stripe.

MONSOON

A wind that reverses its direction with the season. It is a steady wind that blows from the centre of a continent towards the sea in winter and from sea to continent in Summer.

MOVEMENT AREA

The movement area of an aerodrome is classed as the runways, taxiways and other areas that are used for taxiing, take off and landing of aircraft excluding loading ramps and parking areas.

NEAR GALE - Winds - Meteorological

According to the Beaufort Wind Scale a near gale is a force 7 wind. If the wind reaches 28 - 33 knots (32 - 38 mph) it is said to be near gale force.

NIGHT AND DAY - Official Interpretation

Officially (ICAO) Night means the time between half an hour after sunset and half an hour before sunrise. Sunset and sunrise being determined at surface level. From this we can surmise that Day means any other time. Flights to qualify for Night flights require a more technical interpretation, as follows.

NIGHT RATING

A night rating is an extended privilege of a pilot's licence which allows a pilot to act as pilot in command providing he/she has within the preceding 13 months carried out as pilot in command not less than 5 take-offs and 5 landings at a time when the depression of the Sun's centre was not less than 12 degrees below the horizon. And **you** thought it just had to be dark!

NIMBOSTRATUS CLOUD
A grey, dark cloud often dark enough to blot out the sun. Usually associated with continuous falling rain and snow.

NON DIRECTIONAL BEACONS
Refer to the section on Automatic Direction Finding Equipment for further information on the operation and use of these systems.

Bearing Signal	Identification	Use
NON	A1A	Long Range NDB
NON	A2A	Short Range NDB

The difference between A1A & A2A is that it governs the requirement to use the Beat Frequency Oscillator (BFO). NONA1A requires that the BFO be selected on to hear both parts of the transmission. NONA2A requires that the BFO is selected on to display the bearing but off to be able to ident the audio identification signal.

NDB Ranges
An NDB must not be used outside its **Promulgated Range**. This range is published in the COM Section of the UK Air Pilot. The published range is based on a daytime protection ratio of wanted and unwanted signals of not less than three to one. This limits bearing errors to +/- 5° or less. Errors above this limit will be found at distances outside of the published range or at night.

NDB Checks & Inspections
NDBs are not normally flight inspected by the CAA Flight Calibration Service except on initial installation. In the event of any unusual indications it is a pilot's responsibility to advise their current ATC unit of the problem.

NORMALLY ASPIRATED ENGINE
A phrase frequently mis-used to describe an engine fitted with a carburettor. The definition is a reciprocating aircraft engine having a rated take-off power that is only produced at sea level. It may also be referred to as a **Sea Level Engine**.

NOTAM - Notice to Airman
The word NOTAM evolved from the term **Notice to Airmen**. They are issued by the Aeronautical Information Services of National Air Traffic Services. They are used to promulgate information relating to the establishment, condition or change of any aeronautical facility service, procedure or hazard. They may be used to change details in the **Air Pilot** on a temporary basis until new pages can be issued. It is essential to check any NOTAMS affecting the departure aerodrome, en-route phase, alternate and destination aerodrome before the departure of a flight. A Class I NOTAM is distributed by the AFTN telephone system. A Class II NOTAM is distributed by post. The Series A is classed as a general NOTAM, a Series B is reserved for temporary navigation warnings.

Some NOTAMS are marked **AIRAC** which contain advance information such as changes in airspace limits or heights, introduction or deletion of danger areas, frequency changes or removal of radio aids. AIRAC NOTAMS are published 4 weeks in advance of the changes, on a Thursday.

OBSTACLE CLEARANCE HEIGHT - OCH
The lowest height above the elevation of the relevant runway threshold or above the

aerodrome elevation as applicable, used in establishing compliance with the appropriate obstacle clearance criteria.

OBSTACLE CLEARANCE LIMIT

The height above the aerodrome elevation below which the minimum prescribed vertical clearance cannot be maintained either on approach or in the event of a missed approach.

OCCLUSION - Meteorological

This is the name given to the point at which the boundaries of two fronts have met. The most common occlusion is a cold front occlusion. This is because a cold front moves faster than an associated warm front and must inevitably catch up. It is also possible, under certain circumstances for a warm front occlusion to form. The defining factor is whether the air behind the occlusion line is warmer or colder than the air in front.

OCCURRENCES AND ACCIDENTS - Mandatory Reporting

It is mandatory for an occurrence and accident classified as reportable to be advised to the CAA. The definition of reportable is defined in CAP393 Section 8/3.

The qualification for a reportable accident or occurrence and the details that the report should included can be found in the Air Pilot. In such cases that qualify the Department of Transport must be notified by the quickest means available. The notice must be sent to the Chief Inspector of Accidents, and also to the local police.

OCULOGYRAL ILLUSION

Thought to be the reason for the occasional WWII night escort aircraft spiralling off from the formation and crashing. These pilots were required to follow only the red tail light of a bomber for many hours.

The illusion occurs if a source of light is viewed from an aircraft which is subject to angular acceleration. The light source, although in a static position in reference to the viewing aircraft, will appear to develop a movement of its own, even after straight and level flight is resumed.

The illusion is produced by involuntary eye movements and unless the pilot changes his vision reference, for instance looking back into the cockpit until the effect has cleared, the illusion will greaten. The pilot will naturally attempt to place the aircraft in a attitude where the light remains static, which, of course, is not possible. Spatial disorientation will quickly follow. The illusion can also occur where limited ground reference lights can be seen.

OHM'S LAW

Ohm's Law states that the current flowing in a circuit is directly proportional to the applied voltage and inversely proportional to the resistance. Computations may be made by use of the following formulas where I = Amps R = Resistance (in Ohms) & V = Volts.

$$I = \frac{V}{R} \quad \text{or} \quad R = \frac{V}{I} \quad \text{or} \quad V = I \times R$$

OMNI-BEARING INDICATOR - OBI

Refer to the reference section on **Very High Frequency Omni-Directional Range** for information on the transmission and reception of a VOR signal.

Most modern omni-bearing indicators may also be used for **Instrument Landing System** glideslope and localiser indications. This is explained under that heading. The OBI is also known as a **Course Deviation Indicator**.

The various parts of the omni-bearing selector are:-

The Alarm/Failure Flag - This is coloured red to show its importance. It will appear in the event of a signal of insufficient strength or no signal at all reaching the receiver. This may be caused by:-

(a) Cone of Confusion - as an aircraft passes overhead the beacon at angles of up to 40° of the transmitter's vertical axis it enters the cone of confusion. No useful navigation information will be displayed until the aircraft is clear of this area.

(b) Range Limitations - a signal may be too weak to be used even if the limits are inside of the Designated Operational Coverage due line of sight limitations.

(c) Sectors of Ambiguity - at close range whilst passing through the radials of up to 10° either side of the radials which are at 90° to that selected on the OBS.

(d) VOR transmitter failure - being off the air due to a fault or for scheduled maintenance. During periods of maintenance or test VOR stations may radiate normally but will ident 'TST'. This period will usually be publicised by NOTAM. Regardless of the bearing information received it should not be used.

Course Deviation Needle - VOR - The needle is used across a five dot display to show if the aircraft is on the required radial. Each dot off the centre line shows 2° off the required bearing up to a maximum of 10°.

Omni-Bearing Selector - VOR - This is a selection knob which rotates the compass omni-bearing card, the bearing shown at the top of the display is also that to which the receiver is then tuned.

Course Deviation Needle - ILS - Localiser - The needle is used across a five dot display to show if the aircraft is on the required approach path. Each dot off the centre line the course deviation needle strays shows 0.5° off the required track.

Glidepath Indicator - A five dot display in line with the vertical axis shows a displacement of 0.14° per dot. The UKAIP states that the maximum permitted deflection of this needle in an ILS approach is half scale deflection below the glideslope. If this is exceeded a go around should be initiated.

Omni-Bearing Selector - ILS - Contrary to VOR mode the OBS will not alter the displayed information. When using instrument approaches the magnetic runway heading should be rotated to the top of the OBI.

To and From Flags - One or the other flag will show dependent on the omni-bearing selected. Overhead the beacon neither flag will be visible. When referring to tracking on a radial always quote the 'from' radial.

VOR Tracking with the OBI

Tracking en route using an OBI must take into account any wind drift as any heading will only hold good in zero wind conditions. A wind drift allowance, i.e. the difference between the heading and the track must be laid in.

If the aircraft is blown to the right of the required track the OBI needle will drift to the left showing that a turn to the left to recapture the needle to the centre line.

Needle left turn left.
Needle right turn right.

If the aircraft is blown to the left of the required track the OBI needle will drift to the right showing that a turn to the right to recapture the needle to the centre line. . A heading can be worked out by trial and error that will hold a radial and maintain the OBI needle on the centre line.

Using the OBI for a position fix requires two beacons. The first beacon must be chosen and idented. The OBS must then be turned until the needle is centred. If a 'TO' flag shows, rotate the OBS by 180° until the needle is again centred. The bearing at the top of the display gives the radial on which the aircraft is positioned (QDR). A second beacon can then treated in the same way to provide a cross reference. Some VORs have a co-located DME which makes position fixing very simple. Refer to the **Distance Measuring Equipment** reference section for more details.

OROGRAPHIC LIFTING

This is the term given to the disturbing effect of hills or mountains on an air mass flowing horizontally across the Earth's surface.

OWNERS MANUAL

Usually found with older US built light aircraft. The manual contains information regarding the safe operation of the aircraft together with performance statistics.

PAN MESSAGE - Urgency

An urgency message is transmitted by an aircraft to notify a ground station of a situation affecting the safety of the aircraft, a person on board or a third party in sight of the aircraft. It should be used if, for instance, you are getting erratic oil pressure readings, a situation which may or may not develop into a serious problem. It helps to share the worry with ATC! It is also the format to be used to report another person's possible distress. From an airborne position you may be the only person able to report a fire in an isolated farmhouse or get assistance to a wind surfer 20 miles off Lands End.

The message should be transmitted on the frequency that the aircraft is currently working.

Mnemonic - **R**est **I**n **P**eace **H**orace **H**edgehog

    PAN PAN, PAN PAN, PAN PAN
    NAME OF STATION YOU ARE CALLING
    CALL SIGN OF AIRCRAFT

R - *REASON FOR CALL AND NATURE OF URGENCY*
I - *INTENTION OF THE PILOT*
P - *POSITION*
H - *HEIGHT, FLIGHT LEVEL OR ALTITUDE*
H - *HEADING*

! - Any other useful information. Your qualification*, number of people on board, anything that will help the controller to help you.

* Knowing that you do/don't have an instrument or IMC rating will ensure that the controller does not give you headings into conditions beyond your experience. Inexperienced civil pilots should use the call sign prefix TYRO to indicate their lack of experience.

The ATC Unit dealing with a PAN call is put on a state of **urgency**, which is officially a condition concerning the safety of an aircraft or its occupants, or a situation in sight of the aircraft occupants, but does not require any immediate assistance.

PARALLAX ERROR

The reading error resulting from interpreting an instrument display at an angle other than head on. Also referred to as Slant Error.

PARALLEL RUNWAYS

Where an airfield has two parallel runways each runway is suffixed L (Left) or R (Right). If there is an additional centre runway it is suffixed C.

PILOT'S OPERATING HANDBOOK

Usually found with more modern US built light aircraft. The manual contains information regarding the safe operation of the aircraft together with performance statistics.

PITOT PRESSURE

Pitot pressure is used by the air speed indicator. It is fed to the instrument by a pitot tube and it is a combination of static pressure and dynamic pressure.

PITOT TUBE

The pitot tube is the device used to feed a combination of dynamic & static pressure to the **air speed indicator**. Refer to reference section for more details. Errors occur in the indications due to the fixed position of the tube. Various configurations of the aircraft mean that the pitot head cannot always be pointing directly into the airflow. Position error correction tables are produced by aircraft manufacturers and can be found in the aircraft operators manual.

The pilot tube is normally heated by an electrical element which is used to prevent an ice blockage. The use of pitot heat is essential when an aircraft is in an area of visible moisture and the ambient temperature is +5°C or less. The pitot head is a very efficient collector of ice, by virtue of its design, and will ingest ice crystals which will not collect elsewhere on the aircraft. Its blockage, especially in IMC conditions, can lead to fatal consequences.

If the pressure inlet port is blocked but the moisture drain remains open, the indicated airspeed will be erroneously low and eventually read zero. If both ports are blocked it will tend to read as an altimeter, increasing as the aircraft climbs, reducing as it descends. On encountering seemingly illogical ASI indications it is possible for the pilot to become fixated on attempting to recover to a normal cruise speed. By reacting to the indicated speed, control movements opposite to those which would help, will increase the ASI error, eventually reaching a point where structural failure occurs if the surface of the Earth does not intervene first.

POINT OF NO RETURN

The point calculated for in flight planning beyond which an aircraft will have insufficient fuel to return to the starting point.

POLAR FRONT - Northern Hemisphere

The term used to describe the divide between cold polar air in the North and the warmer air to the South. The mixing of these two air masses provides a great influence on the weather affecting the UK and Northern Europe. It lies between Newfoundland and the North of Scotland in winter and Florida and the South West of England during the summer.

POLARISATION

Polarisation refers to the direction or plane of an electrical field. A vertically polarised signal is one who's electrical field is vertical to the Earth's surface. The polarisation of a signal remains constant when transmitted. To achieve the greatest gain in reception the receiving aerial should be set to the same polarisation as the transmitter.

PORTABLE TELEPHONES

Telephone systems developed for Trans-Atlantic and similar jet traffic routes use discrete frequencies and work to a totally different basis to the modern portable cellular telephone. By virtue of their name cellular telephone systems are designed to hold a frequency on a geographical cell ready for a transmitting phone to be 'nearest to it'.

As the system works on a line of sight basis, a telephone in an aircraft with a height of a few thousand feet could tie up hundreds of frequencies even through it only requires two at most. It is for this main reason that the use is discouraged. In addition, it contravenes the aircraft and telephone users licencing agreements and may interfere with VOR/DME/GPS/COM equipment.

PRECIPITATION

Solid and liquid precipitation is classified to enable a common description to be given and understood. The durations are:-

Duration	Description
Showers	Sunshine between periods of precipitation
Intermittent	Overcast between periods of precipitation
Continuous	Continuous!

In the case of liquid they are:-

Droplet Size	Description
0.2mm diameter	Drizzle
2.9mm diameter	Moderate
5.5mm diameter	Heavy

For solids:-

Title	Description
Sleet	Rain & sleet falling together or snow that melts as it falls
Granular Snow (grains)	Opaque white ice less than 1mm in diameter
Ice Needles	Ice crystals less than 2mm long, needle shaped
Snow	Large combinations of opaque and feathery crystals in complex branched hexagonal shapes
Snow Pellets	Opaque white snow like structures about 2mm diameter. Crisp, will rebound from a hard surface and break up
Soft Hail	Opaque white round pellets of snow

Snow on the Ground

Title	Description
Dry Snow	Snow that can be blown if loose and if compacted by hand will fall apart
Wet Snow	Snow that if compacted by hand will form a snowball
Compacted Snow	Snow which has been compressed and resists further compression. Will break up in lumps if picked up
Slush	Water saturated snow which can be splattered with a heel and toe motion

Precipitation will also affect **Visibility**, refer to the reference section covering the variations in more detail.

PRECISION APPROACH PATH INDICATORS - PAPI

These are a system of angled lights, red in the lower half, white in the top. They a classed as having sharp transition characteristics which effectively means that as opposed to showing a pink colour transition they will either show red or white.

PAPIs are usually installed as a four unit display on the left hand side of the runway, in a full array eight units are mounted adjacent to the touchdown point, four units each side of the runway. The outermost units (4) are set 0.5° lower than the approach angle, the next (3) 0.17° lower, (2) 0.16° higher and the innermost (1) 0.5° higher.

For use by large eye/wheel height aircraft the wing bar is positioned 120 metres further upwind and the on slope channel opened out to 0.5°.

The system is usable down to 50 feet and on a theoretical 3° glideslope will give the following indications:-

	Left	4	3	2	1	Right
Too Low (less than 2.5°)		Red	Red	Red	Red	
Slight Low (2.7°)		White	Red	Red	Red	
Correct - On Slope (3°)		White	White	Red	Red	
Slightly High (3.3°)		White	White	White	Red	
Too High (more than 3.5°)		White	White	White	White	

PRECISION APPROACH RADAR - PAR

Primary radar equipment which is used to determine the vertical and lateral position of an aircraft during an approach. The controller is able to pass the pilot corrective actions to prevent or correct any deviations from the correct approach path.

Refer also to the reference section on Decision Height and Radar.

PRESSURE GRADIENT

A pressure gradient is the rate of change of pressure with distance. It is measured in at the surface in millibars, at right angles to the **isobars** and usually at 100 nautical mile intervals.

PRESSURE GRADIENT FORCE

This is the force created by the difference between high and low pressure systems. The force moves from high to low as it attempts to equalise the atmospheric pressure. This movement of air is referred to as wind. If the isobars are plotted close together a steep pressure gradient is said to exist, if they are widely spaced the gradient is slack. Pressure reduces with height and although actual situations will vary it may be assumed to reduce at 1 millibar per 30 feet.

The pressure gradient force is affected by the Coriolis Force producing the **Geostrophic Wind.** Refer to the reference section for more details.

PRIME MERIDIAN

The prime meridian is also known as the **Greenwich Meridian**. It passes through Greenwich, London and has a value of zero degrees. It is used as the datum for positions East and West of this line.

PRIVATE PILOT'S LICENCE - PPL

The full privileges and restrictions of the PPL are given in the Air Navigation Order (ANO) 1985. Very briefly a few points are:-

a) The minimum age is 17 years for the issue of a PPL

b) There is no expiry date once granted

c) A minimum of 5 hours must be flown as pilot in command within 13 months of the last certificate of experience, or issue of the original licence, for the licence to remain valid.

d) A personal flying log book must be maintained. Refer to Article 22 of the ANO for clarification.

PROCEDURE TURN

A standardised left turn of 45° to the reciprocal of an inbound track. Normally used in an instrument approach to intercept a final approach track. Banking within the turn is at 3° per second.

PROHIBITED AND RESTRICTED AREAS

Unlike danger areas where an activity service is available and they may be crossed when inactive, prohibited and restricted areas should always be taken as active unless hours or months of activity are published.

The following are in this category and further details will be found under the individual reference sections:-

a) Bird Sanctuaries

b) High Intensity Radio Transmission Areas

c) In Flight refuelling Areas

d) Military Training Areas

PROPELLER

Fixed Pitch Propellers are, by virtue of their name, fixed in pitch. The blade angle at any particular section cannot be changed. If the rpm is constant the **Angle of Attack** (AoA) and direction of the relative airflow is determined by the forward speed. The AoA will decrease as the airspeed increases, so ultimately, no thrust will be produced. A fixed pitch propeller is at its most efficient at one airspeed and therefore, one angle of attack.

Variable Pitch Propeller

The limitations of a fixed pitch are overcome by the introduction of a **Variable Pitch (VP), Constant Speed Propeller**. A **Constant Speed Unit** (CSU) contains a governor which regulates the propeller rpm. It automatically adjusts the blade angle so that the rpm is maintained irrespective of airspeed and the power delivered by the engine.

At low airspeeds an optimum angle of attack is achieved with a small blade angle, known as **Fine Pitch**. With increased speed such as in the cruise, a **Coarse Pitch**, large angle of attack, is required for maximum efficiency.

The advantages of a variable pitch propeller are:-

a) If the aircraft is climbed the blade will fine off to maintain the rpm and the power will remain unchanged

b) If the aircraft dives the speed will increase but the propeller will coarsen preventing over-revving of the engine

c) Full engine power is instantly available in the event of a go around

d) Reverse pitch or ground-fine pitch may be available to reduce a ground run by acting as a braking action

e) In the event of an engine failure the propeller may be feathered

When a propeller is feathered the blades are rotated so that the leading and trailing edges are nearly parallel with the aircraft's flight path. This reduces drag to the minimum possible and is part of the standard shutdown drill for a variable pitch propeller. For associated engine failure effects refer to the section on Critical Engine.

PULSE LIGHT APPROACH SLOPE INDICATOR - PLASI

The system emits pulsing red or white lights when the approach slope is too high or low. A steady white light indicates when the aircraft is on the glideslope and a steady red light when just below the glidepath.

The installation is located to 15 metres to the left of the runway and 150 metres upwind of the threshold.

PYROTECHNICS

A grand sounding name for firework-type flares. They are used by ground based personnel to warn pilots of an airspace infringement or possible danger. Inadvertently entering an active danger area at night would probably result in pyrotechnics being directed towards the aircraft. Refer to the reference section on **Light Signals** for the meanings of the lights used.

QUADRANTAL RULE

For all flights in Instrument Meteorological Conditions outside controlled airspace it is compulsory to comply with the quadrantal rule. It is also a strong recommendation that VFR flights above 3,000 feet amsl comply with it.

The rules applies for all flights below 24,500 amsl after which the **Semi-Circular Rules** apply.

The rule states that for a given **magnetic track** an aircraft should be:-

Magnetic Track	Rule	Available Flight Levels
000° - 089°	Odd Levels	30, 50, 70, 90, 110 etc
090° - 179°	Odd + 500	35, 55, 75, 95, 115 etc
180° - 269°	Even Levels	40, 60, 80, 100, 120 etc
270° - 359°	Even + 500	45, 65, 85, 105, 125 etc

In the United Sates a similar rule exists and is known as the hemispheric rule

RADAR ALTIMETER

A very sophisticated narrow beam radar system aimed directly below the aircraft. As with conventional primary radar the time taken for the returning pulses to be received is used to display the actual height above terrain or sea. The display effectively gives constantly updated QFE information without a sub-scale setting or input from the pilot.

RADAR - PRIMARY

Primary radar systems transmit a continuous train of pulses from a revolving parabolic aerial. The pulses are transmitted typically for one millionth of a second. The transmitter then cuts off for around one thousandth of a second for its receiving phase and then restarts. The number of pulses sent per second are referred to as the Pulse Repetition Frequency.

This frequency controls the range of the radar as the returning pulse must be received back before the next pulse is sent. The transmissions are in the UHF band and are affected by line of sight restrictions. Weather also affects radar returns. Thunderstorms will emit electrical pulses across the full frequency spectrum and large quantities of water droplets will reflect the pulses, showing on the cathode display as weather clutter.

When these pulses strike an object of sufficient mass, some of the pulses are returned and received by the station. The direction of the object can be displayed on a Cathode Ray Tube as this will directly relate to the direction in which the aerial was pointing when the signal struck it. The slant range distance can be displayed by the receiver calculating the time taken for the signal to leave the transmitter and be received back divided by two. It then converts this to distance by using speed x time, using the fact that radio waves travel at the speed of propagation, 300×10^6 Mt/Sec.

To calculate an actual ground distance of an aircraft from the radar head the aircraft's height would need to be taken into account.

Ground Clutter affects primary radar by giving ghost ground returns from certain areas. This effect is reduced by **Moving Target Indicator (MTI)** intelligence circuits which are able to distinguish between clutter and moving targets. Radar signals reflected from fixed objects on the Earth's surface are discernible from ground clutter by being in fixed locations. This is known as **Permanent Echo** and are sometimes used to check radar alignment.

Thunderstorms affect displays which would block out any returns in the area, modern equipment has suppressors fitted to reduce this influence in a similar way to the MTI circuits. Temporarily removing the suppressors from the system can enable the controller to give a pilot routing information around thunderstorm activity.

RADAR - SECONDARY SURVEILLANCE - SSR

Refer to the Transponder section for information on the receiver.

The SSR transponder should be operated in accordance with the following:-

a) If proceeding from an area where a specific code has been assigned, maintain that code setting unless otherwise instructed.

b) Select or re-select, switch off or to standby only when instructed to by ATC.

c) Acknowledge code settings instructions by a read back.

d) Select Mode C with Mode A unless instructed by ATC.

e) When reporting levels under routine procedures or when requested, state the displayed reading to the nearest 100 feet to confirm Mode C data. If a variation of +/- 300 feet exists ATC will instruct the pilot to de-select Mode C and select code 0000.

SSR with Mode 3/A 4096 code and Mode C is compulsory in the UK for all aircraft:-

a) When flying under IFR within controlled airspace.

b) When flying at and above FL 100.

c) When flying within airspace notified as having special rules.

d) In the Scottish TMA above 6,000 feet amsl.

e) Except for gliders.

f) Except for aircraft below FL 100 in controlled airspace receiving an approved crossing service.

Secondary Radar requires a participating receiver to be fitted in an aircraft. The ground based transmitter emits a train of pulses normally omni-directionally which is recognised by an aircraft receiver. The receiver then sends a reply from its transmitter at a different frequency. This is known as a **Transponder**.

Modes - The pulse trains used are able to carry additional information. The transmitted interrogation signal is composed of two pulses, the space between the pulses determines the mode used.

Mode	Spacing	Transponder's Reply
Mode A	8 microseconds	Omni-directional up to 14 pulses
Mode B	17 microseconds	N/A in Europe
Mode C	21 microseconds	Height Read Out
Mode D	25 microseconds	Various (Experimental)

Secondary Surveillance is the phrase commonly used to describe systems which provide additional information on primary radar targets. As well as displaying the Transponder discrete code and height to the controller, it may be to display a registration number, aircraft type, TAS and route details.

RADAR SEPARATION

Various minimums are applied, a summary is as follows. They are applicable between aircraft under IFR flights, IFR and Special VFR flights and Special VFR flights. The terrain clearances relate to aircraft under radar advisory service in or out of controlled airspace, not those under RIS, SVFR or VFR even if they are accepting radar vectors.

Standard (basic minimum) separation is 5nm horizontal which may be increased if the situation warrants, or reduced to 3nm when within 40nm of the radar head below FL 245 (when authorised by NATCS Headquarters). This is increased to 8nm when SSR only is available.

Lateral Separation

a) **Dead Reckoning** - Tracks diverging by at least 45° and at a distance of 15nm or more from the point of intersection of the tracks. The point is determined visually or by reference to a navigation aid.

b) **Geographical** - Positive position reports at different geographical locations determined visually or by reference to a navigation aid.

c) **NDB** - Tracks separated by at least 30° and a distance of 15nm or more from the facility.

d) **VOR** - Tracks separated by at least 15° and a distance of at least 15nm from the facility.

Longitudinal Separation - Time Based

For aircraft on the same track and at the same cruising level.

a) 15 minutes normal time separation.

b) 10 minutes in a rapid fixing area.

c) 5 minutes when the preceding aircraft has a TAS at least 20kts faster.

d) 2 minutes when the preceding aircraft has a TAS at least 40kts faster.

Crossing Tracks

Time - 15 minutes normal time separation reduced to 10 minutes in rapid fixing areas.

Distance - 20nm distance to DME or, if the crossing aircraft is at least 20kts faster 10nm. Climbing or descending, 10nm at the time the level is crossed.

Climbing or Descending

15 minutes normal time separation reduced to 10 minutes in rapid fixing areas, or 5 minutes when the level change commences within 10 minutes of the time the second aircraft has reported over an exact reporting point.

Vertical Separation

This is achieved by allocating aircraft different flight levels. The minimum separation between two aircraft on reciprocal tracks is 1,000 feet up to FL 290 and 2,000 feet above.

Vertical separation is also provided between holding aircraft and aircraft en-route when the en-route aircraft is five minutes flying time away.

An aircraft at a cruising level has priority over other aircraft, for two aircraft at the same cruising level the preceding aircraft has priority.

Terrain Clearance

Within 30nm of the radar head but excluding the final and intermediate approach area - 1,000ft above any fixed obstacle which is closer than 5nm to the aircraft or which is situated within the area 15nm ahead of and 20° either side of the aircraft's track. These distances may be reduced to 3nm and 10nm respectively where official CAA approval has been promulgated. Levels assigned to aircraft during initial approach will also provide this terrain clearance.

30nm or more from the radar head, for flights on airways or advisory routes - 1,000ft above any fixed obstacle within 15nm of the centreline. Otherwise 1,000ft above any fixed obstacle within 30nm of the aircraft.

RADAR SERVICES - Air Traffic Control

Precision Approach Radar - PAR

This service is available to traffic approaching to land at suitably equipped aerodromes. The service is similar to en-route radar coverage except that precise heading and glide path instructions will be given to enable the flight to complete a visual landing.

The service is terminated 400 metres from the end of the runway except when:-

a) Carrying out an emergency approach and landing.

b) Carrying out a practice emergency approach in conditions better that 500 ft cloudbase and 1nm visibility.

c) ATC requests a practice emergency approach for ATC training purposes.

ILS Approach Monitored by Precision Approach Radar.

An approach radar controller will, whenever PAR is available, monitor an ILS approach if requested by the pilot, or when the weather is at the prescribed minima.

The radar controller will advise the pilot that the approach is being monitored and providing the flight path remains within 0.5° above or below the glide path and 2° either side of the centreline no instructions will be issued. The pilot will be advised if the aircraft exceeds these parameters and if requested by the pilot will issue heading and height instructions, effectively taking control of the flight.

Radar Vectoring for an ILS Approach

Aircraft being positioned for a final approach will be given vectors to close on the localiser at a range of at least 5nm from the runway threshold and at a level below the glidepath. The last vector will be a turn onto the localiser and the pilot will be asked to confirm **localiser established**.

If requested by the pilot ATC will give another vector to bring the aircraft onto the localiser.

Occasionally, to maintain adequate separation, an aircraft may be vectored through the localiser for an approach from the other side. Pilots will be fore-warned of this action.

Surveillance Radar Approach - SRA

Similar to a precision approach except that no height information is available. Height checks will be given to the pilot as the aircraft passes various distances from the threshold and headings will be passed to maintain the centreline.

The service will terminate at 0.5nm, 1nm or 2nm dependent on the type of equipment. The termination distance will be stated by the controller at the beginning of the procedure to enable the pilot to check for the appropriate decision height. The **No Gyro Approach** or **No Gyro Vectors** is a radar approach procedure used in the case of gyrocompass or directional gyro failure, it may be used with PAR or SRA equipment. The pilot is instructed to turn left, right or stop turn as appropriate by the radar controller observing the radar track.

Radar Control Service

This is provided in **Controlled Airspace** and **Special Rules Zones** and provides the following services:-

a) Radar separation and monitoring of arriving, departing and en-route aircraft.

b) Radar vectoring and assistance with navigation.

c) Information on observed weather.

d) Assistance in distress.

e) Proximity hazard warning.

f) Assistance in crossing controlled airspace.

Lower Airspace Radar Service - LARS

LARS is available in UK controlled airspace up to FL 95 and within 30nm of each unit. The majority of the participating aerodromes are military, so the service is mainly restricted to 'office hours' on weekdays, 0800 - 1700hrs local time. Other units may operate on a 24 hour basis. Details of coverage, operational hours and contact frequencies are in the Air pilot.

Outside controlled airspace upon contacting a ATCU a pilot will be, by default, offered a **Flight Information Service**. If a radar service is required it must be specified on the initial call. *'ATC Callsign, this is callsign, request Lower Airspace Radar Service'*. On receiving the *'pass your message'*, pass the normal information end with *'Request Radar Information/Radar Advisory Service'*. On receiving verbal confirmation from the controller that you have an agreed service, act accordingly. The differences between the services are as follows:-

Radar Advisory Service - RAS

This service is available to any aircraft under any flight rules or conditions. It will be provided subject to workload and is granted in priority to aircraft on an ADR, in Advisory Airspace, in the vicinity of aerodromes and IMC conditions.

The service offered is similar to that of a control service but under an RAS the controller will expect the pilot to comply with radar vectors or flight level allocations for avoidance of other traffic. That may involve flight into IMC, if the pilot is unable to fly in IMC the controller must be advised. Under these circumstances the service will probably be downgraded to a Radar Information Service (RIS) or Flight Information Service. The RAS is an advisory service and the final responsibility for collision avoidance lies with the pilot. The pilot **must** state that he/she is not going to comply with ATC instructions if he/she does not intend to.

Under RAS the pilot should not make any changes of heading or height without a request an ATC approval. Quadrantal rules apply. Separation sought will be; 3nm horizontal separation between identified aircraft working the same unit, or 5nm horizontal separation between identified and other observed aircraft unless 1,000 feet vertical separation is known to exist.

Further LARS information can be found in the UK AIP RAC 3-6-13.

Military Middle Airspace Radar Advisory Service

In all respects the same as LARS RAS except that it is available only from Military ATC Radar Units. It is offered to all aircraft flying outside controlled airspace in UK FIR (except those on ADRs) and transponder equipped between FL 100 and FL 240. The coverage in the Brize Radar area is restricted to FL 150.

Details of coverage, operational hours and contact frequencies are in the UK Air Pilot RAC 3-6-17.

Radar Information Service - RIS

This service may be offered if RAS is impracticable. Again the services available are similar to a Radar Control Service but traffic information will be limited to range and bearing with no avoidance action offered. The pilot may request an upgrade to RAS at any time which may be granted at the controllers discretion.

Handover or Termination of Service

As an aircraft reaches the limits of a control area, or is unable to maintain radar contact, the controller will:-

a) Advise the pilot of his position and suggest a freecall to the next controller. This will normally only be done if the airspace is clear and the flight is VMC, even under IFR. The pilot must then contact the next controller making a full contact message.

b) Talk to the next radar controller by landline, obtain a new squawk and pass the aircraft's details. The pilot will then be advised of the squawk and given a contact frequency. The pilot may then contact the new controller confirming only his call sign and height, ATC will request any further details if required.

c) Use the **Radar Point Out** procedure where the current radar controller retains RT communication with the aircraft whilst it penetrates another controller's airspace.

d) Advise **Radar Service Terminated**, this may be because the aircraft has reached the limits of the controller's area or that because of terrain he is unable to provide the required service. In the later case he may offer a reduced service, for instance FIS, until able to upgrade.

e) If the flight is in controlled airspace or an airway the message *Continue with ....(Unit) on .... Frequency,* and any other relevant instructions. Refer also to the reference section on Flight Information Services.

RADIATION FOG

Radiation fog forms over low lying, moist, inland areas and is caused by the radiation of heat from the surface into the atmosphere. As the surface temperature drops, usually late afternoon, the air closest to the surface is cooled to its dewpoint temperature causing condensation to occur. If the wind is within 3 to 10 knots the droplets will be held in suspension forming a fog. This will usually persist overnight until sunrise when the surface is warmed by the sun. If the fog is sufficiently thick it will prevent the Sun's rays from reaching the surface. It will therefore remain until a stronger wind or a change of air mass occurs.

RADIO MAGNETIC INDICATOR - RMI

Refer to the reference section on **Very High Frequency Omni-Directional Range** and **Automatic Direction Finding** for information on the transmission and reception of signals used by the RMI.

The RMI displays magnetic bearing information. It can be used with ADF or VOR receivers or a dual needle display combining both system displays. They are also available with dual ADF and dual VOR needles.

The RMI display is a rotating compass card which is slaved to the magnetic compass so that the magnetic heading of the aircraft is always shown at the top of the card. The needles on the RMI regardless of whether they are VOR or ADF will always point towards the ground position of the relevant transmitter and will show the aircraft's QDM.

Tracking en route using an RMI must take into account any wind drift as any heading will only hold good in zero wind conditions. A wind drift allowance, i.e. the difference between the heading and the track must be laid in.

If the aircraft is blown to the right of the required track the OBI needle will drift to the left showing that a turn to the left to recapture the needle to the centre line. Needle left turn left. If the aircraft is blown to the left of the required track the RBI needle will drift to the right showing that a turn to the right to recapture the needle to the centre line. Needle right turn right. A heading can be worked out by trial and error that will hold a radial and maintain the RMI needle on the correct indication.

Using the RMI for a position fix requires two beacons and may be displayed simultaneously making it the easiest navigation instrument to use for this purpose. Ideally the two beacons should be selected for their locations so that their intercept angle lines to the aircraft are at least 30° and not more than 150°.

RADIOSONDE

An electronic weather station carried aloft by balloon with equipment that is able to record humidity, pressure and temperature (plus other information dependent on type) and transmit the information to a ground station. For high level recordings the device is launched by rocket and returns to Earth by parachute. It is then referred to as a **Rocketsonde**.

RADIO WAVES

There are three basic types of radio waves used in aviation, sky waves, surface waves and direct waves.

Direct Wave

Direct wave transmissions are in a straight line from transmitter to receiver. They are used for VHF transmissions and above. The maximum theoretical range of a transmission is:-

$$R = 1.25 \text{ x (Square root of H1 + square root of H2)}$$

Where H1 = the height of the transmitter (AMSL). H2 = the height of the receiver (AMSL). R = the range in nautical miles.

The practical restrictions of this are:-

a) the power of the transmitter.

b) the sensitivity of the receiver in its ability to extract the correct signal from that of interference

c) the selectivity of the receiver to be tuned to exactly that of the transmitted frequency.

d) any physical obstructions, all transmissions rely on 'line of sight'.

Surface Waves

Surface waves are also known as ground waves. This is because frequencies in the LF & MF bands follow the curvature of the Earth due to diffraction. Because of the relatively low frequencies in these wave bands the amount of surface attenuation is small and high power transmitters may be used to achieve ranges of typically 300nm over land and 1000nm over the sea.

Sky Waves

Sky waves are chiefly restricted to the HF frequency band. If a HF frequency is directed towards the **ionosphere** it will be subject to refraction within the inonospheric layer. An angle of transmission is selected so that the refraction will cause the wave to return to the Earth's surface. The radio wave that returns to Earth closest to the transmitter is referred to as the **first returning sky wave.** The angle between the vertical and the angle of the transmitted wave is referred to as the **critical angle.**

Transmission angles of less than the critical angle will result in the wave passing through the ionosphere and out in to space, and not being refracted back to Earth.

Due to the properties of an HF transmission it is subject to a high amount of surface contact and accompanying attenuation. This results in a small range of **surface wave cover**. The area between the point where the surface wave cover ends and the first returning sky wave starts is referred to as the **dead space**. In this area no transmission can be received.

Carrier Waves

The simplest method of transmitting radio waves is by carried wave. This is a wave that is transmitted at a constant frequency and amplitude. This is designated a **NON** emission. If interrupted by a Morse code ident it is designated an **A1A** emission. Both of these emissions use a frequency too high for detection by the human ear and so the receiver must be fitted with a modulator to make the signal audible. This is referred to as a **Beat Frequency Oscillator.**

Modulation

Human speech cannot be transmitted directly in the form of radio waves as the frequencies are too low to be sent efficiently. Speech, music and single audio frequencies are combined with a carrier wave to raise the frequency to an efficient level. This is known as **modulation.**

A modulated carrier wave can then be transmitted to a receiver that then separates the carrier wave from the audio wave, it discounts the carrier wave and passes the remaining audible signal to a speaker or headset.

The types of modulation used are:-

AM   -   Amplitude Modulation
FM   -   Frequency Modulation
P   -   Pulse Modulation

Amplitude Modulation - The amplitude of a carrier wave may be varied in accordance with an audio signal, transmitted, and decoded at the receiver. For instance if an audio frequency of 2Khz needs to be transmitted it can be combined with a carrier wave of say, 128Khz. The resultant will be the carrier wave frequency of 128Khz plus two **Side Band** frequencies, one of 130Khz and one of 126Khz. The highest frequency is referred to as the **Upper Sideband,** the lowest as the **Lower Sideband**. The spread of the frequencies is known as a **Bandwidth** and in this example would have the value of 4Khz and would be an A2A emission suitable for a fixed tone audio transmission.

This type of transmission would use a large range of frequencies and can be made more economical by removing the upper or lower sideband as they are mirror images of each other and contain no unique information. The resultant is known as a **Single Sideband Transmission.** In the above example the frequencies used in the transmission would be from 128Khz to 130Khz if the 126Khz sideband was suppressed. The 126Khz band is now released for another channel. AM signals tend to suffer from unwanted interference as noise frequencies tend to modulate the amplitude of the signal.

Frequency Modulation - In this type of transmission the amplitude of the carrier wave remains constant but the frequency is altered in accordance with the modulations of the audio wave. The amplitude of the audio wave determines the size of the bandwidth and greater frequency separation is required for FM transmissions than those of AM. FM signals are less prone to interference when compared to AM.

Pulse Modulation - Pulses are normally a short burst, normally around one microsecond, followed by a equivalently long pause, conventionally of around one millisecond, before a further burst. Pulse modulation is used in Distance Measuring

Equipment, Secondary Surveillance Radar and Primary Radar.

Interference - Most radio transmissions are affected by interference. This will either be from a natural atmospheric source classed as **Static** or from a man made source classed as **Noise**.

Noise - Any electrical equipment will produce noise interference. Equipment which has moving parts and electrical connections will produce electronic pulses of random frequencies.

Static - is used to describe any type of natural interference. Sun Spot activity will affect HF transmissions. All types of active weather causing movement of air and moisture molecules will produce a static charge. As this discharges it produces electro-magnetic energy which affects HF, MF and LF frequencies.

Precipitation Static particularly affects ADF receivers when precipitation strikes an airframe and static discharges take place. **Static Wicks** are often attached to the trailing edges of the wings to minimise this effect.

RATE ONE TURN

A turn made at 3° a second, 180° in one minute. It is the rate of turn recommended for non-instrumented pilots to use to reverse direction upon inadvertently entering cloud. It is also the rate of turn that should not be exceeded in normal instrument flight.

It is indicated to the pilot by the Turn Indicator which will show a rate one line as it is calibrated to the aircraft, or as an angle on the artificial horizon arrived at by the calculation of; TAS(Knots)/10 + 7 = Rate of Turn°.

REFERENCE HUMIDITY

ISA reference humidity is defined as:-

a) At temperatures at or below (ISA) +15°C
   80% relative humidity

b) At temperatures at or above (ISA +28°C) +43°C
   34% relative humidity

c) At temperatures between (ISA) +15°C and (ISA +28°C) +43°C

The relative humidity varies linearly between the humidity specified for those temperatures.

REFRACTIVE SURGERY

Procedures are available where laser surgery is performed to etch the cornea surface. This may be considered by some pilots as an alternative to wearing spectacles. The procedure may produce side effects such as glare or distortion and the long term effects are as yet unknown. Pilots considering any type of voluntary eye surgery should consult the CAA Medical Division for advise prior to committing to an operation.

RELATIVE BEARING INDICATOR

Refer to the section on **Automatic Direction Finding** for further information on the transmission and reception of NDB signals.

A typical relative bearing indicator has a fixed compass card showing a full 360°. The 360° indication is normally aligned with the nose of the aircraft. On some RBI instruments it is possible to adjust the compass card to any desired setting but the needle indications may then become confusing and many pilots and instructors recommend against this method.

Information from the display is shown by a needle which displays the bearing to the beacon relative to the fore-aft axis of the aircraft. It is a very simple and basic indication and has no other function that to display this **relative** bearing.

Tracking en route using an RBI must take into account any wind drift as any bearing indication will only hold good in zero wind conditions. A wind drift allowance, i.e. the difference between the heading and the track, would also be shown by the RBI as the same number of degrees off 360° when tracking directly to a beacon.

The RBI can be used for a position fix and requires two beacons. The magnetic heading of the aircraft must be added to the relative bearing on the RBI (less 360 if the figure exceeds 360) which will give the magnetic track to the first beacon. The track must then be adjusted to convert to a true value taking into account the variation at the aircraft's position. A second beacon can then treated in the same way to provide a cross reference.

RELATIVE HUMIDITY

Relative Humidity is the ratio between the actual amount of water present in a parcel of air in comparison to the amount of water that parcel could hold at that temperature. It is expressed as a percentage.

When air is saturated the relative humidity is 100%, after this point (the **Dew Point**) cloud, dew, fog or mist forms. Relative humidity is directly affected by the temperature, the higher the temperature of the air the more water vapour it will hold before reaching saturation. Relative humidity and Dew Point can be evaluated by use of a **Wet and Dry Bulb Thermometer**.

REPETITIVE FLIGHT PLAN - RFP

A flight plan related to a series of regularly repeated flights with identical basic features. The plan may be submitted by the pilot or aircraft operator and retained by Air Traffic Services for retrieval and activation.

ROTOR CLOUDS

Often found in areas of **Mountain Wave** activity where turbulent up and downdrafts swirl around. The clouds are usually cumulus and are accompanied by severe turbulence.

RUDDER

The rudder is attached to the trailing edge of the fin and is for directional control in **Yaw.** It is operated by left or right pressure to foot controlled rudder pedals. If the right pedal is depressed the rudder will move to the right of the fin, and into the airflow causing a yaw to the right.

The use of the rudder in flight is to achieve a balanced turn by complimenting the aileron roll. On some aircraft the ailerons and rudder are coupled to overcome adverse aileron yaw.

RULES OF THE AIR

The Rules of the Air and Air Traffic Control Regulations 1985 are far too complex and details to be fully covered in this book. The following are extracted as the most commonly referred to and included as an aide memoir. Refer to the Air Pilot RAC Section for full details.

In the Air

a) Two aircraft approaching in flight - each turns right.

b) Two aircraft converging in flight, order of precedence is Balloons, Gliders, Airships, Flying Machines.

c) An aircraft being overtaken in the air has the right of way.

d) Right Hand Rule, an aircraft flying within sight of the ground following a road, railway or similar is to keep it to its left.

On the Ground

a) Two aircraft approaching head on, on the ground - each turns left.

b) Aircraft or vehicles converging on the ground, order of precedence is taking off and landing aircraft, vehicles towing aircraft, aircraft, vehicles.

c) Two aircraft converging on the ground - the one which has the other on its right shall give way and avoid crossing ahead of it unless well clear.

d) An aircraft being overtaken has the right of way, the overtaking aircraft shall keeping to the left until ahead and well clear.

Lights

Basic lights are:-

1) **Green light** of at least 5 candela showing to the starboard side through an angle of 110° from dead ahead in the horizontal plane.

2) **Red light** of at least 5 candela showing to the port side through an angle of 110° from dead ahead in the horizontal plane.

3) A **White light** of at least 3 candela showing through angles of 70° from dead astern to each side in the horizontal plane.

For aircraft over 5,700Kg MTWA registered after April 1988 this must also include an **anti-collision light**, red or white. For aircraft registered prior to this date they must display a) the basic lights or b) the basic lights plus an anti-collision lights or c) three basic lights, flashing, plus an additional 20+ candela light showing in all directions flashing in alternation with the three basic lights.

a) **Captive Balloons and Kites** - must be lighted at night if over 60 metres high.

b) **Free Balloons** - must display a steady red light of at least 5 candela showing in all directions not less than 5m and not more than 10m below the basket of lowest part of the balloon.

c) **Gliders** - must display the same basic lights as an aircraft or a steady red light of at least 5 candela showing in all directions.

d) **Airships** - must display basic lights as aircraft but with additional lights for the control car when the engines are stopped.

RUNWAY MARKINGS

All CAA runways have a centreline, threshold and runway designator markings. Non-instrument runways more than 1,100 metres without VASIS have fixed distance markers 300 metres from the threshold.

Precision approach runways have touchdown zone markings up to a distance of 600 metres, placed 150 metres apart. These are made up of the **Threshold Marker**, **Fixed Distance Marker** and **Runway Markers** each at 150 metres. The Threshold and Fixed distance markings bracket the optimum touchdown area.

Arrows showing a **Displaced Threshold** are used to indicate the correct threshold upwind of the actual runway due to obstructions on the final approach.

RUNWAY USAGE

Normally only one aircraft is permitted on the active runway at any one time. An aircraft may be allowed to land on a runway before the preceding aircraft has cleared if:-

a) It is during daylight.

b) The runway is of adequate length.

c) The aircraft on the runway has been warned.

d) The landing aircraft is able to see the aircraft on the runway and taxiway throughout its approach and landing.

It is the pilot's responsibility to ensure adequate separation. ATC will advise *'Land After'* instead of *'Cleared to Land'*. If the pilot does not wish to proceed he/she should Go Around.

If an aircraft is cleared to take off from the active runway while another aircraft is on a final or long final approach ATC will call *'Cleared Immediate Take Off'*. In response the pilot should:-

a) If already lined up on the runway, take off immediately.

b) If waiting at the hold taxi to the runway and commence a take-off run without stopping.

c) If unable to comply (perhaps checks are incomplete) advise ATC immediately. You may be asked to hold or clear the runway. Alternatively the approaching aircraft may be instructed to go around.

To expedite traffic ATC may call *'Callsign - are you ready for immediate take off?'*. If checks are incomplete or you are unable to comply with a) or b), reply, *'Callsign - Negative'*.

RUNWAY VISUAL RANGE - RVR

Runway Visual Range is the visual distance over which the pilot of a landing aircraft can expect to see centreline or runway edge lights on touchdown. It is a range taken from the surface. Actual slant vision will normally be worse and the RVR should be taken as a coarse indication. RVR is essential information at times when visibility is limited and will, if it falls below certain criteria, prevent an aircraft from even making an attempt to land.

There are two methods of measurement. RVR by a human observer or IRVR (**Instrumented Runway Visual Range System**) which is an optical/electronic measurement system known as a **Transmissometer**. The data from this can be manually or automatically converted to a figure of IRVR.

RVR is measured by a ground observer 76 metres perpendicular to the runway centreline abeam the touchdown point. He then counts the number of markers or lights visible to him in the landing direction. This number is converted to a distance as assessed from a point 5 metres above the centreline, and passed to the pilot as the RVR. RVR is assessed when the visibility falls below 1,500 metres (2,000 metres in some countries). It is always an actual report and is never forecast. The most recent measurement is passed to the aircraft throughout the approach.

The standard UK RVR reporting increments are:-

Every 25 metres when the visibility is between 50 and 150 metres

Every 50 metres when the visibility is between 150 and 800 metres

Every 100 metres above 800 metres

IRVR systems provide touchdown, mid-point and stop-end visual range values and are switched on when the RVR at any of these points falls below 1,500 metres. The distances are passed to the pilot in the above order.

The latter two are not given if they are higher than the touchdown distance or in excess of 800 metres. If only one of the two later values is not given it is qualified with a distance value.

Although the IRVR system is in the majority of cases much quicker and efficient it does have its machine linked quirks. There have been occasions when a London airport's main runway has been technically closed due to a measured IRVR below limits, whilst according to a human observer, and the control tower, the actual visibility has been several miles.

Note:- A non-public transport aircraft approaching to land on a runway in respect of which there is a notified instrument approach procedure must comply with any relevant aerodrome operating minima in respect of that runway (ANO Am 1990 Article 32A). If the weather falls below these minimas an approach ban applies.

SEA BREEZES

Sea breezes have a very localised effect rarely extending further than 15 miles inland and 1,000 feet vertically. The wind strength will not normally exceed 10 knots.

The breeze is caused by the difference in surface heating of land in comparison to water. Sea temperature remains almost constant even when solar radiation is at its diurnal peak. The land temperatures can vary dramatically (consider the sand on a continental beach after midday).

Sea breezes are most prolific when a slack pressure gradient is present and cloud cover is minimal. The cycle starts after dawn when solar radiation begins to warm the Earth's surface, the air in contact with this is warmed and rises. This causes the geostrophic (2,000 feet) pressure to rise and it drifts towards the area of low pressure which in this case is over the sea. As the cycle continues the high pressure flow begins to build over the sea leaving a low pressure area over the land. The surface air now flows from the sea to the land where it is heated and the cycle continues.

The reverse effect which occurs at sunset is referred to as a **Land Breeze**.

SELECTIVE CALLING SYSTEM - SELCAL

SELCAL is a high frequency speech system. A unit fitted to an aircraft is allocated a code which may be altered. This discrete code is noted on filed flight plans and may be used to contact the aircraft on long range flights. Because the system notifies the crew that a contact call is incoming it alleviates the need for a listening watch.

SEMI-CIRCULAR RULE

For flights in airways at any height and for all flights above 24,500 feet amsl outside controlled airspace in IFR the semi-circular rule must be followed.

Below 24,500 feet amsl in airways (unless authorised by ATC)

Magnetic Track 000° to 179° - Odd Flight Levels, 30, 50, 70, 90 etc
　　　　　　　　180° to 359° - Even Flight Levels, 40, 60, 80, 100 etc

Outside Controlled Airspace

Magnetic Track 000° to 179° - Flight Levels 250, 270, 290, 330 and every 4,000 feet
　　　　　　　　　　　　　　　thereafter.
　　　　　　　　180° to 359° - Flight Levels 260, 280, 310, 350 and every 4,000 feet
　　　　　　　　　　　　　　　thereafter.

A similar rule applies in the USA, from 3,000 feet to FL 290 and is known as the **Hemispheric Rule**.

SEVERE GALE - Winds - Meteorological

According to the Beaufort Wind Scale a severe gale is a force 9 wind. If the wind reaches 41 - 47 knots (47 - 54 mph) it is said to be severe gale force.

SHORT FIELD TAKE-OFFS AND LANDINGS

The aim of a short field take off is to use as little runway as possible. To achieve this the run should be aimed as close as possible into the prevailing wind. The optimum flap setting should be selected and the roll started from as close to the end of the runway as possible.

Full power should be applied whilst the aircraft is held on the brakes.

Lift off should be at the minimum recommended flying speed, and the best rate of climb angle immediately selected. The lift off and best rate of climb figures will be found in the owner's or operators manual.

Landings using the minimum possible distance are accomplished by carrying out a powered approach with full flap being lowered in the final stages. Accurate control of airspeed is achieved by power adjustments so that the aircraft should pass over the threshold by only a few feet, and at the correct threshold speed.

When full flap is used due consideration must be given to the crosswind. The limits will reduce with the amount of flap lowered. The owner's manual or operators handbook will give the recommended limits.

Retractable Undercarriage Aircraft - If flaps are raised immediately after touchdown to improve braking, tyre adhesion, or elevator effectiveness, great care must be taken to avoid selecting the gear up lever. The electric flap and gear levers are on some aircraft, almost identical.

SIGNIFICANT METEOROLOGICAL INFORMATION - SIGMET

A SIGMET is a warning message passed by ATC to aircraft at subsonic cruising levels liable to be affected by meteorological conditions of one or more of the following:-

a) Active thunderstorm

b) Heavy hail

c) Marked mountain wave activity

d) Tropical revolving storm

e) Severe airframe icing

f) Severe line squall (50kts +)

g) Severe turbulence

h) Duststorms/sandstorms that reduce visibility to less than 3 miles

At transonic and supersonic levels warning messages are sent in respect of:-

a) Cumulus Cloud

b) Hail

c) Moderate or severe turbulence

For aircraft approaching or in the vicinity of an aerodrome the following warning will be given:-

Fog - when visibility is expected to fall below 1,000 metres.

For aircraft on the ground:-

Strong wind warning - when gales (35kt +) gusts (43kt), squalls or snow is imminent.

SIMULATED INSTRUMENT FLIGHT

The Air Navigation Order states that an aircraft shall not be flown in simulated instrument flight conditions unless:-

a) The aircraft is fitted with dual controls.

b) An additional pilot (in this rule called a safety pilot) is carried in a second control seat of the aircraft for the purpose of rendering such assistance as may be necessary to the pilot flying the aircraft; and

c) If the safety pilot's field of vision is not adequate both forward and to each side of the aircraft, a third person, being a competent observer, occupies a position in the aircraft from which his field of vision makes good the deficiencies in that of the safety pilot, and from which he can readily communicate with the safety pilot.

For the purpose of this rule the expression 'simulated instrument flight' means a flight during which mechanical or optical devices are used in order to reduce the field of vision or the range of visibility from the cockpit of the aircraft.

SLANT VISIBILITY

During anticyclonic periods stable air may cause a haze layer to be trapped near the ground. This layer may be many hundreds of feet thick. Under these conditions a ground object that may be seen from overhead will be hidden from a slant distance. This can be particularly problematical for visual flights.

If, for instance, the haze layer is 1,000 feet thick, flying overhead an airfield you would be looking down through 1,000 feet of haze. If however you were cruising at 2,000 feet looking for the airfield from a distance of 5 miles you would be looking through a haze depth of more than 30,000 feet.

SMALL CIRCLE - Geographical

A small circle is an imaginary circle drawn on the surface of the Earth, with a radius that is not the same as that of the Earths' and with a plane that does not pass through the centre of the Earth.

SNOWTAM

Snow clearance plans (SNOPLAN) are issued annually by Class II NOTAM for each airfield. These are plans which may or may not be put into effect. The plan for each airfield contains:-

a) The equipment held and the type of clearance.

b) Height and distance of snow bank if permitted.

c) Contact authority for current information.

d) Any local deviation from standard practice.

If snow does affect an airfield a SNOWTAM is issued. If the snow effects an airfield to the extent that it is forced to close, a **SNOCLO** message will be added to **VOLMET** and **OPMET** messages. Braking action will also be advised to the pilot by ATC or by OPMET.

A SNOWTAM is issued every 24 hours or when a significant change occurs.

Runway conditions are re-assessed every half hour. The reports take a standard format with depth and condition of precipitation and its affect on **runway braking action**.

The priorities for snow clearance are:-

1. Main Runway   2. Run Up Areas   3. Aprons 4.   Taxiways   5. Airport Roads

Runway braking action is measured by a **Mu-Meter** contained within a friction measuring trailer which will verify the possibility of slush-planing when it indicates a low co-efficient of friction.

Braking action is not assessed in slush-planing conditions. A **Tapley Meter** is used to assess braking action on ice and dry snow.

Information is passed to the pilot in the following form:-

Type of Precipitation	Report	Categories
Snow	Braking	Good, Medium good, Medium, Medium Poor, Poor
Snow	Density	Dry, Wet, Compressed, Slush, Standing water
Water	Braking	Good, Medium, Poor
Water	Quantity	Damp, Wet, Water patches, Flooded.

Snow Banks are only passed if they exceed the height outlined in the SNOPLAN.
Any runway contamination greater than 3mm of water, slush or wet snow, or 10mm of dry snow are likely to affect the aircraft's performance by:-

a) Increased drag effect on the wheels and areas impacting the spray.
b) Possible power loss or malfunction due to spray saturation.
c) Reduced braking performance and possible aquaplaning resulting in directional control problems.
d) Possible structural damage.

Take off should not be attempted if the depth of:-

a) Water, slush or dry snow is greater than 15mm.
b) Dry snow is greater than 60mm.
c) Very dry snow is greater than 80mm.

SOFT FIELD TAKE-OFFS & LANDINGS

The soft field take off procedure is used when operating out of soft surface or high friction runways. These may be snow, sand, long wet grass or a rough surface. Firstly the criteria for the aircraft's take off distance requirement must be calculated and met.

The aim is then to reduce the surface wheel weight as soon as possible. This is achieved by maximum power and optimum flap. Full power should be applied against the brakes. On reaching take off power the roll is commenced holding the control stick well back to keep weight off the nose wheel. The aircraft will lift off at a lower speed than normal.

As soon as this is achieved the climb should be checked and the aircraft flown as close as possible to the ground (within 10 feet) to take advantage of the **ground effect**. As soon as normal climb speed is reached a climb can be initiated and at a safe height the flaps retracted.

Landings using the minimum possible speed are accomplished by carrying out a powered approach with full flap being lowered in the final stages. Accurate control of airspeed is achieved by power adjustments so that the aircraft should pass over the threshold at the correct threshold speed. If the landing distance is restricted the threshold height should only be a few feet.

When full flap is used due consideration must be given to the crosswind. The limits will reduce with the amount of flap lowered. The owner's manual or operators handbook will give the recommended limits.

Retractable Undercarriage Aircraft - If flaps are raised immediately after touchdown to improve braking, tyre adhesion, or elevator effectiveness, great care must be taken to avoid selecting the gear up lever. The electric flap and gear levers are on some aircraft, almost identical.

SOMATOGRAVIC ILLUSION

An illusion affecting, primarily, pilots operating from aircraft carriers. A rapid acceleration during take off stimulates the sensory organs to the extent that it creates the illusion of being in a nose-up attitude. A pilot suffering from the illusion will instinctively push the controls forward into a dive. Pilots are trained not to input any control movements in the first few seconds of take-off.

The reverse illusion occurs with rapid deceleration, as caused by arrester gear, giving the pilot a nose down illusion, instinctively resulting in a pull back on the controls.

SPECIAL RULES ZONES - SRZ

At certain major aerodromes Special Rules Zones are established. The dimensions vary and are shown on the appropriate charts. Entry into the zone is subject to prior permission which must be requested by radio whilst at least 10 minutes from the zone boundary. The zone rules only apply during the working hours of the aerodrome ATCU.

If a pilot wishes to enter a SRZ and is unable to comply with IFR he/she may request a **Special VFR Clearance**. The clearance may or may not be granted. If it is granted it does not absolve the pilot of complying with all other rules regarding visibility, terrain clearance and low flying rules.

The permission will normally include a height limit, *'not above .... feet on QNH, route via ... and report at ....'* ATC will provide separation from IFR traffic. The Special VFR permission is not in accordance with IFR and the pilot must remain clear of cloud and in sight of the surface at all times. A private pilot should not accept a Special VFR clearance if the visibility is less than 5nm unless he/she holds an IMC rating.

SPOT WIND CHARTS - Form 214

Spot Wind Charts are issued by the UK meteorological office at Bracknell. The chart shows the time of issue and validity of the charts. The boxes overlaid on the chart itself are placed at intersections of meridians and parallels. When using this chart plot your route and if it passes between two boxes interpolate between the indicated values for the planned height.

The charts are issued at the following times, UTC:-

Fixed Time Validity Hrs	Suitable for flights within the periods	Available at Hrs
0300	0000 - 0600	2300
0800	0600 - 1100	0500
1200	1000 - 1500	0900
1600	1400 - 1900	1300
2100	1800 - 2400	1700

SQUALLS - Meteorological

A squall is the term given to an temporary and sudden increase in windspeed of at least 15 knots to a peak of 20 knots or more which lasts at least one minute at the peak speed. A shorter increase is known as a **Gust**.

STABILITY - Meteorological

There are four expressions used to describe various states of atmospheric stability or instability:-

Absolute Stability - When the **environmental lapse rate** is less than the dry and saturated adiabatic lapse rates absolute stability is said to exist.

Absolute Instability - When the environmental lapse rate is greater than the dry &

saturated adiabatic lapse rates absolute instability is said to exist.

Conditional Instability - When the environmental lapse rate is between the dry and saturated adiabatic lapse rates conditional instability is said to exist.

Neutral Stability - When the environmental lapse rate is equal to the lapse rate of the parcel of air that is being lifted neutral stability is said to exist.

STANDING WAVES - Meteorological

Standing Waves are also known as **Mountain Waves** or **Lee Waves**. As the name implies this refers to air wave formations that are effectively static in position in relation to the mountain. For these waves to be created certain criteria are required:-

a) A range of mountains sloping on the windward side and steep on the leeward side.

b) A wind with a constant direction in height and blowing within 30° of the face of the range.

c) A windspeed of more than 20 knots, increasing with height.

d) A stable layer of air just above the summit of the range with layers of unstable air above and below.

The following cloud types may be present:-

Cap Clouds - covering the windward side and peak of the mountains created by the same process as Foehn Winds. Adiabatic cooling that occurs as the air is forced over the range reduces the freezing level.

Lenticular Clouds - remaining stationary in the stable air in the peak of each wave and may occur at various heights. The high liquid content held in these clouds may cause severe icing.

Roll Cloud - found below the peak on the leeward side, this cloud is created by extreme up and downdrafts known as rotor zones and will mark the area of most turbulence. If there are strong surface winds rotor zones may flow downwind causing **Rotor Streaming.**

If no cloud is present, standing waves will be impossible to detect visually. They will influence the area downwind by up to 250 miles and from the surface to some 30,000 feet in extreme cases. The wavelength of a standing wave may be up to 5 miles.

STATIC ELECTRICITY - Meteorological

A general term used to describe any form of audio radio interference.

It is more likely to affect MF and HF than VHF. Aircraft radio communications are often affected by precipitation static due to discharges into the atmosphere from the airframe following self generated charging in flight. Extreme cases of static discharge produces a visual show of static known as **St Elmo's Fire** or **Corposant**.

STATIC PRESSURE

This is the ambient atmospheric pressure. The variations of static pressure with height (approximately 1 millibar for each 30 feet) is measured by various aircraft instruments and used to display relevant data to the pilot. The instruments that use static pressure are the Airspeed Indicator, Vertical Speed Indicator and Altimeter.

STATIC VENT

The static vent is a small hole, usually on the side of the aircraft fuselage, via which static pressure (see above) is measured. On sophisticated aircraft dual vents will usually be fitted, one each side of the fuselage, to reduce any position errors. An alternate static selector may also be found on some aircraft. This is used in the event that ice formation blocks the external vent, selecting alternate air will feed cabin pressure directly into the static line. If selected the static pressure fed to the altimeter will be lower than the external static pressure causing the instrument indications to be slightly erroneous.

In aircraft where no alternate static exists an alternative is to crack the glass, and therefore the pressure seal of the Vertical Speed Indicator. This will feed static to the other instruments but significant lag will be experienced due to the air having to flow through the VSI's restrictive choke.

STORM - Winds - Meteorological

According to the Beaufort Wind Scale a storm is a force 10 wind. If the wind reaches 48 - 55 knots (55 - 63 mph) it is said to be storm force.

STRATIFORM - Clouds

Stratiform or **Layer Cloud** usually has a uniform base, it is low and grey in appearance. It can appear in ragged patches, often with layers of clear air between further cloud layers. It seldom produces precipitation, if it does it will be light or moderate drizzle or snow grains. Airframe icing no worse than moderate. Small detached stratus fractus clouds below a layer of higher stratiform or nimbostratus clouds are referred to as **Scud**.

Over high ground stratiform clouds form when the air is moist and cools to its dew point as it is forced to rise over a range of hills. The hill itself may be totally covered in cloud, and as the cloud is so dense and close to the ground is referred to as **Fog** or **Hill Fog**. As the air flows over the hill and back to lower ground the cloud will disperse.

Stratocumulus is a low cloud, its base is stratiform in appearance, sometimes with breaks. Grey with whitish patches or layers. It is differentiated from a thick stratus layer by the comparatively uneven tops.

STRATOSPHERE

The stratosphere is the atmospheric layer above the tropopause and starts at around 30 miles above the Earth's surface. This layer has a constant or increasing temperature.

Its upper limits are defined by the stratopause, above which lies the Mesosphere.

STRONG - Winds - Meteorological

According to the Beaufort Wind Scale a force 6 wind is known as strong. If the wind reaches 22 - 27 knots (25 - 31 mph) it is said to be strong.

SUBLIMATION - Meteorological

The name given to the process in which a gas changes directly into a solid without going through a liquid state. In icing conditions water vapour may change directly to ice crystals when coming into contact with an aircraft.

SUBSIDENCE

A phenomenon frequently occurring in **Polar Highs** where there is an extensive area of sinking air. The subsiding air is warmed adiabatically and becomes stable.

SUPER HIGH FREQUENCY - SHF

Frequencies in the range 3 to 30 Ghz with a wavelength of 1 to 10cm. They are used for **precision approach, secondary surveillance,** weather radar and **radio altimeters**. Frequencies in the SHF band are sometimes referred to as **centimetric** or **microwave**.

SURFACE WINDS - Local Winds

The geostrophic wind passing over the surface of the Earth is disturbed if it encounters any obstacles. These may take the form of a man made constructions, natural formations or vegetation.

Their effect on the wind flow in the Northern Hemisphere will be to cause it to slow down and back. **Backing** or to back is the expression given to a wind if it changes direction anti-clockwise when measured from a fixed point or is compared with the direction of the wind at another point. The opposite, changing clockwise, is referred to as **Veering**.

The mixing effect of the wind upon meeting surface obstacles results in a vertical wind layer known as the **Turbulence Layer** or **Friction Layer**.

The friction layer is affected in degree by the wind strength and by the amount of surface heating. Surface heating results in **Thermal Turbulence** by the effect of warmed air rising away from the surface.

The strength of the wind as it encounters an obstacle relates to the amount of turbulence and is known as **Mechanical Turbulence**.

The depth of the friction layer is judged to be thick or thin in comparison with the 2,000 feet geostrophic wind. The thicker the friction layer the less difference there will be between the surface wind and the geostrophic wind.

The friction layer will exhibit predictable diurnal variations. At night when there is no thermal turbulence the friction layer will be at its thinnest.

TACTICAL AIR NAVIGATOR - TACAN

TACAN is the military equivalent of a co-located civil VOR/DME station. They are usually located within a Military Air Traffic Zones and on the airfield. The DME system is identical to the civil equipment and so this may be used by any DME equipped aircraft. The bearing information uses an ultra high frequency rho-theta air navigation system not accessible to un-equipped civil aircraft. A combined VOR/TACAN installation is referred to as a **VORTAC.**

VOR, VORTAC and TACAN Stations are classified according to their operational use. T - Terminal, L - Low Altitude, H - High Altitude.

TECHNICAL LOG

A technical log must be kept for any UK registered aircraft which has a Certificate of Airworthiness valid in either the transport or aerial work category. Various criteria and exceptions apply to this requirement. They may be found under Article 10 of the Air Navigation Order 1985.

TEMPERATURE

The most commonly used aeronautical unit for temperature is **Centigrade.**

Other units used in aviation are **Fahrenheit** and **Kelvin** (also known as **Absolute**). Conversions involving centigrade and Fahrenheit can be made with the navigation computer or by use of the following:-

Celsius to Fahrenheit	(x 1.8) + 32
Fahrenheit to Celsius	(-32) x 0.555

One degree Kelvin has the same value as one degree of centigrade but the units have different datum points.

$$0°C = +273° \text{ Kelvin } -273°C = 0° \text{ Kelvin}$$

0°K is known as absolute zero and is the temperature at which all molecular motion ceases. At standard sea level pressure the freezing point of water is 273°K and the boiling point 373°K.

TERMINAL AERODROME FORECAST - TAF

TAFs are prepared between one and two hours before the start of the period of validity. This elapsed period should be taken into account when considering their accuracy. For civil aerodromes they are valid for either a 9 or 18 hour period, the latter are valid for 24 hours by omission of the first 6 hours and are intended for long duration flights. The 9 hour TAFs are updated every three hours and the 18 hour TAFs every six hours.

Both have routine issue times commencing at 0100 hrs UTC for 9 hour and 0600 hrs UTC for the 18 hour.

Full details of a TAF decode are given in AIC (Yellow) 108 but will always take the following form.

Location Identifier - The ICAO four letter code for an aerodrome.

Time - The date and time of origin followed the letter Z (Zulu Time).

Validity Time - The hours of validity, from and to, in UTC.

Wind - The direction in degrees **true from** which the wind is flowing followed by the measuring unit (usually KTS Knots but could be KMH or MPS).

Horizontal Visibility - The visibility given in metres, 9999 means visibility in excess of 10Km. If the visibility varies in different directions only the lowest value will be indicated.

Weather - Indications will follow some logic for example SHRA - Showers of Rain, +BLSN - Heavy Blowing Snow. The abbreviations in the glossary section will give the decode. If no significant weather is expected this group will be omitted. After a change group if the weather ceases to be significant NSW will be shown (No Significant Weather).

Cloud - This will be given as SCT - Scattered, BRK - Broken or OVC - Overcast followed by the height of the base of the cloud in hundreds of feet above aerodrome level. If significant cloud types are around it will be given after this. Example:- CB-Cumulonimbus. CAVOK, NSC (No Significant Cloud) or SKC (Sky Clear) may also be used.

Trend - This will indicate significant changes during the period of validity and is a self contained TAF within the TAF for the indicated period. For a further explanation refer to trend in the reference section.

Information that is missing from a TAF will be shown by diagonals or slashes (////). If a TAF consists of forecasts for more than one aerodrome the code name TAF will be replaced by FC or FT. Runway Visual Range is not shown in a TAF as it is **never** forecast.

Forecast Temperature, Airframe Ice Accretion and Turbulence are shown on overseas and UK Military TAFs. For decode information refer to AIC 124/1992 (as at time of publication).

THERMAL WIND

In the Northern Hemisphere the thermal wind component blows parallel to the isotherms with the low pressure system to the left. See Buys Ballot's Law. Thermal wind results from the temperature difference between two air masses.

It is possible for two air masses to have similar pressures but differing temperatures. The air will tend to flow from warm to cold and will be affected by the geostrophic force deflecting it to the right in the Northern Hemisphere. Jet streams, found in the upper atmosphere are a result of the thermal gradient.

TORNADOES

These occasionally form within a very large cumulonimbus cloud. They are intense vortices of circulating air which lower towards the surface as **Funnel Clouds.** They are also known as **Cyclones** or **Twisters.** They are micro-systems which have a very low pressure at the centre surrounded by very strong winds. The base of the tornado does not always reach the ground but when it does it will suck up any loose debris in its path. If a tornado occurs over the sea it is then referred to as a **Waterspout.**

TOUCH AND GO

A procedure when an pilot, normally in the process of training for landings, will allow the aircraft to touch down on the runway but then apply full power to take off without making any attempt to slow or stop. A **Stop and Go** is a procedure where the aircraft will come to a complete stop on the runway before taking off into the circuit. The call for a touch and go or stop and go should be made downwind. At the end of training the downwind call will be for a **Full Stop Landing** which advises the controller that it is the final training circuit.

A **Go Around** is a procedure instructed by ATC, when an approaching aircraft is on finals, if there is a reason why the landing would not be safe. It may also be advised by the pilot to ATC if for any reason he/she is not happy with the approach.

TRACK ERROR - ONE IN SIXTY RULE

Track Error = $\dfrac{\text{Distance Off} \times 60}{\text{Distance Gone}}$ Closing Angle = $\dfrac{\text{Distance Off} \times 60}{\text{Distance to Go}}$

TRADE WINDS

Predominant, nearly continuous wind, which blows from the sub-tropical high pressure areas towards the inter-tropical convergence zone. The flow is north easterly in the northern hemisphere and south easterly in the southern hemisphere.

TRANSITION ALTITUDE/LEVEL

The Transition Altitude is the height above mean sea level, above which Instrument Flight Rules traffic must use flight levels.

In the UK this is usually 3,000 ft amsl but may be higher around some airports. It is indicated on approach and departure charts and will usually be advised to the pilot by ATC. The Transition Level is the lowest available flight level.

The **Transition Layer** is the distance between the transition level and the transition altitude. The depth of this layer varies in accordance with the local barometric pressure.

TRANSPONDER

The operation of the transponder system is detailed in the reference section under **Radar - Secondary.** The actual equipment carried in the aircraft requires very little input from the pilot. Apart from the dials to change the displayed numbers there is only one knob.

The possible settings are:-

SBY - STANDBY - Stops the unit's output This may be requested by ATC with the instruction '*Squawk standby*'. This mode should be selected by aircraft within an ATZ.

ON - This selects Mode A and displays the pilot selected (or ATC instructed) number on the controllers screen.

ALT - (Altitude) This selects Mode C (spoken as Mode Charlie) and displays the aircraft's height, in 100 foot increments, on the radar controller's display.

Discrepancies in excess of 300 feet between the altimeter and the Mode C readout requires the Mode C to be de-selected and Mode A selected. If the aircraft is in controlled airspace specific permission is required for the flight to continue.
S - Selects Mode S (if fitted) and contains a 24-bit address of the transponder installation together with a capability report in its message field.
See page 271 for full details of specific transponder codes.
The carriage of a working transponder with Mode A & C is mandatory in all controlled airspace when operating IFR except for:-
i) Gliders.
ii) Aircraft below Flight Level 100 in controlled airspace receiving an approved crossing service.
If instructed to *'Squawk Ident'* the pilot should press the ident key momentarily, the ident light will remain illuminated. On the controllers screen a circle will appear around your aircraft's radar return or the return will be highlighted.

TREND - Meteorological

A trend is a short term landing forecast valid for 2 hours which is added to a TAF, METAR or VOLMET. It may contain the following terms:-

CAVOK -   Visibility 10Km or more.
No cloud below 5,000ft or below the highest minium sector altitude, whichever is the greater, and no Cumulonimbus
No precipitation, sandstorm, duststorm, thunderstorm, shallow fog or low drifting snow, dust or sand.

Note : Conditions could deteriorate within two hours from this to a visibility of 6km and/or a ceiling of 1,600ft without the TREND being considered incorrect. The criteria for significant changes for TREND type forecasts are given in Table K of the MET Section of the UK AIP.

GRADU -	Gradual Change at a constant rate
INTER -	Intermittent changes with conditions fluctuating
NOSIG -	No significant changes expected
PROB -	Percentage of probability of a change occurring
RAPID -	Rapid change occurring in 1/2 hour of less
TEMPO -	Change expected to last for less than one hour
TREND -	Forecast of an expected change follows....

TRIM TABS

An aircraft is in trim when it maintains steady flight without any input from the pilot. It is not possible for an aircraft to be designed to achieve this, taking into account changes in airspeed or centre of gravity, without the use of trim tabs.
A **Elevator Trim Tab** is located on the trailing edge of the elevator and is operated manually or electrically from the cockpit. It is used to increase or decrease the lift of the elevator, removing the need for strong pressure to be exerted by the pilot at any stage of the flight. A similar tab is often found on the rudder and is known as the **Rudder Trim Tab**, this works on a similar basis and will correct for any slight adverse yaw.

TROPICAL STORMS

Tropical Storms originate over tropical seas where warm, moist air travels westward at first before turning east into middle latitudes.
Wind speed tend to decrease as the storms pass over land but precipitation may increase due to the adiabatic cooling as the air is forced to rise over high ground. They are often

referred to as **Cyclones** because of the very visual effect of their circulating winds. The term **Tropical Cyclone** is reserved for low pressure storms having a wind speed of more than force 8 but less than force 12.

TROPOSPHERE

This is the term given to the layer of atmosphere from the Earth's surface to the **Tropopause.** The height of the tropopause varies according to temperature and is approximately 52,000ft deep over the equator and reducing to 26,000ft deep over the poles. The tropopause is usually at around 38,000ft over the UK in winter time. The area above this is known as the Stratosphere.

TURN & SLIP INDICATOR

The turn and slip indicator is a combination instrument, the turn indicator is more correctly referred to as a **Rate of Turn Indicator** whilst the slip indicator will verify any **Yaw** being experienced by the aircraft.

Rate of Turn Indicator - This contains an electrically driven rate gyro. It is a safety back-up in the event of a failure of the Artificial Horizon or the engine suction pump operating it.

The instrument only has one gimbal and only has freedom of movement about two axis. The spin axis is aligned horizontally along the aircraft's lateral axis. The gimbal axis is aligned to the aircraft's longitudinal axis with its movement restricted by two calibrated springs. The instrument has no freedom of movement about the aircraft's normal axis and force applied about this axis will attempt to make the gyro topple and precess.

In a turn the gyro's rigidity attempts to hold itself in the same position, as this is not possible, a force is applied across the gyro along its axis. This force precesses at 90° as the gyro topples which pulls vertically against a spring which applies a secondary reaction against the turn. The primary precession topples the gyro until the gimbal has rotated sufficiently to tension the spring to a point where it provides a stabilising secondary precession. This holds the gimbal at an angle equal to the rate of turn of the aircraft.

A pointer or aircraft is attached to the gimbal so that the rate of turn can be displayed to the pilot. The action and reaction process sounds long winded but the indication is almost immediate. The scale of the instrument is usually marked to show a rate one, two and three turn. A rate one turn is one that will turn the aircraft 360° in two minutes. The calibrated indication removes the need to calculate the bank angle, for reference this is:-

$$\text{Bank Angle} = \frac{\text{TAS(Kts)}}{10} + 7$$

Errors affecting the Rate of Turn Indicator:-

Calibration Speed - The instrument is calibrated to indicate accurately for a specified True Air Speed. If the aircraft is turned at speed outside the calibrated speed small errors will occur.

Gyro Rotation Speed - if the gyro rotates at less than the correct design speed it will under-read (under-speed - under-read). This will result in a greater angle of bank being flown than is indicated. The technical reason for this is that a lesser amount of secondary torque is required to balance the primary torque. The spring is effectively too strong for the amount of precession.

Pitching Error - this will only occur where the a steep turn is being flown and indicated at the same time as an abrupt pitching movement is made. This causes additional precession which results in over-reading of the instrument.

Slip Indicator - This is a very simple instrument that will indicate Yaw or a skidding turn. A curved glass tube is filled with a dampening fluid in which a heavy metal ball is free to move. The ball will, in straight and level flight, respond to gravity and rest in the bottom centre of the tube.

If the aircraft turns centrifugal force will also act on the ball and if the turn is un-balanced it will be thrown out to the relevant side of the tube. The value of this centrifugal force is proportional to the rate of turn and the true air speed. For the turn to be balanced, and for the slip indicator ball to be centralised, the resultant of the two forces must be an extension of the aircraft's normal axis. To maintain a balanced turn 'same side' rudder pressure is applied to keep the ball centralised. In practice if the ball is out of balance to the right, right rudder must be applied, and vice versa.

ULTRA HIGH FREQUENCY RANGE - UHF

Frequencies in the range 300Mhz to 3Ghz with a wavelength of 10cm to 1 metre. It is used by the military for communications. Frequencies as low as 225 Mhz used for this purpose are referred to a UHF although they technically fall in the Very High Frequency (VHF) band. The band is sometimes known as **decimetric.** It is the range used by the **ILS glidepath, en-route primary radar**, some **secondary surveillance radar** and **distance measuring equipment**.

UNCERTAINTY PHASE - Emergency

The period where uncertainty exists as to the safety of an aircraft and its occupants, it is qualified by:-

a) No communication received within 30 minutes of the time that a communication should have been received.

b) Failure to receive an answer when the aircraft was expected to answer (hence the importance of telling a controller that you intend leaving his frequency).

c) Failure to arrive or make any form of contact within 30 minutes of ETA last notified or estimated by ATC.

During this phase the Rescue Co-ordination Centre (RCC) will brief the appropriate rescue units and evaluate any information. If no further information is received the next phase will be the Alert Phase.

VALLEY WINDS

Any wind blowing across the surface of the Earth will attempt to find the easiest route. If the route is blocked by a range of mountains or hills it will tend to flow around rather than over it. To effect this detour it will change direction significantly to find a valley or ravine.

The air entering this constriction will then have to increase its speed which can cause severe localised effects. Any minor veering or backing of the wind approaching the obstruction can, if the angles are critical, cause a complete reversal of the direction of the valley wind.

VARIATION - Magnetic

The Magnetic North Pole does not lie in the same position as the true or Geographic North Pole. The magnetic meridians (great circles passing through both poles) do not lie in the same position as the true meridians. The angle of difference between the meridians is known as variation.

Variation is either added or subtracted to a true track for flight planning purposes. If

Magnetic North lies to the west of True North variation is westerly and is added to the true track. If Magnetic North lies to the east variation is referred to as easterly and is subtracted. This is easily remembered by:

Variation West - Magnetic Best (more)

Variation East - Magnetic Least (less)

The reason for Earth's magnetic field is not known. One theory is that it emanates from the iron contained within liquid magma at the centre of the Earth. The rate of change of magnetic variation has decreased by 5% in the past 100 years. The changes in variation eventually cause runways to be renumbered to a more accurate magnetic heading. In 1966 Gatwick's main runway was 27-09 it's now 26-08.

VENTURI EFFECT

A venturi is any tube which gently narrows at the centre and broadens at the ends. If air, or any fluid, flows through the tube, the pressure at the narrow section will be less than that at the ends.

This property is used in the design of the carburettor. For the negative side effects of the venturi effect refer to the reference section on Icing - Carburettor.

VERTICAL SPEED INDICATOR

The Vertical Speed Indicator uses the principle of differential pressure to display the rate of descent or climb of an aircraft.

The instrument is located within a sealed case. The static line feeding the instrument is branched to feed both a sealed capsule and a metering device. The metering device will only accept changes of pressure at a fixed rate.

The sealed capsule will expand or contract in response to pressure changes and the difference is displayed by a needle indicator.

Whilst on the ground or in level flight the pressure in the sealed capsule and the instrument case are equal and the needle will display zero. If the aircraft then descends the pressure will increase expanding the capsule and the indicator will show a rate of descent. The metering device will prevent a quick equalisation of pressures. Soon after level flight is re-established the pressures will equalise and the indicator return to zero. If a climb is effected the opposite will occur.

Errors that effect the Vertical Speed Indicator are:-

System Blockages - as the instrument is fed from one static pressure source there will be no change of pressure to the instrument if that source is blocked. The instrument will read zero even if the aircraft is climbed or descended.

Alternate static should be selected in the event of a blockage. If the aircraft being flown does not have internal static source the glass should be broken on the face of the instrument allowing variable pressure to reach the capsule. You should note that as this air will be routed via the metering device significant lag will be encountered.

Lag - the needle will always lag behind the true pressure changes because of the time taken to build up a steady pressure difference. This becomes most noticeable after a long climb or descent.

Position Error - due to different configurations of the aircraft it is impossible for the static head to give invariable results. Refer to the reference section on the Static Vent.

Manoeuvring error, similar to position error but varies with the configuration of the aircraft.

VERY HIGH FREQUENCY

Frequencies in the range 30 to 300 Mhz with a wavelength of 1 - 10 metres.
The band is used for **VHF Communications** and is from 118.000 to 137.000Mhz, with a standard spacing of 25Mhz. 136.025 to 136.775Mhz are used for national and international ATS, 136.800 to 136.875Mhz for international operational control and 136.900 to 136.975Mhz reserved for datalink purposes. **VOR Frequencies** are from 108Mhz to 117.95Mhz using even tenths and tenths + 50Khz from 108.00Mhz to 111.85Mhz and then from 112.00Mhz to 117.95Mhz at 50Khz intervals.
Also used for VHF direction finding and part of the ILS. The **ILS Localiser** uses VHF but the glideslope uses UHF.

VERY HIGH FREQUENCY METEOROLOGICAL REPORT - VOLMET

VOLMET is a service produced on various VHF frequencies to cover weather for selected aerodromes. Each broadcast cycle is preceded by a time announcement. This time was the time at the end of the observing period.
Individual reports are broadcast 30 minutes after the observation and for a period of 30 minutes after that if no fresh observation has been reported in that period. At the end of one hour if no fresh report is available then the report for that aerodrome will be suspended.
The content of the VOLMET is:-
a) Surface Wind
b) Visibility
c) Runway Visual Range (if applicable)
d) Weather
e) Cloud
f) Temperature
g) Dew Point
h) QNH
A TREND may be included if a forecaster is on duty.

VERY HIGH FREQUENCY OMNI-DIRECTIONAL RANGE - VOR

Refer to the reference section on the Omni-Bearing Indicator and Horizontal Situation Indicator for further information on the use of this navigation aid.
The VOR system uses the VHF frequency band and is allocated frequencies from 108.00Mhz to 117.95Mhz but shares the range with ILS equipment. To separate them the VOR uses even tenths and even tenths + 50Khz up to 111.85Mhz and then from 112.00Mhz upwards at 50Khz intervals.
The system functions by the ground station transmitting **Radials.** These are an infinite number of magnetic position lines emanating outwards from the station. The aircraft is equipped with a receiver which by use of an **Omni-Bearing Selector** can determine which radial it is on.
An exact location may then be obtained either by taking a cross reference from another VOR or by using co-located distance measuring equipment (DME) when available. Most airways route via VOR beacons enabling an aircraft to follow the same magnetic radial of several different beacons over several hundred miles.

Principle of Operation of the Ground Transmitter
The transmitter sends two separate signals, a **Reference Signal** and a **Variphrase Signal.** Bearing information is provided by comparison of the signals.
The Reference Signal - this is an omni-directional carrier wave, the allocated frequency is modulated at 30Hz. The signal is omni-directional and so all receiving aircraft will receive the same phase of the signal regardless of their bearing to the beacon.

The Variphase Signal - this is a carrier wave transmitted on the same frequency and has the effect of amplitude modulating the signal. On the 360° radial is at the same phase as the reference signal. On the 180° radial the variphase signal is 180° out of phase. This signal is also transmitted at 30Hz which is the basis of the VOR operation, the system simply compares the phases.

The 360° radial of a VOR is aligned with Magnetic North, all radial indications are magnetic and variation is taken into account. The signal is designated as an A9W emission. Individual VOR stations are identified by a three letter Morse group transmitted every ten seconds.

VOR Theoretical Range and Designated Operational Coverage

160 frequencies are shared by thousands of VOR stations all over the world. It is therefore most important that stations sharing the same frequencies are spaced as far apart as possible.

VHF line of sight range will normally apply with the theoretical range of a VOR is calculated by the formula '1.25 x (H1 + H2)' where H1 = Square root of the height of the VOR Station, H2 = Square root of the height of the receiver (aircraft).

Aircraft flying at high altitudes can receive signals from two VORs simultaneously and the bearing information displayed in the aircraft will be incorrect. A **Designated Operational Coverage** is published in the COM Section of UKAIP and lists the usable distance and height limits, this must be used for all VOR navigation to avoid such occurrences.

Standard airways and en route VOR stations have a power output of 200 watts which normally equates to a range of 200 nautical miles. Terminal and approach VOR stations have an output of 50 watts with a range of around 100 nautical miles.

VOR Stations are classified according to their operational use. T - Terminal, L - Low Altitude, H - High Altitude.

Errors affecting VOR Stations and Receivers

Errors are normally very slight and can either be cumulative or cancel each other out to a certain extent. They should not exceed 5° in total and can be summed up as:-

  1° Maximum from station due to location
  1° Maximum from transmitter
  3° Maximum in receiver

Location - VOR aerials are sited away from hills, mountains and man made obstructions as much as possible. Reflected signals may cause the aircraft to receive its signal slightly later than the direct signal causing the combined result to be incorrect. This is unlikely to exceed 1°.

Transmitter - The transmitter is subject to automatic monitoring to ensure it remains accurate. If this equipment detects an error in excess of 1° a standby transmitter is activated and the errant equipment is shut down. During the change over period any OBI indications will be inaccurate and if idented no Morse ident will be heard. The ident will restart as soon as the monitoring equipment judges the standby transmissions to be within 1°. It is essential that a VOR station is regularly idented en route.

Receiver - Phase difference cannot be measured with totally accuracy with the compact size of equipment carried by an aircraft. Design specifications require that any errors do not exceed 3°.

Station Identification

As with all electronic navigation equipment it is essential that the ident is checked to be correct and not just to be transmitting a Morse ident. A VOR station transmits a three letter Morse group every ten seconds. If it is co-located with a DME every third ident is suppressed with the DME ident. To enhance the difference they are transmitted at different tones.

VOR Checks & Inspections

VOR installations are routinely inspected by the CAA Flight Calibration Service once every five years. In the event of any unusual VOR indications it is a pilot's responsibility to advise their current ATC unit of the problem. For pilots to check the aircraft's equipment some aerodromes provide VOR Test Checkpoints (VOT) at specific ground points. Other VOTs are designated for accuracy tests in flight.

VERY LOW FREQUENCY

Frequencies in the range 3 to 30 Khz with a 10 to 100Km wavelength. They are used for long range navigation aids such as Omega.

VIOLENT STORM - Winds - Meteorological

According to the Beaufort Wind Scale a violent storm is a force 11 wind. If the wind reaches 56 - 63 knots (64 - 73 mph) it is said to be violent storm force.

VIRGA

Virga is the name given to precipitation falling from a cloud, in ice or liquid form, that evaporates before reaching the surface.

VISIBILITY - Meteorological

Ground visibility is the distance at which objects of known distance are visible over at least half the horizon. Visibility at night is expressed by how far you would expect to see in the prevailing conditions if it were daylight. It is reported in kilometres or metres. It is reduced by the following phenomena:-

Blowing Snow - ice crystals picked up from the ground by a strong surface wind to a height of at least 6 feet usually reducing visibility below 1,000 metres.

Drizzle - very small numerous droplets of water falling as precipitation reducing the visibility to between 500 and 3,000 metres.

Dust and Haze - minute solid particles held in suspension in the atmosphere reducing visibility to between 1,000 metres and 10 kilometres.

Duststorms - strong winds and possibly thermal activity lift dust from arid areas reducing visibility to less than 1,000 metres.

Fog - minute water droplets held in suspension with a diameter of less than 0.2mm reducing visibility to less than 1,000 metres.

Mist - minute water droplets held in suspension with a diameter of less than 0.2mm reducing visibility to not less than 1,000 metres.

Rain - Droplets falling as precipitation affecting visibility in proportion to their size and intensity.

Sandstorms - strong winds and possibly thermal activity lift sand from desert areas reducing visibility to less than 1,000 metres.

Smoke - solid particles introduced into the atmosphere as a result of combustion reducing visibility to less than 1,000 metres.

Snow - ice crystals falling as precipitation affecting visibility in proportion to their size and intensity.

Flight Visibility - is stated as being the average forward horizontal distance, from the cockpit of an aircraft in flight, at which prominent unlit objects may be seen and identified by day and prominent lighted objects may be seen and identified at night.

The distances are largely academic. There is no reliable method of measurement and with the variances of slant vision are of little use.

VISUAL APPROACH SLOPE INDICATORS - VASI
Standard System VASI or (Abbreviated) AVASIS
The full system comprises of twelve units arranged to form two lighted wingbars each side of the runway. The abbreviated system has a reduced number of lights in each wingbar on one or both sides of the runway. They indicate to the pilot a white light if the aircraft is above the glideslope and a red light if below. A correct approach slope is maintained by the white sector of the nearer bars and the red sector of the far bars being visible throughout.

The wingbars are located at 150m and 300m up the runway, not more than 15m from the runway edge. The azimuth coverage is between 10° either side of the centreline during daylight and 15° at night. As with all types of VASI systems below 200 feet visual judgment should override the light indications.

On precision approach runways with VASI attempts are made to collate with the ILS glidepath but variances may occur of up to 1.5 dots up and down (where the full scale deflection is 5 dot) with the VASI still indicating an approach within limits.

Three Bar VASI System
For long bodied and high eye/wheel height aircraft a third, upper, bar is added. This enables use where there is a difference of more than 15 feet between the pilot's eye and the landing gear. Conventional aircraft use the first two bars whilst high eye/wheel height aircraft use the upper two bars, ignoring the other. To be on the slope either type of aircraft should have one red, one white. Two reds indicate too low, two whites indicating too high.

'T' Type VASI System
The T system consists of a group of lights each side of the runway. The T indications are:-

White T sloping away from the aircraft	Too High
White T sloping towards the aircraft	Too Low
White Cross Bar Only	On Slope
Red T sloping towards the aircraft	Very Low

The azimuth coverage is between 10° either side of the centreline during daylight and 15° at night. As the system is visible from angles where obstruction clearance is not guaranteed it must only be used for descent when the aircraft is lined up with the runway.

During light ground fog conditions all the white lights of the system may be visible at the same time as a result of light being reflected from water droplets adjacent to the units. In these conditions, in addition to the correct indication the pilot may see a 'fuzzy' T fly up or down indication, usually less distinct than the direct lights. If the difference is not distinctive the T VASI should not be used.

For long bodied, high eye/wheel height aircraft the system may be used by flying a slope which shows two lights high on the away facing T. This will result in a slope increase of less than 0.25° and will move the visual aiming point further up the runway.

Low Intensity Two Colour Approach Slope System - LITAS
LITAS is a simplified version of the standard VASI system consisting of two units, one upwind, one downwind, usually placed on the left of the runway. It is a low intensity system designed to be used at night but can also be effective during the day in poor light conditions.

VISUAL DESCENT POINT - VDP
This is a point shown on an approach chart. It defines the point on the final approach path of a non-precision, straight-in approach, from which a normal descent from the Minimum

Descent Altitude to the runway touchdown point may be made, providing the approach end point is clearly visible.

The VDP is normally identified by a navigation aid fix and with a 75Mhz marker beacon on Non-directional beacon procedures. They are not a mandatory part of the procedure but provide additional guidance when used in conjunction with the Visual Approach Slope Indicators.

VISUAL FLIGHT RULES - VFR

A set of minimas required to fly in Visual Meteorological Conditions.

WEATHER MINIMA FOR VFR FLIGHT
BELOW FL245 IN UK BY PPL/BCPL HOLDERS-NO RATINGS

NO rating	CLASS F and G AIRSPACE			CLASS D AIRSPACE UNLESS NOTIFIED FOR THE PURPOSES OF ANO SCH 8			CLASS D and E AIRSPACE NOTIFIED FOR THE PURPOSES OF ANO SCH 8		
		VMC+ LIMITATIONS OF LICENCE			VMC+ LIMITATIONS OF LICENCE		SPECIFIED MINIMUM WEATHER PROVISIONS		
	FLT VIS	DISTANCE FROM CLOUD		FLT VIS	DISTANCE FROM CLOUD		FLT VIS	DISTANCE FROM CLOUD	
		Hor	Vert		Hor	Vert		Hor	Vert
AT AND ABOVE FL100	8km*	1500m* in sight of surface	1000ft	8km*	1500m* in sight of surface	1000ft	10km	1800m in sight of surface	1000ft
BELOW FL100	5km*	1500m* in sight of surface	1000ft	5km*	1500m* in sight of surface	1000ft	10km	1800m in sight of surface	1000ft
AT AND BELOW 3000ft AMSL	5km	1500m in sight of surface OR	1000ft	5km	1500m in sight of surface	1000ft	10km	1800m in sight of surface	1000ft
	5km	clear of cloud in sight of surface		5km	IAS 140kts OR LESS clear of cloud in sight of surface				
	3km**	IAS 140kts OR LESS clear of cloud in sight of surface							
SVFR		Not Applicable		10km#	clear of cloud in sight of surface		10km#	clear of cloud in sight of surface	

* With passenger(s) 10km 1800m
** With passenger(s) 5km

UK VMC Differences from ICAO printed in *italics*

Except on notified route or in notified ATZ

AN INSTRUMENT RATING IS REQUIRED FOR FLIGHT IN AIRSPACE NOTIFIED FOR THE PURPOSES OF ANO SCH 8 IN CONDITIONS LESS THAN THE SPECIFIED MINIMUM WEATHER PROVISIONS.

CLASS D AIRSPACE NOT NOTIFIED FOR THE PURPOSES OF ANO SCH 8		CLASS D AIRSPACE NOTIFIED FOR THE PURPOSES OF ANO SCH 8	CLASS E AIRSPACE NOTIFIED FOR THE PURPOSES OF ANO SCH 8
Aberdeen CTR/CTA	Leeds Bradford CTR/CTA	Belfast CTR	Belfast TMA
Alderney CTR	Liverpool CTR	Birmingham CTR/CTA	Scottish TMA at and below 6000ft
BELFAST/City CTR/CTA	LONDON/City CTR	Cardiff CTR	Scottish CTR
Bournemouth CTR	LONDON/Gatwick CTA	East Midlands CTR	
Bristol CTR/CTA	Lyneham CTR/CTA	Edinburgh CTR	VFR flight is not permitted in Class A Airspace ie Airways, Channel Is. CTR/CTA, Cotswold CTA, Daventry CTA, London CTR, London TMA, Manchester TMA, Shanwick OCA, Worthing CTA.
Brize Norton CTR	Manston Cross Channel CTR	Glasgow CTR	
Cardiff CTA	Newcastle CTR/CTA	Isle of Man CTR	
Cross Channel CTA	Prestwick CTR	LONDON/Gatwick CTR	
East Midlands CTA	Southampton CTR/CTA	LONDON/Stansted CTR/CTA	
Guernsey CTR	Southend CTR	Luton CTR/CTA	Special VFR flight is permitted in London CTR and Channel Is CTR.
Isle of Man CTA	Sumburgh CTR/CTA	Manchester CTR/CTA	
Jersey CTR	Teesside CTR/CTA	Scottish TMA above 6000ft	Upper Airspace FL245-FL660 is Class B Airspace.
			No Class C Airspace currently allocated in UK.
NOTES			Airspace information correct at 28 MAY 1992. Check UKAIP amendments for changes.

ANS2 Drg. No. G1068 5/92

WEATHER MINIMA FOR VFR FLIGHT BELOW FL245 IN UK BY PPL/BCPL HOLDERS WITH IMC RATING

IMC rating	CLASS F and G AIRSPACE VMC+ LIMITATIONS OF LICENCE			CLASS D AIRSPACE UNLESS NOTIFIED FOR THE PURPOSES OF ANO SCH 8 VMC+ LIMITATIONS OF LICENCE			CLASS D and E AIRSPACE NOTIFIED FOR THE PURPOSES OF ANO SCH 8 SPECIFIED MINIMUM WEATHER PROVISIONS		
	FLT VIS	DISTANCE FROM CLOUD Hor	Vert	FLT VIS	DISTANCE FROM CLOUD Hor	Vert	FLT VIS	DISTANCE FROM CLOUD Hor	Vert
AT AND ABOVE FL100	8km	1500m	1000ft	8km	1500m	1000ft	10km	1800m	1000ft
BELOW FL100	5km	1500m	1000ft	5km	1500m	1000ft	10km	1800m	1000ft
AT AND BELOW 3000ft AMSL	5km	1500m OR clear of cloud in sight of surface	1000ft	5km	1500m	1000ft	10km	1800m	1000ft
	5km			5km	IAS 140kts OR LESS clear of cloud in sight of surface				
	1500m†	IAS 140kts OR LESS clear of cloud in sight of surface							
SVFR	Not Applicable			3kmØ	clear of cloud in sight of surface		3kmØ	clear of cloud in sight of surface	

† 1800m taking off or landing

UK VMC Differences from ICAO printed in *italics*

Ø Except on those notified routes which specify a higher minimum

AN INSTRUMENT RATING IS REQUIRED FOR FLIGHT IN AIRSPACE NOTIFIED FOR THE PURPOSES OF ANO SCH 8 IN CONDITIONS LESS THAN THE SPECIFIED MINIMUM WEATHER PROVISIONS.

CLASS D AIRSPACE NOT NOTIFIED FOR THE PURPOSES OF ANO SCH 8		CLASS D AIRSPACE NOTIFIED FOR THE PURPOSES OF ANO SCH 8	CLASS E AIRSPACE NOTIFIED FOR THE PURPOSES OF ANO SCH 8
Aberdeen CTR/CTA	Leeds Bradford CTR/CTA	Belfast CTR	Belfast TMA
Alderney CTR	Liverpool CTR	Birmingham CTR/CTA	Scottish TMA at and below 6000ft
BELFAST/City CTR/CTA	LONDON/City CTR	Cardiff CTR	Scottish CTR
Bournemouth CTR	LONDON/Gatwick CTA	East Midlands CTR	
Bristol CTR/CTA	Lyneham CTR/CTA	Edinburgh CTR	VFR flight is not permitted in Class A Airspace ie Airways, Channel Is. CTR/CTA, Cotswold CTA, Daventry CTA, London CTR, London TMA, Manchester TMA, Shanwick OCA, Worthing CTA.
Brize Norton CTR	Manston Cross Channel CTR	Glasgow CTR	
Cardiff CTA	Newcastle CTR/CTA	Isle of Man CTR	
Cross Channel CTA	Prestwick CTR	LONDON/Gatwick CTR	
East Midlands CTA	Southampton CTR/CTA	LONDON/Stansted CTR/CTA	
Guernsey CTR	Southend CTR	Luton CTR/CTA	Special VFR flight is permitted in London CTR and Channel Is CTR.
Isle of Man CTA	Sumburgh CTR/CTA	Manchester CTR/CTA	
Jersey CTR	Teesside CTR/CTA	Scottish TMA above 6000ft	Upper Airspace FL245-FL660 is Class B Airspace.
			No Class C Airspace currently allocated in UK.

NOTES

Airspace information correct at 28 MAY 1992. Check UKAIP amendments for changes.

CAA
CIVIL AVIATION AUTHORITY

Designed by Peter Grant

VISUAL MANOEUVRING AREA

Also referred to as the **Circling Area**. This is a selected area near an aerodrome considered suitable for visual manoeuvring after an instrument approach. The minimum circling height is published with the minimas for each particular airfield.

WAKE TURBULENCE

Wake turbulence is the name given to the effect caused by **Wake Vortices** that are generated by all aircraft, including helicopters. The effect is strongest when generated by heavy aircraft. They are most hazardous to light aircraft during take off, initial climb, final approach and landing, but may also affect taxiing or parked aircraft.

The larger an aircraft the greater the strength and size of its wake vortices. The actual vortex is generated from the wing tips of aircraft or from the main rotors of a helicopter in forward flight. The vortices are made up of two counter rotating cylindrical air masses trailing behind the aircraft. They will tend to drift slowly downwards and will be drifted or halted in progress by any local winds.

Aircraft Classifications for Wake Turbulence

Category	ICAO & Flight Plan	UK
Heavy (H)	136,000 Kg +	136,000 KG +
Medium (M)	<136,000 Kg and > 7,000 Kg	<136,000 and > 40,000 Kg
Small (S)		17,000 KG or 40,000 KG or less
Light (L)	7,000 Kg or less	17,000 Kg or less

Wake Turbulence Spacing Minima - Final Approach - Distance & Time

Leading Aircraft	Following Aircraft	ICAO		UK	
		nm	min	nm	min
H	H	4	-	4	2
H	M	5	2	5	3
H	S	-	-	6	3
H	L	6	3	8	4
M	H	3	-	*	*
M	M	3	-	3	2
M	S	-	-	4	2
M	L	5	3	6	3
S	H	-	-	*	*
S	M	-	-	3	2
S	S	-	-	3	2
S	L	-	-	4	2
L	H	3	-	*	*
L	M	3	-	*	*
L	S	-	-	*	*
L	L	3	-	*	*

* Separation for wake vortex alone in not necessary

Wake Turbulence Spacing Minima - Departures - Time

Leading Aircraft	Following Aircraft	Departure Position	Minimum spacing at the time Aircraft are Airborne
H	M/S/L	Same	2 Minutes
M/S	L	Same	2 Minutes
H	M/S/L	Intermediate	3 Minutes
M/S	L	Intermediate	3 Minutes

For further details refer to the CAA General Aviation Safety Sense Leaflet 15 and/or AIC 122/1992 (Pink 61).

WATER VAPOUR

Water vapour is the term used to describe particles of water suspended in the atmosphere. The amount of water vapour in an air mass is dependent on the temperature of the mass. Higher temperatures hold a higher proportion of vapour than cold.

Water vapour is introduced into an air mass by evaporation and whilst it remains in vapour form the air is said to be unsaturated. If the air cannot absorb any more evaporated water vapour or is cooled so that it can no longer retain the vapour the air is said to be saturated and condensation takes place. Condensation on this scale is said to be saturated and condensation takes place. Condensation on this scale results in cloud formation which in turn leads to precipitation.

WET AND DRY BULB THERMOMETER

The instrument is used to evaluate the **Relative Humidity** and **Dewpoint**.

It consists of two identical thermometers mounted side by side. One has its bulb covered in a wick which is kept moist by being dipped in water. Evaporation of the water from the wick extracts heat from the bulb and its reading is always lower than that of the dry bulb.

The amount of moisture in the air is proportional to the rate of evaporation of the wick. The drier the air, the greater the rate of evaporation. If the air is saturated the evaporation will be zero and both thermometers will read the same. The Dew point and relative humidity can be calculated from tables. The dew point is approximately as far below the wet bulb temperature as the wet bulb temperature is below the dry bulb temperature.

WIND DIRECTION

The wind direction is always stated by the direction it is blowing from. The shifting of the wind across a specific ground point in the anti-clockwise direction is known as **Backing**. If it shifts in a clockwise direction it is referred to as **Veering**. The wind direction quoted by air traffic for take off and landing is usually referenced to magnetic north. METAR and SPECI reports are referenced to true north.

WINDSHEAR

Windshear is the change of wind direction and/or speed over a short distance. These variations may be vertical, horizontal or a combination of both.

The most severe windshear is associated with thunderstorms but may also coincide with the passage of a front. Thunderstorms tend to have an area of cold air that causes a downdraught in all directions but is often well marked along the line of its movement. This is known as a **Gust Front**. This area may extend up to 6,000 feet high and 20 miles of the centre of the storm. Frontal windshear occurs in active fronts that are moving at speed in excess of 30 knots and where there are large temperature differences.

Low level windshear is a particular hazard to aircraft during the take off or landing phases of a flight. Take for example a case where windshear is purely horizontal and the windspeed on the distant side of the shear line is 25 knots lower than the side containing a landing aircraft. If the aircraft is approaching at 90 knots airspeed this IAS will reduce to 65 knots as it passes through the line. The aircraft may be placed within its stall envelope.

If the shear is purely vertical and in the form of a downdraft the angle of attack can effectively be changed at the instant it passes through the shear line. If the shear line variation has a combined vertical and horizontal component it can critically affect an aircraft's approach or take off.

WING LOADING

The load carried by the wings whilst in straight and level flight is described as the wing loading or the weight supported for each unit area of wing. It is calculated from:-

$$\text{Wing Loading} = \frac{\text{Weight of the Aeroplane}}{\text{Wing Area}}$$

ZERO THRUST - Twin Engined Aircraft

During asymmetric flight training it is necessary to practice engine failures and procedures. To avoid risks to safety most of this time will be spent with one or the other engine set at Zero Thrust.

Needless accidents have occurred in the past due to power failures on the approach and climb out in training flights when one engine has been shut down. Zero Thrust is a manifold pressure setting that will simulate the reduction in drag experienced when an engine is actually feathered and shut down.

The power setting for individual aircraft is usually found in graph form in aircraft manuals or can be calculated by formula. Alternatively a setting of 10 to 12 inches of manifold pressure will usually be suitable and can be fine tuned by trial and error.

ZULU TIME

Another name for Greenwich Mean Time (GMT). GMT is quoted as a datum. GMT + 1 hour = Alpha Time, GMT + 2 hours = Bravo Time, etc. British summer time (BST) is Alpha Time.

QUICK REFERENCE SECTION

PHONETIC ALPHABET

A - Alpha	B - Bravo	C - Charlie	D - Delta
E - Echo	F - Foxtrot	G - Golf	H - Hotel
I - India	J - Juliet	K - Kilo	L - Lima
M - Mike	N - November	O - Oscar	P - Papa
Q - Quebec	R - Romeo	S - Sierra	T - Tango
U - Uniform	V - Victor	W - Whisky	X - Xray
Y - Yankee	Z - Zulu		

RADIO TELEPHONY NUMERIC CODES

1 - WUN	2 - TOO	3 - TREE	4 - FOWER
5 - FIFE	6 - SIX	7 - SEFFEN	8 - AIT
9 - NINER	0 - ZERO	100 - HUNDRED	
	1000	TOWSAND	

800 feet is passed as AIT HUNDRED FEET
2500 feet is passed as TOO TOWSAND FIFE HUNDRED FEET
3000 feet is passed as TREE TOWSAND FEET

1017 millibars is passed as WUN ZERO ONE SEFEN
1000 millibars is passed as WUN TOWSAND

STANDARD ALLOCATED FREQUENCIES AND TRANSPONDER CODES

Frequencies

500.000 Khz	International distress/calling frequency.
2182.00 Khz	International distress/calling frequency.
121.500 Mhz	Aeronautical emergency frequency.
121.600 Mhz	Airport fire service emergency frequency (All category 5 - 9 fire & rescue vehicles).
122.100 Mhz	Standard VHF tower frequency for military aerodromes (other frequencies may be allocated for operational reasons).
123.100 Mhz	Civil aircraft in a search and rescue area.
130.425 Mhz	A VHF UNICOM channel used when a temporary danger area has been set up around the scene of an incident.
243.000 Mhz	Survival craft frequency.
282.800 Mhz	Military aircraft in a search and rescue area.

To conserve battery power the following times have been internationally allocated for distress frequencies.

1. VHF/UHF	Switch on only when it is thought that the search aircraft are within range.
2. 500Khz	Transmit on hour + 15 minutes and hour + 45 minutes for 3 minutes.
3. 2182Khz	Transmit on hour and hour + 30 minutes for 3 minutes.

Transponder Codes

0000	Selected on ATC instructions when Mode C readout differs by more than 300 feet (Mode C to be de-selected).
0033	Parachuting drop code to be selected with Mode C (unless another code is assigned by ATC) five minutes before the drop commences and maintained until parachutists are estimated to be on the ground.
2000	Selected when a flight enters UK airspace from an adjacent region where transponder operation has not been required.
7000	Conspicuity code to be used at all times except when:- a) ATC allocate a specific code. b) Operating in controlled airspace. c) In an aerodrome pattern below 3,000ft agl.
7001	Military low level conspicuity code.
7500	Unlawful interference (normally in the event of hi-jack) This results in a **special emergency** being declared.
7600	Radio failure.
7700	Emergency.

Meteorological Non Alpha-numeric Symbol Codes

<	Less than.
>	More than.
+	Heavy.
-	Slight.
///	Cloud or visibility, indicates view totally obscured. Temperature and dewpoint, indicates missing information.

Meteorological Numeric Codes

0000	Visibility less than 50 metres.
00000	Wind calm.
9999	Ten kilometres or more.

Conversion Tables

TO CONVERT	FROM	TO	MULTIPLY BY
WEIGHT			
	Lbs	Kilograms	0.453
	Kilograms	Lbs	2.204
DISTANCE			
	Feet	Metres	0.305
	Metres	Yards	1.094
	Metres	Feet	3.280
	Statute Miles	Nautical Miles	0.869
	Nautical Miles	Statute Miles	1.150
	Nautical Miles	Kilometres	1.852
	Kilometres	Nautical Miles	0.534
CONSUMPTION			
	Litres per Km	Imp Gals per Mile	0.354
	Litres per Km	U.S. Gals per Mile	0.425
	Litres per Hour	U.S. Gals per Hour	0.264
	Litres per Hour	Imp Gals per Hour	0.220
	Imp Gals per Mile	Litres per Km	2.825
	U.S. Gals per Mile	Litres per Km	2.352
	Imp Gals per Hour	Litres per Hour	4.546
	U.S. Gals per Hour	Litres per Hour	3.785
VOLUME			
	Imperial Gallons	Litres	4.546
	Litres	Imperial Gallons	0.220
	U.S. Gallons	Litres	3.785
	Litres	U.S. Gallons	0.264
	Imperial Gallons	U.S. Gallons	1.201
	U.S. Gallons	Imperial Gallons	0.833
	Imperial Gallons	Cubic Feet	0.160
	Cubic Feet	Imperial Gallons	6.229
	U.S. Gallons	Cubic Feet	0.134
	Cubic Feet	U.S. Gallons	7.480
	Litres	Imperial Pints	1.760
	Imperial Pints	Litres	0.568
	U.S. Pints	Litres	0.473
SPEED			
	Knots	Miles per Hour	1.151
	Metres per Second	Knots	1.944
	Miles per Hour	Knots	0.868

Conversion Tables (Contd.)

TO CONVERT	FROM	TO	MULTIPLY BY
PRESSURE			
	Hectopascals	Millibars	1
	Inches	Millibars	33.860
	Millibars	Hectopascals	1
	Millibars	Inches	0.0295
TEMPERATURE	APPLY FORMULA		
	Celsius	Fahrenheit	(x 1.8) + 32
	Fahrenheit	Celsius	(-32) x 0.555

Quick Reference Section

AIRBORNE EMERGENCIES

Emergency Triangle
A procedure to be adopted in VMC conditions when radio failure is compounded by the pilot being lost. The pattern has three 2 minute legs each followed by a 120° turn. Right hand for transmitter failure and left hand for transmitter and receiver failure. See the reference section, page 190 for further details.

Frequencies

121.500 Mhz	Aeronautical emergency frequency.
121.600 Mhz	Airport fire service emergency frequency.
122.100 Mhz	Standard VHF tower frequency for military aerodromes.
123.100 Mhz	Civil aircraft in a search and rescue area.
130.425 Mhz	A VHF UNICOM channel used when a temporary danger area has been set up around the scene of an incident.

Light Signals - Ground to aircraft

Light Signal	Meaning to aircraft on the ground	Meaning to aircraft in the air
Flashing Green	Authorises movement on the manoeuvring area and apron	Return to the circuit or remain in the circuit and await for permission to land
Steady Green	Authorises take-off	Authorises landing
Flashing Red	Move clear of landing area immediately	Aerodrome is unfit for landing, go away, land elsewhere
Steady Red	Movement prohibited	Give way to other aircraft and continue circling
Flashing White	Return to your starting point	Land after receiving a green light and then after receiving green flashes proceed to the apron.
Red Pyro or Flare		Landing prohibited for the time being, previous landing permission withdrawn.
Red or Green Lights or Stars		You are in an active danger area, do not alter your height and get out by the shortest route OR you are about to enter a danger, prohibited or restricted area.

Light Signals - Aircraft to Ground

Signal	Meaning
Red Pyro or Flare	Immediate assistance is requested.
Continuous Green Green Flashes or pyro	By Night: May I land? By Day: May I land in a different direction to that indicated by the landing T?
White Flashes, Pyros or switching on and off of aircraft lights	I am compelled to land.

Speechless Code

Used in distress situations where an aircraft's transmission is weak, distorted or unintelligible but received signals are audible. The pilot should transmit carrier wave only by depressing the aircraft transmit button for less than a second for a short code and two seconds for a long code.

Transmission	Morse	Meaning
One Short	. (E)	Yes
Two short	.. (I)	No
Three Short	... (S)	Say again
Four Short	.... (H)	Request homing*
One Long	- (T)	Manoeuvre complete steady on heading
One Long, Two Short, One Long.	-..- (X)	My aircraft has developed another emergency

* ATC will respond to the aircraft using the call sign *speechless aircraft* if the identity is not known.